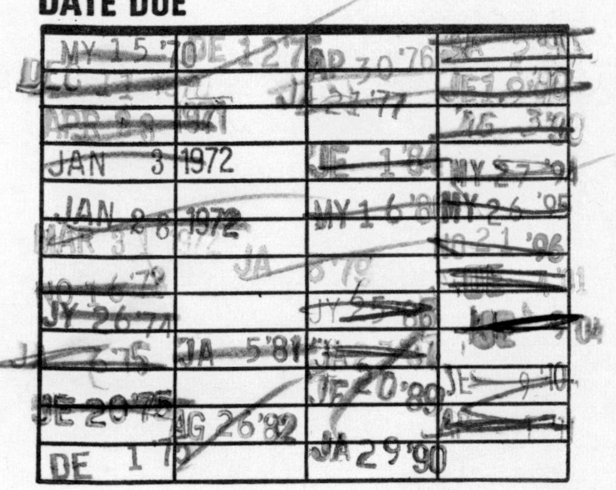

Insecticides

ACTION AND METABOLISM

Insecticides

ACTION AND METABOLISM

R. D. O'BRIEN

SECTION OF NEUROBIOLOGY AND BEHAVIOR
AND
DEPARTMENT OF ENTOMOLOGY
CORNELL UNIVERSITY
ITHACA, NEW YORK

ACADEMIC PRESS New York and London 1967

ACADEMIC PRESS INC.
111 Fifth Avenue, New York, New York 10003

United Kingdom Edition published by
ACADEMIC PRESS INC. (LONDON) LTD.
Berkeley Square House, London W.1

LIBRARY OF CONGRESS CATALOG CARD NUMBER: 66-30096

PRINTED IN THE UNITED STATES OF AMERICA

To My Parents,
in Affection and Gratitude

Preface

The aim of this monograph is to provide a rather complete account of today's knowledge of the action of insecticides and a survey of their metabolism. Its two major predecessors in English, Brown's "Insect Control by Chemicals" and Metcalf's "Organic Insecticides," are now 15 and 11 years old, respectively, and in the interim important advances in the understanding of insecticide action and metabolism have taken place. This work differs somewhat in its aims from its predecessors. The utility and modes of formulation and application of insecticides will not be described; texts on economic entomology must provide that information. I have never found the full description of organic synthetic routes very edifying or attractive to any but organic chemists, so I have omitted them. By contrast, the full understanding of modern studies on mode of action demand a working knowledge of neurobiology, and I hope that the introductory chapter will suffice to provide that knowledge. Also, the understanding of relations between structure and activity, when conceived as an exercise in logic and comprehension rather than as a dreary catalogue of which substituents help and which hinder, requires some knowledge of electronic aspects of chemistry, and the section on this topic was written to provide knowledge sufficient for the purposes of this book.

I have striven to produce an account which is up-to-date, critical, and readable. I have taken the position that it is appropriate to sift good evidence from bad, but I hope I have made it clear when I am stating fact and when opinion.

No attempt has been made to give total descriptions of all the theories of action for all the compounds described; often the early views have fallen into an appropriate neglect as more precise observations or concepts have developed. Similarly, I have not attempted to describe all metabolic paths for every representative of the classes of compounds mentioned, but I have tried not to omit any that have interest extending outside one particular compound. These two condensations have been made in the interests of presenting a contemporary view at modest length. On the other hand, certain subjects, such as A. R. Main's work on the interaction of organophosphates with cholinesterase and the debate on the ion permeability of insect nerve, have been gone into very fully because I believe them to be exceptionally important and yet not previously brought together for full discussion. I hope that these parts will be of particular interest to advanced researchers; in addition, such extensive treatment is necessary in these subject areas for students also, for the ideas are rather new and fairly complex.

I hope that any reader with a modest introductory knowledge of chemistry and biology will read this work with ease. If the facts are not clear, the fault is in my writing, not in any deep obscurity of the subject.

The spirit in which this monograph was written, and I hope that in which it will be read, was well expressed by the eminent physical chemist, G. N. Lewis [quoted by H. A. Bent in *Science* **143,** 1425 (1964)]:

> Scientific theories are not those beautiful structures so delicately designed that a single flaw may cause the collapse of the whole. The scientist builds slowly and with a gross but solid kind of masonry. If dissatisfied with any of his work, even if it be near the very foundations, he can replace that part without damage to the remainder. On the whole he is satisfied with his work, for while science may never be wholly right, it certainly is never wrong; and it seems to be improving from decade to decade.

June, 1967 R. D. O'BRIEN

Contents

Insecticides

ACTION AND METABOLISM

CHAPTER I

Introduction

Toxicology

This book is about the toxicology of insecticides. The term toxicology is much abused; it is commonly applied in medical and veterinary usage to problems of analysis of food and organs for toxic substances. A recent two-volume treatise on toxicology is devoted almost entirely to this aspect. In agricultural schools, the term is often applied to work on the application of toxicants to animals and the evaluation of toxicity. In my view, "toxicology," like any other "-ology," should be reserved for a logical study of a body of knowledge, the subject matter in this case being the toxic effects of substances on organisms. From this viewpoint, toxicity testing and toxicant analysis are minor components of a subject whose central theme is the mechanism whereby toxicants exert their effects. Such mechanisms are the principal topics of this book.

In practice, toxicology is concerned with highly toxic substances, although it is recognized that even essential substances, such as sodium chloride, can be lethal in large excess. We are here concerned instead with compounds used in a dose range commonly of the order of 0.1–25 mg/kg,* which might be better visualized as 0.1–25 parts per million (ppm) if evenly distributed. Such extreme effectiveness can only be achieved if the toxicant has considerable specificity,

* Toxicities are commonly expressed as weight of toxicant per given body weight, most often mg/kg or, when discussing small animals such as insects, μg/g, which is the same thing. A better system, rarely used, is to use mmoles/kg, permitting comparison on a molar basis. A highly undesirable practice is to use μg or mg per animal, making it impossible to compare species directly or to get an immediate grasp of the order of magnitude of the toxicity being described.

so that it avoids consuming its substance by combination with body components in great excess, and if it interferes specifically with a component which is not in excess and is vital for life. Usually, at doses which are just sufficient to kill, only one component will be "attacked." At much larger doses, many other components with lesser affinities will become affected. The special mystery to be disentangled is why the toxicant has such special affinity; for example, why does nitrogen mustard preferentially alkylate the guanine of nucleic acids (2) or the organophosphates phosphorylate the serine of cholinesterase (p. 39), when the body contains billions of other alkylatable and phosphorylatable groups? The disentanglement is made very difficult by the existences of these less important reactions encountered at high concentrations. The older literature on organophosphates, and much of the literature on chlorinated hydrocarbons, is full of examples of effects which researchers have observed when extremely high concentrations of toxicant have been applied to tissue preparations, and such effects have often been "red herrings," tempting one to believe a vital mechanism has been uncovered. It is not easy to say what concentrations *are* adequately low, but they should certainly be not more than 100 times larger than the concentration achieved by just-toxic doses *in vivo*, in cases where roughly equal distribution in the body may be assumed. This means that for a compound of molecular weight 250, whose LD_{50} (dose which is lethal to 50% of the population of the organism) is 1 mg/kg, a concentration of 0.4mM is maximal and, to make a convincing case, one would like to see a concentration 100 times smaller. But the most convincing case of all is to show that, in an animal poisoned with an LD_{50}, the system under study is profoundly affected. Such a demonstration should be buttressed by showing that nontoxic close analogs at similar doses produce no effect on the particular system.

Modes of Killing

Organisms of any kind may be killed mechanically, physically, or chemically. All of these modes are forms of disruption. Living organisms are elaborately ordered arrays of organic and inorganic components, whose ability to carry on the essential life processes, such as the utilization of energy sources, the synthesis of body constituents, movement, and reproduction, depends upon the integrated activity of these ordered components. Organisms differ vastly in the ease with which disruption of this order is lethal; for instance, insects can survive decapitation or anoxia for days. But all organisms can be lethally disordered by the above three modes, and only by them.

This triple classification of modes is somewhat arbitrary, but convenient. By "mechanical" is meant gross destruction, by flyswatter, by fire, by squashing and entangling materials, such as Tanglefoot and polybutenes (7), and by mechanical abrasives, such as inert dusts. By "physical" is meant the action of agents which kill by interacting with body components, but not chemically. Examples would be those fumigants and organic solvents which we believe to act by modifying the physical properties of a poorly understood lipid biophase, and silica aerogels, which adsorb cuticular grease and lead to desiccation (6). The hallmarks of a physical toxicant are: little dependence of activity upon precise structure, little species specificity, common symptoms from very diverse groups of agents, usually a low order of toxicity, and often rather ready reversibility. Such compounds will be discussed in Chapters 2 and 13.

By far most interesting to the chemist and biologist are those agents which kill chemically, i.e., by reacting, usually specifically, with a body component. This class of compounds includes most of the insecticides. In some cases a clear-cut chemical reaction involving covalent bonding occurs, as with some hydrazides, which react with pyridoxal phosphate (vitamin B_6) to form a Schiff base, or as with the carbamates, which carbamylate cholinesterase. In other cases weaker bonding may be involved, such as ionic, van der Waals, or hydrogen bonding, but the molecular specificity of the reaction, and the fact that there is not merely a modification in the physical properties of a phase, allow us to classify the mode as chemical. Clear examples would be poisoning by reversible enzyme inhibitors such as malonate or organomercurials. There are cases which are difficult to classify, such as the chlorinated hydrocarbons, which seem to cause a specific modification of the electrical properties of a nerve component, and which show marked dependence of activity on structure.

It is not the intention of these comments to imply that there is any tidy set of categories which permits a precise classification of modes of action. Rather, it is desired to dispel the mists which hang around the concept of death by poisoning, and to bring home the realization that one is dealing with classes of physical and chemical reactions which are susceptible to experimental examination. Furthermore, although the symptoms of poisoning may be elaborate and it may be difficult to view dispassionately the extinction of a life, most potent toxicants have the primary effect at one or a very few highly specific loci, and the reactions at these loci are of the type familiar to the physical and organic chemist.

The Causal Chain Leading to Death

Probably the first clear demonstrations that poisons may kill by interacting highly specifically with vital body components were those of Claude Bernard, the celebrated French physiologist. In the middle of the last century, Bernard showed (1) that the South American poison, curare, acted by blocking only the neuromuscular junction, and that carbon monoxide reacted with blood to block its oxygen-carrying capacity. The concept thus implied, that the complex set of symptoms observed in poisoning (or in nutritional deficiencies or in diseases) may often be traced to a single crucial reaction with a body component, has been captured in the phrase "the biochemical lesion." The phrase was introduced in 1931 by Sir Rudolph Peters (9) when he showed that thiamine-deficient pigeons had brains whose ability to oxidize pyruvate was impaired because the pyruvic-oxidizing enzyme needed thiamine as a cofactor. He extended the concept by showing that biochemical lesions occurred in poisoning by arsenicals and by sulfur mustard, both of which react with sulfhydryl groups, and from this biochemical concept was developed (12) an antidote to the vesicant (blister-producing) action of sulfur mustard. The antidote was BAL (British anti-lewisite), which offered an alternative source of

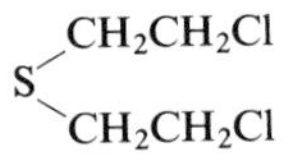

$$S\begin{matrix} \diagup CH_2CH_2Cl \\ \diagdown CH_2CH_2Cl \end{matrix} \qquad \begin{matrix} CH_2SH \\ | \\ CHSH \\ | \\ CH_2OH \end{matrix}$$

Sulfur mustard 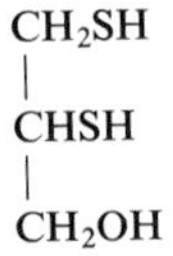 BAL

sulfhydryl groups with which the mustard could react. This strikingly successful outcome of a biochemical approach was so dramatic, and has led to so many other findings in which the actions of drugs, vitamins, and poisons are attributable to their interaction with enzymes, that it is by now very difficult not to think of the concept of the biochemical lesion as self-evident. The complementary phrase "physiological lesion" has not, as far as I know, been used. I suggest that it has application to those cases where the agent interacts not with an enzyme but with a component whose significance is only apparent in the functioning, fully integrated cell. The most likely example would be agents which affect nervous conduction, yet have negligible effects upon broken-cell preparations. Arguments will be given in Chapter 6 to support the view that DDT causes a physiological lesion. If it does, this will explain why the exhaustive attempts to locate an effect of DDT upon individual enzymes have been entirely unsuccessful.

One must beware of the "dormitive principle" argument: Molière has one of his characters explain that opium causes sleep because it contains a dormitive principle. Precise analogs of this statement, in which the "explanation" simply restates the phenomenon, may be rare, but equally delusive claims are not. For instance, it is tempting to state that fluoroacetate kills rats by blocking aconitase, or organophosphates kill insects by inhibiting cholinesterase; but in neither case has there been any success in tracing out a detailed causal chain of events leading from inhibition of those enzymes (which undoubtedly occurs) to death. By contrast, in the poisoning of several mammals by several organophosphates, it has been possible to demonstrate each step of the poisoning process, e.g., inhibition of cholinesterase, thence accumulation of acetylcholine, consequent blockade of the intercostal muscles, therefore respiratory failure, followed by death due to brain anoxia (see p. 56). In insects, by contrast, all we know is that cholinesterase is inhibited and acetylcholine accumulates. Since respiration is achieved by passive diffusion, and since insects are also highly resistant to anoxia, the rest of the chain is undoubtedly different from that in mammals, and is still entirely unknown to us. The only basis we can find for saying that organophosphates probably kill insects through inhibition of their cholinesterase is that of an indigestible accumulation of correlations: of toxicity with anticholinesterase activity, of analogies with mammals, and of failures to suggest other causes. This indirect evidence, widely accepted, is frankly declared to be insufficient by Chadwick (3), one of our most eminent authorities.

Background Chemistry

The following notes are designed to give a condensed statement of certain aspects of chemistry which must be completely understood if later arguments are to be followed, but which may have been too lightly touched on in introductory chemistry, or may be too distant in the past of some readers.

pK_a

Many compounds of toxicological interest are weak acids or bases, and consequently they ionize in aqueous solutions. The extent of this ionization is governed by the dissociation constant of the compound and the pH of the solution. Strong acids are those which ionize (deprotonate) easily, even at low pH; strong acids have low pK_a values (e.g., trichloroacetic acid, 0.7). Strong bases are those which ionize (protonate) easily, even at high pH, when there are few protons available; that is, strong bases have high pK_a values (e.g., ethylamine, 10.7). The factors which weaken and strengthen acids and bases will be discussed below (p. 10).

Let us first consider an acid such as acetic acid, which dissociates thus

$$CH_3COOH \rightleftharpoons CH_3COO^- + H^+$$

It can be shown that, under given conditions, $[CH_3COO^-][H^+]$ bears a fixed relation to $[CH_3COOH]$, where the square brackets indicate concentrations. We define K_a, the dissociation constant, as

$$K_a = [CH_3COO^-][H^+]/[CH_3COOH]$$

Clearly the relative amounts of CH_3COO^- and CH_3COOH present will depend on $[H^+]$, and since we can adjust $[H^+]$ (or its negative logarithm, pH) with buffers, we can adjust those relative amounts. The pK_a is defined as the negative logarithm of the K_a, e.g., a K_a of 10^{-6} gives a pK_a of 6. It turns out that when we adjust the pH of the solution to equal the pK_a of the compound

$$[CH_3COO^-] = [CH_3COOH]$$

so that 50% of the acid is ionized. This is a particular case; a more general statement is given by the Henderson-Hasselbach equation:

$$\mathrm{pH} = \mathrm{p}K_a - \log(\text{Protonated form}/\text{Unprotonated form})$$

The advantage of using the term "protonated form" for CH_3COOH and "unprotonated form" for CH_3COO^-, is that the above equation is precisely applicable for bases too. For instance, dimethylamine in water behaves thus:

$$(CH_3)_2NH + H^+ \rightleftharpoons (CH_3)_2NH_2^+$$

and the above equation applies directly. In older work the pK_b of bases was used, about which we need only say that pK_b = 14 − pK_a.

By inserting values into the Henderson-Hasselbach equation, one can easily show that for acids and bases, when the pH is 1 unit below the pK_a, 90% is protonated, and so on. Similarly, when the pH is 1 unit above, 10% is unprotonated; when 2 units above, 99% is unprotonated. Thus acetic acid (pK_a 4.8) is present 90% as CH_3COOH at pH 3.8, and only 1% as CH_3COOH at pH 6.8.

The significance of all this, toxicologically, is that the protonated and unprotonated forms differ radically in polarity, and hence in permeability and partitioning properties. Under physiological conditions the commonest pH is about 7; at this pH, bases with a pK_a much above 7 are almost all in the ionized form, and behave very differently from those with a pK_a much below 7, which are mostly un-ionized (unprotonated). It will be shown below that one can modify the pK_a of a compound by inserting substituent groups; in fact, one can do so with considerable precision. This is one of the ways in which we can "build in" desirable properties of molecules.

Electronic Interpretations

Consider any covalent molecule containing more than one element; it is found that the valency electrons are not evenly distributed, for some elements have a greater affinity for electrons than others, and consequently draw to them some of the electrons which belong to their neighbors. We have the molecule A→B if B has a greater affinity for electrons than A. The arrow here implies a shift of electrons to B. In fact, if A and B are different, we can only have A→B or A←B, for the electron affinities of A and B must differ. Whole groups also differ in electron affinities; for instance, —NO_2 can draw electrons away from —CH_3. An atom or group which can draw electrons to it is said to be electron attracting or electrophilic. The reference point is the hydrogen in a hydrocarbon chain: electrophilic groups are defined as those which are better than hydrogen at drawing electrons from, for instance, —CH_3.

A group which is less electron attracting than hydrogen is said to be electron repelling, or nucleophilic as we shall call it. The terms electrophilic and nucleophilic are more correctly used to describe the properties of reagents rather than substituents, but there are certain advantages to our incorrect usage which will be commented on below. We shall use the terms both for reagents and for substituent groups.

There are two important reasons for studying electronic effects. They influence properties such as polarity, acidity, and basicity, and they influence rates and directions of reactions.

There are five different electronic effects: inductive, field, resonance, inductomeric, and electromeric. We shall discuss only the first three, which are of importance in influencing polarity, acidity, and basicity. These three and also the inductomeric and electromeric effects are of importance in reaction rates; but the latter two effects are rather complex, and cannot be considered here.

It is important to note that one cannot say "chlorine is an electrophilic substituent." The electronic effect must also be specified; for instance, many groups have an electrophilic inductive effect but a nucleophilic resonance effect. If, by an oversight, one does say "X is electrophilic," the implication usually is that one is discussing the inductive effect.

The Inductive Effect

This is the simplest and most important effect. We can arrange certain groups in order of their increasing tendency to draw electrons from neighboring atoms and, consequently, to create local changes in electron density. These local changes are indicated by the signs δ^- for an increase in electron density and δ^+ for a decrease. The inductive effect is this simple attraction of electrons along a bond. It is symbolized by placing an arrowhead on the bond indicating the direction of electron movement. For instance, Cl has an electrophilic inductive effect, so that we may represent methyl chloride as:

```
   H
   |
H—C^δ+→Cl^δ−
   |
   H
```

The δ signs represent partially charged states known as "formal charges." The inductive effect can be transmitted along a chain of atoms, but becomes rapidly weakened in the process. Thus, in

```
 |  |  |
—C—C—C→Cl
 |  |  |
```

the furthest carbon is influenced very little by the chlorine. However, a double bond transmits the effect better than a single bond, so that the furthest carbon in

$$-\overset{|}{\underset{|}{C}}{=}\overset{|}{\underset{|}{C}}-\overset{|}{\underset{|}{C}}\rightarrow Cl$$

is subject to some influence.

Now, we must consider what groups are inductively electrophilic and why; and what importance this effect has. The simplest effects are with ions; negatively charged groups naturally repel electrons, positively charged groups attract them. Hence $-COO^-$ is strongly nucleophilic and $-N^+(CH_3)_3$ is strongly electrophilic. In this connection it is important to note that the $-NO_2$ group has the form

$$-N^{+}\begin{matrix}\nearrow\!\!\!\!= O \\ \searrow O^-\end{matrix}$$

The N^+ is nearer to the point of attachment than the O^-, and the overall effect is therefore that of a cation. The reasons why other groups and atoms behave as they do cannot be entered into here. Table 1.1 shows the inductive effects for some common groupings.

TABLE 1.1

INDUCTIVE EFFECTS

Inductive effect	Group
Nucleophilic	$-O^- > S^-$
	$-C(CH_3)_3 > CH(CH_3)_2 > CH_2CH_3 > CH_3$
Electrophilic	$-F > -Cl > -Br > -I$
	$=O > =S > OH > SH$
	$-OR > SR$
	$F > OH > NH_2 > CH_3$
	$-C{\equiv}C- > -C{=}C-$
	$-\overset{+}{N}R_3 > -NO_2 > -NR_2$

The effects produced by the inductive effect are discussed below.

Polarity. If a compound has an electronic asymmetry, which can arise as discussed above, such that one end of the molecule has a significant partial charge relative to the other end, then it would align itself in a magnetic field as would a magnet. It has, even in the absence of such a field, two "poles," like a magnet, and is said to be "polar." Compounds lacking this property are "apolar." The property is of great importance when one considers solubility and partitioning, because solutes tend to dissolve in and to partition into solvents whose polarity (or lack of it) resembles their own. Polarity can be measured by finding the dipole moment, i.e., the strength of the tendency to orient in a magnetic field, or it can be measured operationally, for instance by measuring a compound's tendency to dissolve or partition into a solvent whose polarity is taken as the reference point. A favorite measurement is the "partition coefficient": A compound is shaken in a mixture of two immiscible solvents, whose immiscibility implies that they differ a great deal in polarity, e.g., water and hexane. The solvents are allowed to separate, and the concentration of the compound in them is measured. The ratio of the concentrations in the two solvents is the partition coefficient. It does not depend on the volumes of solvents, nor (in dilute solutions) on the quantity of compound.

The many methods of measurement give substantially the same order of polarities for any set of compounds. Because water is very polar and fats or oils (lipids) are very apolar, the term "hydrophilic" is often used for polar compounds which partition in favor of water, and "lipophilic" for apolar compounds which partition readily into lipids.

Some common solvents, in order of decreasing polarity, are: salt solutions, water, acetone, ether, chloroform, benzene, and hexane. Solvents close to each other in this series are miscible with each other. A guide which may be used in guessing polarity is that the following factors *tend* to increase polarity: small size (many common compounds, such as ethers, esters, and amines, are water soluble if they have less than six carbon atoms); ionization, such as in —COO^- groups, —NH_3^+ groups, —SO_3^- groups; nitro groups, which have ionic character,

$$\mathrm{O{=}\overset{+}{N}{-}O^-}$$
$$\quad\;\;|$$

and oxygen atoms, particularly in —OH, but also in esters, aldehydes and ethers.

A factor which may disturb predictions that neglect it is aromaticity. Aromatic compounds, such as phenyl compounds, tend to dissolve or partition into aromatic solvents, other things being equal. Phenol, for instance, would have a higher solubility in benzene than in aliphatic solvents of identical polarity. The cause is the affinity that aromatic rings have for each other (particularly if their substituents permit or encourage close side-by-side approach), because the π-electrons, which are free to wander around the ring, can interact with those of other rings and cause resonance stabilization.

The great importance of polarity considerations to toxicology arises from the fact that the body components differ immensely in polarity. Thus nerve tissue has tremendous lipid levels, and tends to accumulate apolar compounds; the kidney is designed to excrete very polar compounds, with favored exceptions; the skin of mammals has very apolar layers; the integuments of many insects have intensely apolar grease or wax coverings. Consequently the toxicity of a compound can be dramatically altered by small changes in polarity. The topic is discussed in detail in Chapter 16 with respect to penetration problems. The great apolarity of chlorinated hydrocarbons contributes to their extraordinary persistence in the body, for they are stored in body fat, safe from metabolic degradation.

Acidity and Basicity. Acids, by definition, release protons (i.e., hydrogen ions, H^+). The more readily they release protons, the stronger acids they are. Weak acids have a high pK_a (see p. 5); the environment must be very deficient in protons (high pH) before such acids will release many protons. If we consider acetic and chloracetic acids, we note that the chlorine of the chloroacetic acid has made the hydroxyl oxygen more electrophilic by an inductive effect. Consequently, the oxygen binds the proton less strongly and the proton escapes more easily, so that chloroacetic acid is a stronger acid than acetic acid.* But as the chlorine is moved further away from the carboxyl

$$CH_3-C(=O)-O-H$$
Acetic acid
pK_a 4.7

$$Cl^{\delta-} \leftarrow CH_2-C(=O)-O^{\delta+}-H$$
Chloroacetic acid
pK_a 2.9

group, its influence rapidly decreases: one extra CH_2 group interposed (chloropropionic acid) gives a pK_a of 4.1; two extra groups (chlorobutyric acid) give a pK_a of 4.5.

Basicity can be defined as proton-binding capacity. A low pK_a in this case means a weak base, for it implies that a high proton concentration (low pH) is necessary before the base can be induced to bind many protons. Electrophilic groups close to the binding site reduce the negative character of the site and, thus, weaken proton-binding capacity and hence the basicity. Thus, the electrophilic hydroxyl group is base weakening:

NH_3
Ammonia
pK_a 9.3

$NH_2 \rightarrow OH$
Hydroxylamine
pK_a 6.0

Reaction Rates. Let us consider any one class of reactions such as the hydrolyses of organophosphates. The rate of the reaction is entirely controlled by three factors: the nature of the organophosphate (the "reactant"), the nature of the reagent (OH^-, H^+, or H_2O), and the environment (solvent,

* In the formulas, the important electrophilic effect of the carbonyl oxygen upon the —OH has been neglected for simplicity, since it is common to both molecules.

temperature, etc.). Now let us consider a series of reactants, and ask why, with one particular reagent and in one particular environment, the extent of the reaction differs. For instance, why do various organophosphates differ in alkaline hydrolyzability? Why do organophosphates differ in the ability to inhibit cholinesterase?

Reactions involving a reagent can be considered in two parts. In the first step the reagent must approach the reaction site and (usually) combine with it. In the second step some rearrangement may occur. In fact, these two steps may occur concurrently, so that in the hydrolysis the "intermediate" (I) has, in

$$OH^- + (RO)_2P(=O)X \xrightarrow{\text{Step 1}} (RO)_2(HO\cdots)P(=O)\cdots X \xrightarrow{\text{Step 2}} (RO)_2(HO)P{=}O + X^-$$

(I)

most cases, no finite existence. Even in these cases, one may discuss the factors influencing step 1, realizing that the factors that promote step 1 are likely to affect step 2 differently. In the case of organophosphates it seems that step 1 is usually the most critical, i.e., is rate controlling. Let us consider the factors which influence it.

As long as we are considering only differences in the nature of the reactant, only two factors are important: steric and electronic. The steric factors are the spatial, geometric aspects which decide the effectiveness with which the reacting center in the reactant is exposed to the reagent. In organophosphates, the reacting center is commonly the phosphorus, as far as the toxicologically interesting reactions are involved. The electronic factors are those which control the effectiveness of the reaction when the reacting center meets the reagent. Reactions are of two kinds: 1. Those in which the reagent attacks a negative site; the reagent is then said to be electrophilic. This is the case when a phosphate (the reagent) phosphorylates the esteratic site of cholinesterase (the reactant). 2. Those in which the site attacked is positive. The reagent is then nucleophilic. An example is an attack on the phosphorus (now a reactant) by the reagent OH^- in alkaline hydrolysis. The terms negative and positive indicate not only fully ionized sites, but more often those bearing only a formal charge. The prevailing rule is simply that opposites attract, and the more opposite the more the attraction. We would, therefore, expect alkaline hydrolyzability to increase in a series of organophosphates whose phosphorus is rendered progressively more positive by varying its substituents:

$(C_2H_5O)_2P^{\delta-}(=O)\leftarrow COO^-$	$(C_2H_5O)_2P(=O)—CH_3$	$(C_2H_5O)_2P^{\delta+}(=O)\rightarrow CH_2\rightarrow {}^+NO_2^-$
Difficult to attack by OH^-	Intermediate	Easily attacked by OH^-

The Field Effect

We have seen how the inductive effect fades away as the number of atoms through which it must be transmitted is increased. However, if the chain of atoms involved is long enough, the electron-affecting group may be brought close to the active center and produce an effect transmitted not via the chain but via the solvent. This is the field effect.

Consider, for instance, a dicarboxylic acid: The removal of the first H^+ leaves a negative carboxylate ion which greatly reduces the tendency of the second H^+ to be removed. This is seen in the fact that the second pK_a is far larger than the first, e.g., oxalic acid:

```
COOH        COO⁻ + H⁺          COO⁻         COO⁻
 |      →    |                  |       →    |     + H⁺
COOH        COOH               COOH         COO⁻
   First ionization              Second ionization
     pKa = 1.23                     pKa = 4.19
```

We anticipate that, in a dicarboxylic acid with its more separated carboxyls, the difference in pK_a values will be less. But with maleic acid and fumaric acid, which have identical numbers of atoms interposed between the carboxyls, we find that the pK_a values are quite different, and that the difference between the first and second pK_a is far less for fumaric than maleic acid.

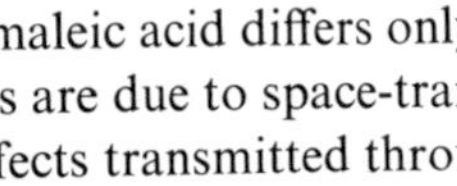

```
          CH—COOH                         CH—COOH
          ||                              ||
     HOOC—CH                              CH—COOH
        Fumaric acid                       Maleic acid
pKa:   first = 3.0 }                pKa:   first = 1.9 }
      second = 4.4 } difference, 1.4      second = 6.2 } difference, 4.3
```

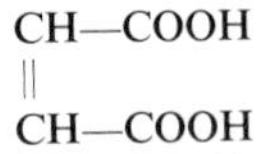

Since maleic acid differs only geometrically from fumaric acid, the different behaviors are due to space-transmitted (or rather solvent-transmitted) effects, not to effects transmitted through the atomic chain.

In acetoxon acid, the carboxylate ion is too far from the phosphorus to have an inductive effect; but the ion can approach the phosphorus and have a field effect.

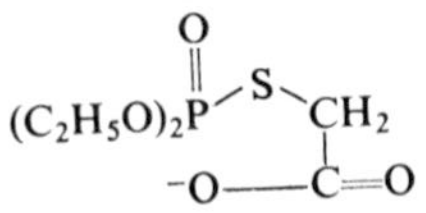

```
            O
            ||
  (C2H5O)2P     S
              /   \
                   CH2
                    |
       -O ———————— C=O
```

The Resonance Effect

When one has a conjugated system, i.e., a system of alternate single and double bonds as in aromatic compounds, the resonance effect may occur. It is important because (as we shall see) it may actually reverse the result expected were a simple inductive effect to be involved.

The underlying principle is: If for a given molecule or ion one may draw different possible structures which all have their nuclei in the same position and all have the same number of paired electrons, the actual structure of the molecule or ion is a form intermediate between these possible structures. This phenomenon is known as resonance or mesomerism. The best known case is that of benzene, which exists in neither of the two possible forms (I) or (II), but instead in the intermediate form (III), where one has six "one and a half" bonds. In order to show that form (I) is an unreal formulation, one can

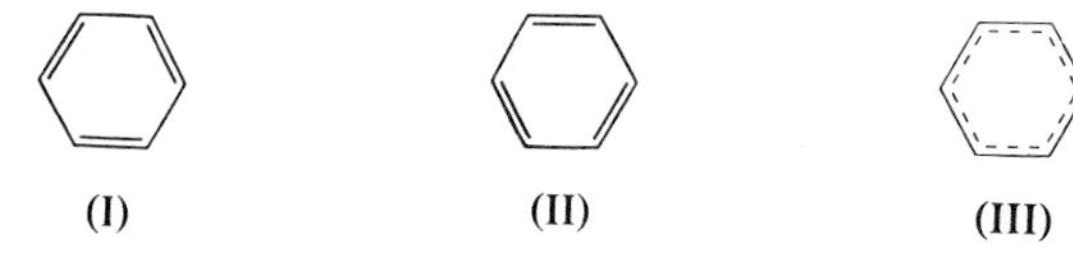

(I) (II) (III)

indicate the shift of electrons towards form (III) as follows:

This helps to remind one that a bond is an electron pair, and that a shift in electrons is, thus, a shift in bonding.

Now, let us consider how this influences electrophilic and nucleophilic effects. Table 1.1 showed that $—NH_2$ has a weak electrophilic effect. But let us consider what happens when the amino group is attached to a benzene molecule. The nitrogen has an unshared electron pair which can tend to turn the single bond to the ring into a double bond, leaving a charge on the nitrogen, i.e., (IV) can go via (V) to (VI).

$—\ddot{N}H_2$ (IV) $—\ddot{N}H_2$ (V) $=\overset{+}{N}H_2$ (VI)

Thus, aniline can be drawn in any of the following ways:

$—NH_2$ $=\overset{+}{N}H_2$ $=\overset{+}{N}H_2$ $=\overset{+}{N}H_2$

In fact, aniline will exist as some intermediate form, but this intermediate form will have a partial negative charge on the para and ortho positions; we may describe the way the partial charge on the para position is formed by:

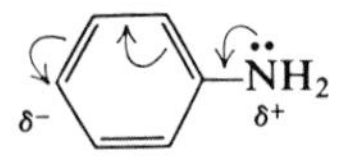

δ^- $\ddot{N}H_2$ δ^+

If a substituent is now attached to the para position, it will be subject to the inductive effect of the δ^- on that position. Summing up, and comparing with aliphatic NH_2:

$\overset{\delta^-}{X}$ $\ddot{N}H_2$ δ^+ $\qquad$ $\overset{\delta^+}{X} \rightarrow CH_2 \rightarrow \overset{\delta^-}{N}H_2$

We see that aminophenyl has a nucleophilic effect, even though aminoethyl has a weak electrophilic effect.

Table 1.2 gives a list of the resonance effects of common groupings. It will be noted that several groups behave as NH_2 in that they have a nucleophilic resonance action in spite of an electrophilic inductive action.

TABLE 1.2

RESONANCE EFFECTS

Resonance effects	Group
Nucleophilic	$—O^- > —OR > —SR$ $—NR_2 > —OR > —F > —Cl > —Br > —I$
Electrophilic	$=\overset{+}{N}R_2 > =NR$ $=O > =NR > =CR_2$ $\equiv N > \equiv CR$ $=S > =O$

When a group with an inductive effect but no resonance effect is attached to a conjugated system such as benzene, one also finds the phenomenon that its influence is mostly on the ortho and para carbons of the benzene. In such cases, an electrophilic inductive substituent always makes those carbons electrophilic, and a nucleophilic inductive substituent makes them nucleophilic. For example, the nitro group has a strong electrophilic inductive effect. If we now attach it to benzene, we can write the following resonance structures:

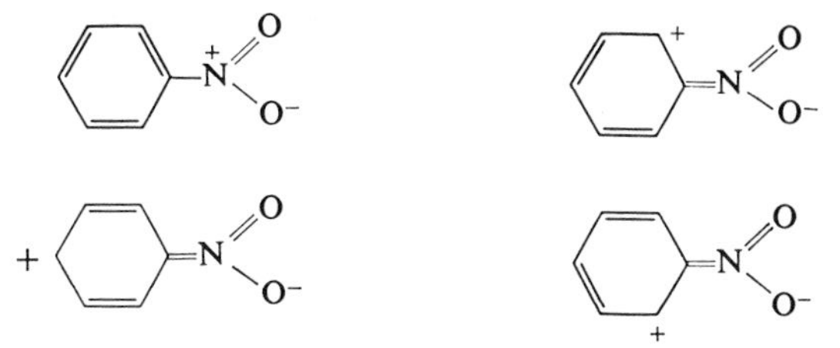

Consequently, the actual form is an intermediate one, with a δ^+ on the ortho and para carbons.

If we compare the *p*-nitrophenyl group with the *p*-aminophenyl group, we see that the first group will have an electrophilic inductive effect on its substituents, and that the second will have a nucleophilic effect. Consequently, the reduction of paraoxon to aminoparaoxon produces a marked change in

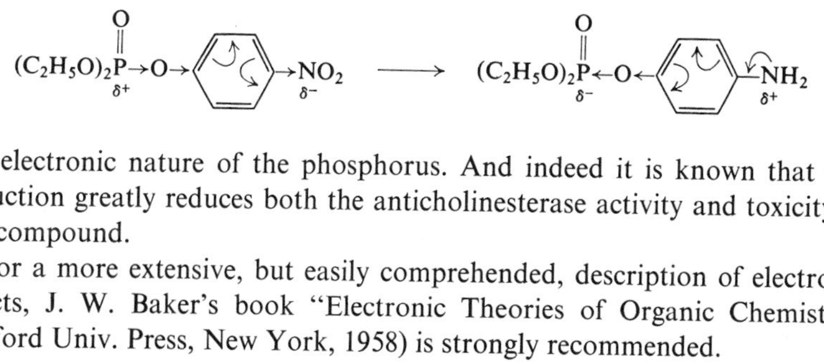

$$(C_2H_5O)_2\underset{\delta+}{\overset{O}{\overset{\|}{P}}}\rightarrow O \rightarrow C_6H_4 \rightarrow \underset{\delta-}{NO_2} \longrightarrow (C_2H_5O)_2\underset{\delta-}{\overset{O}{\overset{\|}{P}}}\leftarrow O \leftarrow C_6H_4 - \underset{\delta+}{NH_2}$$

the electronic nature of the phosphorus. And indeed it is known that this reduction greatly reduces both the anticholinesterase activity and toxicity of the compound.

For a more extensive, but easily comprehended, description of electronic effects, J. W. Baker's book "Electronic Theories of Organic Chemistry" (Oxford Univ. Press, New York, 1958) is strongly recommended.

Background Neurobiology

The majority of insecticides, and indeed the majority of all poisons, kill by virtue of their effects on the nervous system. The reason lies in the special sensitivity of the nervous system, which is the part of the body showing, to the greatest extent, irreversible damage consequent on even transient blockade. Other poisons whose primary target is elsewhere commonly produce their ultimate effect upon the nervous system; thus heart poisons (like atropine) and poisons which block the oxygen-carrying capacity of blood (like carbon monoxide) are lethal because of the brain damage that follows deprivation of the brain's great oxygen requirement.

Very many poisons act directly upon specific parts of the nervous system. The reason again lies in the fact of the marked inability of the nervous system to tolerate even brief interruption. Compounds which act briefly on other tissues have little effect, except in those cases where the tissues, such as heart and lung, are vital in maintaining nervous function. And the body has powerful defense mechanisms, including metabolic degradation and excretion, which make it difficult to produce more than a brief effect with a poison.

The above considerations may be less convincing to the reader than the facts, detailed in this book, which are that in virtually every case where we understand the basis of insecticidal action, the effects are directly upon nerve. So let us now briefly consider the nervous system.

The term "central nervous system" (CNS) refers in mammals to the brain and spinal cord, in insects to the chain of ventral ganglia, which may be partly fused together in some insects, such as the housefly, or present as discrete segmented units in some, such as the cockroach. The CNS is the integrating and determining part. The peripheral nervous system is the residue, consisting of afferent nerves bringing information to the CNS, and efferent nerves taking "instructions" to muscles, glands, etc. The only components of the nervous system whose function is well understood are the neurons, which are nerve cells with long, sometimes extremely long, processes along which nerve impulses pass. A common arrangement is for a cell to have one long process, the axon, carrying impulses away from the cell body, and short branched processes, the dendrites, which carry impulses to the cell body. The long nerves we see anatomically are bundles of axons.

There are two quite different modes of nerve impulse transmission in the nervous system: *axonic transmission*, which conveys an impulse from its arrival point, then along the axon to the meeting place with another cell, which may be another neuron (the meeting takes place on a dendrite or actually on the cell body of this second neuron) or may be a muscle, gland, or sensory receptor cell. Across the junction between cells, *synaptic transmission* occurs. The term "synapse" was formerly used for junctions between two neurons, but is now generally used for junctions of neurons with other cells, even for the junction between neuron and muscle which has the specific name "neuromuscular junction."

Neurophysiologists used to be either "sparks" men or "soup" men: the sparks men believed all transmission was electrical; the soup men argued that it was chemical. In fact, it is now firmly established that virtually all axonic transmission is electrical (in a manner of speaking) and virtually all synaptic transmission is chemical.

Our modern understanding of the basis of axonic transmission is due largely to A. L. Hodgkin and A. F. Huxley. If one pokes an electrode into a resting axon, and measures the internal potential of the axon with respect to some outside point, the inside is found to be more negative than the outside, i.e., the axon is polarized. The resting potential difference is the "membrane potential."

When a nerve impulse goes by, the inside suddenly becomes more negative than the outside, but recovers (with a little overshoot) as the impulse passes on. In fact it is this propagated reversal of polarity that constitutes the impulse. This moving depolarization is called an "action potential" (see Fig. 6.1).

The resting potential is believed to be caused by the existence of a higher K^+ level inside the nerve than outside. There is more Na^+ outside than in. The first or rising part of the action potential is caused by the sudden development of leakiness to Na^+ in the axon's outer membrane, so that sodium rushes in and the potential (recorded by the internal electrode) rapidly drops to zero and even goes positive. Then, microseconds later, the membrane becomes leaky to K^+ which, because it is higher inside than out, rushes out and restores the status quo. It is further believed that a system picturesquely called the sodium pump is always busy pumping Na^+ out of the nerve to maintain its low internal Na^+, and hence its ability to be fired. It will be noted that the question, what causes the sudden Na^+ leakiness in the membrane, is unanswered. Nachmansohn and his colleagues believe that cholinesterase is involved, but their view is not generally accepted (see the review in ref. 10, pp. 23–26).

When an impulse, propagated along an axon as described above, reaches a synapse, the impulse itself dies out. However, it causes release, from the end of the axon, of a little burst or quantum or cloud of a chemical, the transmitter substance, which diffuses across the synapse and triggers off another action potential if the synapse is between neurons, or an appropriate response if the synapse is between a neuron and some effector, such as muscle or gland. The term "neurohumor" was once used instead of "transmitter substance," hence synaptic transmission was stated to be neurohumoral. There are two known kinds of transmitter substance (or simply, transmitter): acetylcholine and norepinephrine; but there are very probably several others. Any given synapse has its characteristic transmitter, as discussed below, with the exception that norepinephrine is commonly accompanied by some epinephrine.

$CH_3C(O)OCH_2CH_2\overset{+}{N}(CH_3)_3$

Acetylcholine

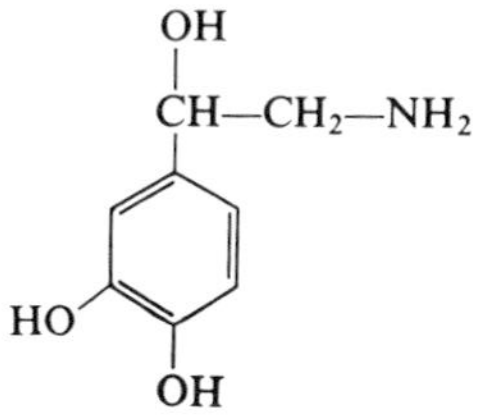

OH
|
CH—CH_2—NH_2
HO OH

Norepinephrine

In Europe the term noradrenaline is often preferred to norepinephrine. Universally, synapses which utilize acetylcholine are called cholinergic, those that utilize norepinephrine are called adrenergic.

The above account assumes that the transmitter stimulates some component on the far side of the synapse (the post-synaptic side), and this component—hypothetical rather than experimental—is called the receptor. One picture is that the transmitter combines with the receptor to produce a configurational change which alters the Na^+ permeability at that point, thus triggering an action potential or appropriate response.

In order to restore the sensitivity of the synapse, the transmitter must be eliminated so that the receptor can return to its resting condition. At cholinergic junctions, it is very promptly removed by cholinesterase, which hydrolyzes it to inactive components, acetate and choline. The cholinesterase is commonly on the presynaptic side of the synapse rather than immediately adjacent to the receptor, but since the synaptic cleft (the zone between the presynaptic and postsynaptic endings) is only about 500 Å wide, and each

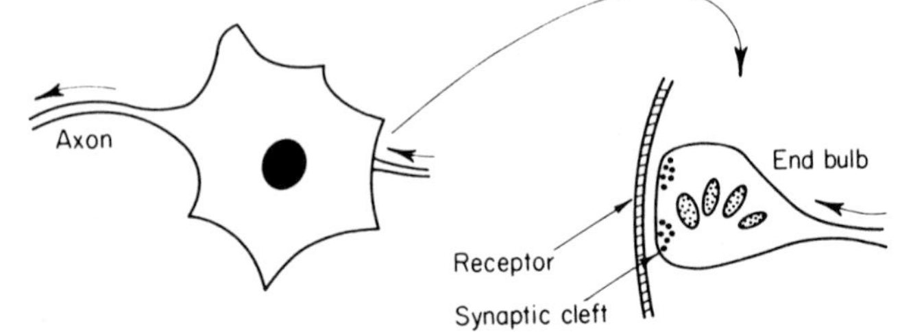

FIG. 1.1. Schematic drawings. Left: cell body of a spinal neuron, with nucleus (black dot). Only one of the thousands of synaptic connections with axons of other neurons is shown, with small arrows showing the direction of impulse flow. Right: greater magnification of the synapse. The end bulb contains mitochondria (large) and clusters of vesicles (small). The small arrow shows the direction of impulse flow.

acetylcholine molecule is about 9 Å long, it is not difficult to imagine that presynaptic cholinesterase could rapidly eliminate acetylcholine throughout the synaptic cleft. In adrenergic junctions, the corresponding degrading enzyme is monoamine oxidase, but its precise localization is not known, and the current view is that diffusion away from the site is the major mode of loss, followed by oxidative removal at a relatively slow pace.

It is believed that the transmitter substances in synapses are stored in small bodies, the presynaptic vesicles. They may be seen in the schematic drawing of a synapse from the spinal cord of a vertebrate (Fig. 1.1).

Now let us consider the gross anatomy of the nervous system. Peripheral nerves belong to either the somatic or autonomic divisions—the sensory somatic nerves are afferent: they carry sensations to the nervous system; the motor somatic nerves are efferent: they carry impulses to the voluntary muscles, i.e., muscles we can move voluntarily, such as those of the arm and leg. The autonomic nerves are all efferent, and carry impulses to glands and also to the muscles which are not voluntarily controlled, such as those of the intestine and the pupil. There are two divisions in the autonomic nervous system, the sympathetic and the parasympathetic. The implication in these names is that the two divisions operate against each other, and this is quite often true. For instance, the pupil is innervated by a sympathetic and a parasympathetic nerve: when the parasympathetic excites it, the pupil contracts; when the sympathetic excites it, the pupil dilates. (It is quite a common arrangement in biological control mechanisms for opposite effects to be under dual positive control, rather than for one effect to occur in the absence of a single control.)

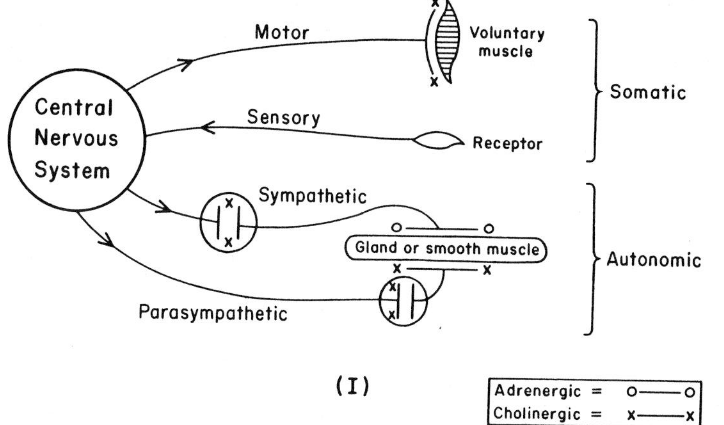

FIG. 1.2. Diagram of the nervous system of a vertebrate showing the locations of adrenergic and cholinergic junctions.

It will be shown in subsequent chapters that some poisons, such as DDT, interfere with axonic transmission; others, such as nicotine and organophosphates, interfere with synaptic transmission, so it is important to know where these components lie. There are axons and synapses in the central and peripheral system. Somatic and autonomic nerves both have synapses in the central nervous system, but as Fig. 1.2 shows, the only peripheral synapse in somatic nerves is the neuromuscular junction. In autonomic nerves, there are always two peripheral synapses: one at the junction with the muscle or gland, the neuroeffector junction, and another intermediate one.

The peripheral synapses of the sympathetic nerves are adrenergic (with two minor exceptions: the adrenal medulla and the sweat glands, where the sympathetic innervation is cholinergic). The peripheral synapses of the parasympathetic nerves are all cholinergic. However, the intermediate synapses of both kinds of autonomic nerve are cholinergic. This biochemical similarity of intermediate synapses is coupled with an anatomical difference: whereas the sympathetic synapses are gathered together in large bundles (ganglia) quite near the nerve cord, the parasympathetic synapses are in small ganglia commonly located on or near the organ innervated. Consequently, the postsynaptic neurons of parasympathetic nerves are usually extremely short while those of sympathetic nerves are usually very long, as Fig. 1.2 suggests.

The cholinergic junctions are not all identical in response to drugs, and probably differ in the nature of their receptor. One group of cholinergic sites in vertebrates, including the neuromuscular junction and the parasympathetic ganglia, is stimulated by nicotine. The symptoms which drugs produce when they stimulate these sites are called "nicotinic": they include effects on voluntary muscles, such as paralysis and fasciculation (a disorganized twitching). A second group of cholinergic sites in vertebrates, the parasympathetic neuroeffector junctions, is stimulated by muscarine, and the corresponding symptoms are called "muscarinic." They include slowing of the heart, constriction of the pupils, urination, and salivation. This aspect is discussed at greater length in a later chapter (pp. 150–152).

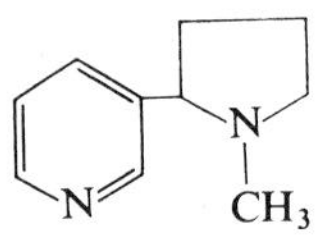

N — CH_3

Nicotine

COOH
|
CH—$\overset{+}{N}(CH_3)_3$
|
CHOH
|
CH_2
|
CH_3

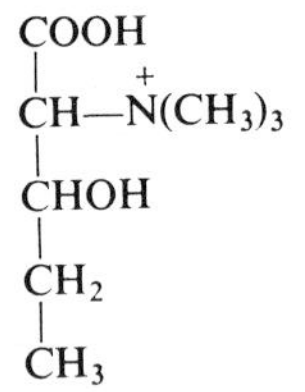

Muscarine

So far we have considered the neurobiology of vertebrates. Insects and other arthropods differ from vertebrates in some very important ways. First, it is virtually certain that the neuromuscular junction of insects is not cholinergic; the evidence is histochemical (15), enzymological (4), and physiological (11). We do not know what transmitter is involved. This appalling lack of knowledge is a challenge not only to physiologists, but to designers of insecticides. Second, we have no knowledge of the transmitters in the insect autonomic system, often called the stomatogastric or sympathetic system. There is no evidence that there are two divisions in this system, comparable to the sympathetic and parasympathetic divisions of the vertebrate.

Because cholinesterase is such an important enzyme in toxicology, comments on its types and occurrence are necessary. There are two types. One is often called "acetylcholinesterase" or "true cholinesterase"; it occurs in vertebrate erythrocytes and the electric organ of electric eels and fishes, and is the principal cholinesterase of vertebrate nervous systems and the insect central nervous system. It is this enzyme which is the target of organophosphate and carbamate toxicants. The second, called "pseudocholinesterase" or "plasma cholinesterase" or "serum cholinesterase" occurs primarily in vertebrate blood plasma, and to a modest extent in brain and other tissues. It has no known biological function, and can be totally inhibited without harmful consequences. The two types are easily differentiated by their substrate preferences and by their different sensitivities to certain inhibitors.

Finally, a brief mention may be made of a class of neurons whose blockade can be lethal, although no insecticides have made use of this principle. These are the inhibitory neurons, present in arthropods and mammals (and elsewhere). When they fire, they counteract the activity of some of the neurons described above, all of which are excitatory. The overall activity that we see is the algebraic outcome of inhibitory and excitatory stimuli. The transmitter substance of these inhibitory neurons is unknown, but it seems certain that strychnine and picrotoxin kill vertebrates by blocking these neurons, thus causing excessive excitation, which shows itself as convulsions. In the coming years, new insecticides could be designed on such a basis. Interested readers would enjoy the splendid little monograph by Roeder (13) for the case of insects, and the detailed review by Curtis (5). Whereas all inhibitory neurons appear to be central in vertebrates, there are at least some peripheral inhibitory neurons in insects (14) and Crustacea (8). These offer a tempting target.

REFERENCES

1. Bernard, C., "An Introduction to the Study of Experimental Medicine" (transl. by H. C. Greene), pp. 157, 159. Schuman, New York, 1949.
2. Brookes, P., and Lawley, P. D., *Biochem. J.* **77**, 478 (1960).
3. Chadwick, L. E., *In* "Cholinesterase and Anticholinesterase Agents" (G. B. Koelle, ed.), pp. 741–798. Springer, Berlin, 1963.
4. Colhoun, E. H., *Advan. Insect. Physiol.* **1**, 1 (1963).
5. Curtis, D. R., *Pharmacol. Rev.* **15**, 333 (1963).
6. Ebeling, W., *J. Econ. Entomol.* **53**, 475 (1960).
7. Fisher, R. W., *J. Econ. Entomol.* **52**, 1015 (1959).
8. Florey, E., *In* "Inhibition in the Nervous System and Gamma-aminobutyric Acid" (E. Roberts, ed.), Macmillan (Pergamon), New York, 1960.
9. Gavrilescu, N., and Peters, R. A., *Biochem. J.* **25**, 1397 (1931).
10. O'Brien, R. D., "Toxic Phosphorus Esters," Academic Press, New York, 1960.
11. O'Connor, A., O'Brien, R. D., and Salpeter, M. M., *J. Insect Physiol.* **11**, 1351 (1965).
12. Peters, R. A., *Proc. Roy. Soc.* (*London*) **B139**, 143 (1952).
13. Roeder, K. D., "Nerve Cells and Insect Behaviour," 188 pp. Harvard Univ. Press, Cambridge, Massachusetts, 1963.
14. Usherwood, P. N. R., and Grundfest, H., *Science* **143**, 17 (1964).
15. Wigglesworth, V. B., *Quart. J. Microscop. Sci.* **99**, 441 (1958).

CHAPTER 2

Physical Toxicants

Indifferent Narcotics

Narcotics are defined as substances which decrease the activity and sensitivity of organisms. The familiar ones are drugs such as barbiturates and opium constituents, but these are probably not physical toxicants. Diethyl ether $C_2H_5OC_2H_5$ and the simple substituted alkanes, such as chloroform $CHCl_3$, carbon disulfide CS_2, ethylene dichloride $ClCH_2CH_2Cl$, and chloropicrin Cl_3CNO_2, may be classified as narcotics. Because they have much in common in their symptomology, are reversible, and are little affected in their potency by substantial structural changes, these are called "indifferent narcotics," and very probably owe their action only to physical effects. The evidence will emerge in this chapter.

Ever since the action of anesthetics was demonstrated in humans by Long in 1842 using ether, a natural interest has existed in the mechanism of action of such compounds. The famous Overton-Meyer hypothesis represents a synthesis of the views of H. H. Meyer in 1899 (9) and Overton in 1901 (12). They were struck by the marked liposolubility of these compounds, coupled with the facts that they presumably act on the nervous system and that the nervous system has a high lipid content. They suggested that narcotic action of anesthetics depends on the concentration achieved in some hypothetical lipid entity, called the biophase. The liposolubility, as measured by the oil/water partition coefficient, was of course extremely high for all the anesthetics they considered.

In 1935, K. H. Meyer and Hemmi (10) extended the above view, proposing that when any substance achieved some threshold concentration in the lipid biophase, narcosis occurred. This striking generalization implied that the detailed structure of compounds was unimportant for narcosis, and only the liposolubility was critical. For such compounds, they coined the phrase indifferent narcotics. One would on this basis predict that if one compound (any compound) had a given narcotic action, then a different compound with twice the liposolubility would be twice as toxic.* Expressed quantitatively, the generalization is

$$PC = \text{constant}$$

where P is the partition coefficient and C is the external concentration necessary to produce a particular effect (e.g., the LD_{50}). Table 2.1 contains data from Meyer and Hemmi which illustrates the constancy of PC in one case.

TABLE 2.1

EFFECTIVENESS OF MISCELLANEOUS NARCOTICS ON TADPOLES[a]

Substance	C, narcotic concentration (M)	P, partition coefficient oil/water	PC
Ethanol	0.33	0.1	0.033
n-Propanol	0.11	0.35	0.380
n-Butanol	0.03	0.65	0.02
Valeramide	0.07	0.30	0.021
Antipyrine	0.07	0.30	0.021
Aminopyrine	0.03	1.30	0.039
Barbital	0.03	1.38	0.041
Diallylbarbituric acid	0.01	2.4	0.024
Benzamide	0.013	2.5	0.033
Salicylamide	0.0033	5.9	0.021
Phenobarbital	0.008	59	0.048
o-Nitroaniline	0.0025	14	0.035
Thymol	0.000047	950	0.041

[a] From Meyer and Hemmi (10).

* This argument holds for the case where the toxicity is measured by the concentration in an external phase whose volume is very large compared to the organism, e.g., a bulk solution or gas to which the organism is exposed. If, instead, the toxicant is injected into or topically applied to the organism, the matter is more complex. Consider a lipid biophase of volume B, and a surrounding aqueous phase of effective volume S; if the partition coefficient between the phases is P (i.e., concentration in B/concentration in S) one can show that the fraction F of any given dose which, at equilibrium, will be in biophase is: $F = PB/(S+PB)$. Consequently, doubling P will only double F when S is much greater than B.

The final refinement of this line of argument was provided in 1939 by Ferguson (3,4) who proposed that the requirement for a given amount of narcotic action (e.g., the amount required to kill the organism) was not that one had to achieve some fixed concentration threshold, but rather some fixed threshold of *thermodynamic activity*. [By "activity" is meant what Lewis and Randall, for instance, call "relative activity" (8).] Let us diverge from the main argument to review the meaning of thermodynamic activity.

Let us consider a solution of solute in a solvent. Certain properties caused by the solute are said to be colligative; approximately speaking, these properties depend only on the molar concentration of the solute, not on the nature of it. For example, any unionized solute at $1M$ will raise the boiling point of water approximately 0.5°C. Clearly the stimulus to Meyer and Hemmi must have been this notion of colligative properties. But let us consider why the above statement is only approximate. First, compounds whose solutions are associated or dissociated give unexpected results because, rather than concentration of *molecules*, it is concentration of *particles* that rules colligative properties; thus dilute NaCl would be about twice as effective as equimolar sucrose. Second, only ideal solutes behave colligatively. By ideal in this context is meant solutes which have no finite size, and do not interact with one another (or with solvent) when in solution. For such hypothetical ideal solutes, increasing the concentration 100-fold would always multiply by 100 any effects upon a solution. But in the real world, solutes may depart far from ideality. For a real solute of concentration C, we can speak of the equivalent concentration of an ideal solute: this is the thermodynamic activity a (often referred to simply as "activity"). Thus if a $1M$ solution of a real solute raised the boiling point of water by 0.25°C instead of the anticipated 0.5°C, clearly its activity would be $0.5M$. Thus the activity represents a sort of corrected concentration indicating what concentration of an ideal solute would give the observed effect. Now concentrations can be expressed as molar (i.e., moles per liter), molal (moles per kilogram), or mole fraction (number of moles of solute divided by total number of moles of solute plus solvent). The mole fraction has the advantages of being dimensionless, and of never exceeding the value of 1, which is the mole fraction for pure solute. It is the activity expressed as mole fraction that Ferguson used.

Now let us state didactically that for a gas at partial pressure p, whose saturated vapor pressure is p_0, the activity, a, is given by

$$a = p/p_0$$

Similarly, for a solute at concentration c whose solubility in the particular solvent is c_0:

$$a = c/c_0$$

Although it does not constitute a proof, it may help to point out that, in the hypothetical case in which a solute is ideal with respect to the solvent, the two would be miscible in all proportions, i.e., $c_0 = 1$. The extent to which the actual conditions depart from this case (as measured by the departure of c_0 from 1) gives the extent of departure from ideality of the solute with respect to the solvent. Thus for an ideal solute, since $c_0 = 1$, then $a = c$, so that concentration and activity are identical, as one would expect. A parallel argument can be made for p and p_0.

There are two virtues to using activity in place of concentration in a theory of this kind. The first is that *concentrations* of different compounds do not necessarily have the same effect upon physical properties, such as the boiling point, whereas *activities* of different compounds do. Therefore, when death is induced in a nonspecific, physical way, compounds producing the same *activity* at the biophase should be equitoxic. The second is the useful property that, in a system containing several phases (for example, an animal body, which contains a great variety of watery and fatty phases), the activity of a solute is the same in all phases if equilibrium has been reached.* Consequently, if one knows the activity in one phase, one knows it in all. And if an organism is immersed in a solution of a certain activity, then when equilibrium has been achieved, the activity in all phases, including the biophase, is the same as in the solution. As in the previous case, discussed in the footnote on p. 23, the bulk of the solution must be large compared to the organism, or else the equilibrium activities will differ from the initial activity of the solute. A precisely parallel argument holds for gaseous agents.

The consequence of Ferguson's argument should be that when one examines the equitoxic dose, such as the LD_{50}, of a variety of physical toxicants, one should find that in spite of great variations in the *concentrations*, their *activities*, as measured by p/p_0 for gases or c/c_0 for solutions, should be very similar, and therefore give rise to similar activities in the biophase. The experimental data look most impressive. In two papers, Ferguson presented no less than 25 sets of data, of which Table 2.2 is representative. Clearly 9 out of 10 compounds, whose absolute toxicities vary as much as 73-fold, all give values for p/p_0 varying only 1.5-fold. Ethylene dibromide is acting in a way different from all the other compounds, producing toxicity at far lower p/p_0; it is therefore not an indifferent narcotic.

Data such as those in Table 2.2 suggest that there are indeed such things as

* A solute will move from one phase to another in an equilibrium system until its free energy F_1 in the first phase is equal to that, F_2, in the second phase. Therefore, at equilibrium $F_1 = F_2$. Since the free energy in phase 1 is given by $F_1 = F_0 + RT \ln a_1$ and in phase 2 by $F_2 = F_0 + RT \ln a_2$, then when $F_1 = F_2$, it follows that $a_1 = a_2$. Therefore, at equilibrium the activities in both phases are identical, and this argument is as true for multiple phases as for two.

indifferent narcotics. A potent compound of this type does not have a special ability to combine with some specific target (as is the case in the vast majority of very potent toxicants), but rather to an ability to achieve a high activity with a relatively low applied concentration. If the lethal dose of an agent is such that it has an activity between 0.1 and 1.0, one is inclined to suspect an indifferent mechanism of this type.

TABLE 2.2

TOXICITIES TO THE GRAIN WEEVIL *CALANDRA GRANARIA*[a]

Substance	Median lethal dose (mg/liter)	P_t/P_s
Ethylene dichloride	98.9	0.24
sym-Tetrachlorethane	15.4	0.24
Tetrachlorethane (asymmetric)	33.4	0.26
Ethyl chloride	1124	0.28
β-Trichlorethane	53	0.30
Ethylidene chloride	380	0.32
Methyl chloroform	290	0.31
Pentachlorethane	16.3	0.32
1,3-Dichloropropane	59	0.36
Ethylene dibromide	0.60	0.06

[a] P_t = vapor pressure at the median lethal dose. P_s = saturated vapor pressure. From Ferguson and Pirie (4).

There have been several cases in which a fairly close dependence of fumigant toxicity upon boiling point has been described with respect to various insects, such as houseflies, confused flour beetles, and wireworms, and for many years, starting in 1917 (1,11,13,15). Boiling point is an inverse measure of vapor pressure, p_0, and the smaller the value of p_0, the less will be the value of p which is required to achieve some fixed value of p/p_0. In other words, all the studies referred to may be looked on as experimental confirmations of Ferguson's principle.

In any homologous series, water solubility, vapor pressure, water–oil partition coefficients, and the reciprocal of surface activity all decrease in an approximately parallel fashion as the series is ascended (3). Consequently, it is a corollary of Ferguson's principle that not only does toxicity in such series increase with decreasing vapor pressure, as just mentioned, but also that there are decreases in the values of the other parameters. An inverse correlation between toxicity and any of the above properties is therefore to be expected in any one series, and to a lesser extent among compounds of diverse series. In every case, a cutoff phenomenon is likely to occur, which we shall now discuss.

The Cutoff Point

It is frequently found that, in some homologous series of poisons, the toxicity increases as the series is ascended. This phenomenon has been referred to (3) as Richardson's rule, and a regular decrease in the concentration needed to produce a given effect has been suggested, specifically 1, 1/3, $(1/3)^2$, $(1/3)^3$, and so on. This pattern was found in such diverse cases as the narcotic action of alcohols, esters, and ketones against tadpoles in 1901; toxicity of alcohols, ketones, and amines against *Bacillus typhosus*; and insecticidal action of alcohols (3), fatty acids (14), and 1,3-indandiones (7). In such series, the toxicity does not increase indefinitely. At some point (the cutoff point), the subsequent member has sharply reduced toxicity, and higher members show a progressive decrease.

An interesting explanation for the cutoff phenomenon was a part of Ferguson's theory. When his p/p_0 data were assembled for a homologous series, it was apparent that although they had far more constancy than the p data, yet there was an upward drift in the values as the series was ascended. For example, the p/p_0 values for mouse narcosis by alkanes for the C_5, C_6, C_7, and C_8 compounds were, respectively, 0.29, 0.34, 0.44, and 0.82. Obviously, if the series was further ascended, the required p/p_0 value would soon exceed 1.0, and clearly this is impossible, for one cannot achieve a pressure (or a solubility) greater than the saturation value under the given conditions.

This is interesting, but leaves open the question of the cause of the upward drift. Ferguson (3) merely comments that cutoff phenomena are not restricted to biological effects, but occur with other effects (such as capillary activity) that derive from the ratio of two parameters which do not increase identically as one ascends the series. One possible reason why p does not keep pace with p_0 would be that as the molecule becomes larger and larger, its ability to diffuse at a reasonable rate becomes progressively reduced, so that although it remains true that the achievement of an appropriate concentration in the biophase would cause death, it becomes excessively difficult to achieve it in practice; an extreme example would be that of the fatty acids, whose larger representatives are waxy and obviously immobile in virtually any system.

The ρ–σ–π Analysis

Hansch and Fujita (5) have attempted to develop a general theory of toxic action centered around partition coefficients, which they measured between octanol and water. Rather than use partition coefficients directly, they refer all results to some parent compound, and invent a π-value, which is a property of the substituent upon that parent; these presumably are responsible for the difference in partition coefficient between the parent and the derivative. Specifically, π is given by $\log(P/P_H)$, where P is the partition coefficient, in octanol–water, of the compound, and P_H is the coefficient for the unsubstituted parent. They then accept as a fact that as π is increased, biological activity increases, achieves an optimum, and decreases. Perhaps (they argue) there is some optimal value* of π, and when the actual value is less than this, the compound partitions only slowly into the hypothetical lipid biophase, whereas a very high π is associated with very large molecules and consequent slowing of the diffusion rate throughout, so that there is a "longer time needed to find the site of action." Now the influence of π would only be upon one of the multiple factors effecting biological potency, i.e., upon the ease of reaching the target. They suggest that, for all toxic compounds, the LD_{50} is reached when

$$ACk_x = \text{constant} \tag{1}$$

where A is a factor describing the probability of reaching the target, C is the external concentration, and k_x is a rate constant or equilibrium constant describing the affinity for the target. It will be noted that it is not necessary in this argument to use activities, for there is no assumption of a colligative property. In fact the above equation is one possible formulation of a common-sense view that total effectiveness depends on how much is applied, how well the compound gets to the target, and how well it reacts when it arrives.

Hansch and Fujita then speculate that π influences only A, and that as π increases (and consequently $\pi - \pi_0$, where π_0 is the value for the parent compound), A passes through an optimum. *If* this dependence has the form of a normal distribution curve (a very dubious proposition!) it would be true that:

$$A = a e^{-(\pi-\pi_0)^2} b \tag{2}$$

where a and b are constants. Combining Eqs. (1) and (2)

$$\log 1/C = -k_1 \pi^2 + k_2 \pi\pi_0 - k_3 \pi_0^2 + \log k_x + k_4 \tag{3}$$

Next they suggest that k_x can be treated as in the Hammett equation, in which the potency of a derivative compared to its parent (i.e., k_x/k_{parent}) is related to a substituent constant σ and a reaction constant ρ, as follows:

$$\log(k_x/k_{\text{parent}}) = \sigma\rho \tag{4}$$

* They actually propose that π is optimal when the partition coefficient "for the cell phases" is 1. It seems hard to imagine that the apolar phases would be so alike that a compound could have the same apolar phase/water coefficient for them all; but this proposal is in fact not necessary to the main argument.

Consequently, one can replace $\log k_x$ in Eq. (3) by $\sigma\rho + \log k_{\text{parent}}$, and using k_5 for $k_4 + \log k_{\text{parent}}$, we have:

$$\log 1/C = -k_1\pi^2 + k_2\pi\pi_0 - k_3\pi_0^2 + \rho\sigma + k_5 \tag{5}$$

The authors now take this as their most general equation, and show that in five categories of action a simplified version holds.

We will consider only one category here (type I) which occurs when π_0 is large with respect to π (so that π^2 is insignificant) and σ is very small or zero; then:

$$\log 1/C = k_6\pi + k_7 \tag{6}$$

where k_6 is a constant equal to $k_2\pi_0$ and k_7 another equal to $-k_3\pi_0^2 + k_5$. It will be recognized that this is a quantitative version of the Overton-Meyer hypothesis, that potency is a direct function of liposolubility, as measured by π. Furthermore, the category of action involved here is a particular case of indifferent narcotic action, for the nature of the substituents (which is measured by σ) is of negligible importance. The particular case is that for which the π's observed are far enough below the optimum that the cutoff effect happens not to be seen. The authors give two sets of data for which an extremely good fit to an equation of the form of Eq. (6) is obtained: the toxicity of 14 benzoic acid derivatives to mosquito larvae (Fig. 2.1) and that of 35 phenol derivatives to a variety of the bacterium *Mycobacterium pyogenes*. The correlation coefficients are 0.977 for both cases.

However, this excellent agreement between prediction and observation does not prove the validity of the theory. The original Meyer and Hemmi hypothesis was that PC=constant, which may be rewritten

$$\log P + \log C = \text{constant} \qquad \text{or} \qquad \log 1/C = \log P + \text{constant} \tag{7}$$

Since the π value of Hansch and Fujita is defined as

$$\pi = \log P/P_{\text{parent}}$$

and P of the parent compound would be constant for any series:

$$\pi = \log P - \text{constant}$$

so that Eq. (6) can be rewritten

$$\begin{aligned} \log 1/C &= k_6(\log P - \text{constant}) + k_7 \\ &= k_6 \log P + k_8 \end{aligned} \tag{8}$$

Clearly Eqs. (7) and (8) become identical if k_6 is approximately 1; so the Hansch-Fujita formulation is not profoundly different from the old Meyer-Hemmi version. In fact the slopes yielded by the data analyzed by Hansch and Fujita are 0.951 for the case of the phenols, which would thus approximately fit the Meyer-Hemmi formulation; but 0.519 for a series of substituted benzoic acids, which would therefore not fit.

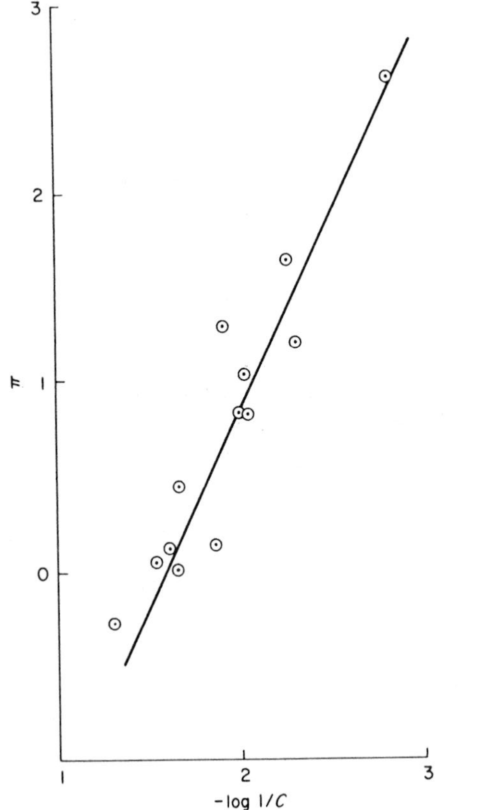

FIG. 2.1. Type I effect in σ–π–ρ analysis. Relation of π to toxicity of various benzoic acid analogs to mosquito larvae. C=concentration for 50% kill. From Hansch and Fujita (5) and Casida (2).

It would be unfair to imply that Hansch and Fujita have added little to the older view. Equation (8) represents only one of the consequences that can follow from introducing general equation [Eq. (5)]. In four other categories, which cover actions other than simply physical, and which consequently cannot be dealt with in this chapter, they succeed in introducing different conditions and producing different equations which fit the toxicity findings for very diverse compounds. This success greatly strengthens the plausibility of their hypothesis. Furthermore, it is intellectually satisfying to consider physical and chemical actions as variations on a basic theme. Or, more precisely, both physical and chemical toxicants have one requirement in common—to reach the biophase from some external point of application. One might expect that there would, therefore, be a common element in their requirements for potency; this common element apparently takes the form of a profound dependence on polarity, as measured by partition coefficients.

One of the problems in any attempt to relate toxicity to partition coefficients is the selection of the pair of solvents with which to measure these coefficients. Hansch *et al.* (6) point out that the relationship between the partition coefficient of a solute for two different solvent pairs is of the form:

$$\log P_1 = a \log P_2 + b$$

where P_1 and P_2 are the coefficients, and a and b are constants. Consequently the results for any given solvent pair have a measure of universality—except for those cases where some special solute–solvent interaction occurs. These cases could occur with an unfortunate choice of, say, the organic solvent employed in the measurement of partition coefficients; or when the solvent properties at the biophase are such as to give a special interaction with the solute.

REFERENCES

1. Brown, A. W. A., *J. Econ. Entomol.* **42**, 399 (1949).
2. Casida, J. E., *Biochem. J.* **59**, 216 (1955).
3. Ferguson, J., *Proc. Roy. Soc.* (*London*) **B127**, 387 (1939).
4. Ferguson, J., and Pirie, H., *Ann. Appl. Biol.* **35**, 532 (1948).
5. Hansch, C., and Fujita, T., *J. Am. Chem. Soc.* **86**, 1616 (1964).
6. Hansch, C., Muir, R. M., Fujita, T., Maloney, P. P., Geiger, F., and Streich, M., *J. Am. Chem. Soc.* **85**, 2817 (1963).
7. Kilgore, L. B., Ford, J. H., and Wolfe, W. C., *Ind. Eng. Chem.* **34**, 494 (1942).
8. Lewis, G. N., and Randall, M., "Thermodynamics," 2nd ed. McGraw-Hill, New York, 1961.
9. Meyer, H. H., *Arch. Exptl. Pathol. Pharmakol. Naunyn-Schmiedebergs* **42**, 109 (1899).
10. Meyer, K. H., and Hemmi, H., *Biochem. Z.* **277**, 39 (1935).
11. Moore, W., *J. Agr. Res.* **10**, 365 (1917).
12. Overton, E., "Studien uber Narkose." Jena, 1901.
13. Shepard, H. H., Lindgren, D. L., and Thomas, E. L., *Minn. Univ. Agr. Expt. Sta. Tech. Bull.* **120** (1937).
14. Siegler, E. H., and Popenoe, C. H., *J. Agr. Res.* **29**, 259 (1924).
15. Tattersfield, F., and Roberts, A. W. R., *Ann. Appl. Biol.* **10**, 199 (1920).

CHAPTER 3

Organophosphates: Chemistry and Inhibitory Activity

There is an extensive literature on these compounds. Two books have been written in English (31,47), one in German (52), and one in Czech (51) concerned exclusively with organophosphates, and a third compendium (40) is much concerned with them. This is a very large class of compounds; it was estimated in 1959 that 50,000 of them had been made (45) and new ones are reported monthly. It is the one class about whose action a great deal is known at the molecular as well as the cellular level.

The discovery of the insecticidal action of these compounds was made in Germany during the last war, and represents one of the remarkably few cases where a sword was later used for a plowshare. The Allies and the Germans both devoted efforts to preparing organophosphates suitable for warfare. A number of such compounds, often referred to as nerve gases, were prepared (the best known are tabun, sarin, and soman) and were available in tank-car lots by the end of the war. Happily, they were never used, but military interests in such compounds continues to be lively (55). It is to Gerhard Schrader in Germany that we owe the discovery of their suitability in agriculture, initially as a substitute for nicotine.

The first preparation used in Germany was Bladan, whose activity we now know to be due to its content of tepp. Then in 1944, parathion was introduced, which, along with the related methyl parathion, continues to be the most widely used organophosphate.

Nomenclature

The indigestible topic of nomenclature must be mastered, at least in its essentials, if sense is to be made of the organophosphate story. A rather full account is available in ref. 47, p. 9. Unfortunately, the reader may encounter in the literature a number of names which do not conform to the standards given herein. In part this is due to the fact that several years ago there were four different "official" systems for nomenclature: competing British, Swedish, German, and American systems (42). Fortunately, Anglo-American agreement was reached in 1952 for the naming of compounds containing one atom of phosphorus, and these make up the great majority of economic compounds. (These rules are described in refs. 8 and 9, but the reader is warned that the legalistic terminology is rather confusing.) But old habits die hard, and the "international" system is not universally used. Furthermore, in cases where side chains attached to the phosphorus are very complex, the naming of the side chain has priority, as we shall see.

It is customary to employ the term organophosphate as a generic term to cover all the toxic organic compounds containing phosphorus. Next we consider the atoms attached to the phosphorus. When the compound contains (I) it is called a phosphate; with (II) it is a phosphonate; with (III) it is a phosphorothionate; with (IV) it is a phosphorothiolate (but many authors choose to call both this and the preceding type a phosphorothioate; they do not distinguish a thiono sulfur, =S, from a thiolo sulfur, —S—); with (V) it is a phosphorodithioate; with (VI) it is a phosphoramidate. The usage will be clearer when examples are given later.

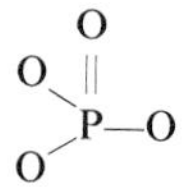

$(O)(O)P(=O)—O$ (I) $(C)(O)P(=O)—O$ (II) $(O)(O)P(=S)—O$ (III)

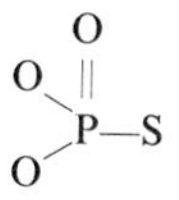

$(O)(O)P(=O)—S$ (IV) $(O)(O)P(=S)—S$ (V) $(O)(O)P(=O)—N$ (VI)

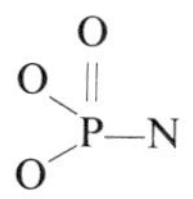

Most organophosphates can be thought of as esters of alcohols with a phosphorus acid, or as anhydrides of a phosphorus acid with some other acid. Thus parathion is an ester of the acid $(HO)_3P{=}S$ with two molecules of ethanol and one of the weakly acidic "alcohol" *p*-nitrophenol:

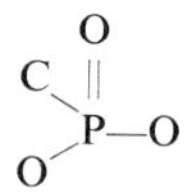

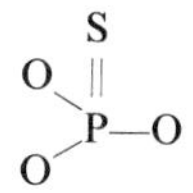

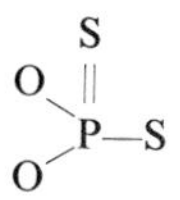

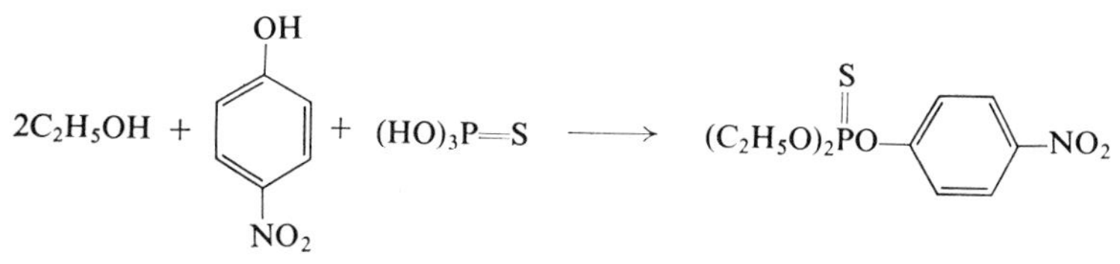

$$2C_2H_5OH + HO{-}C_6H_4{-}NO_2 + (HO)_3P{=}S \longrightarrow (C_2H_5O)_2P(=S)O{-}C_6H_4{-}NO_2$$

In such cases, the chemical name is simply given by naming the alcohols (in alphabetical order) and then the appropriate phosphorus acid ending described above, with spaces after each alcohol. Parathion is, then, diethyl *p*-nitrophenyl phosphorothionate. If there is doubt as to where the alcohols should be attached, one specifies the points of attachment. For instance, an impurity in parathion is:

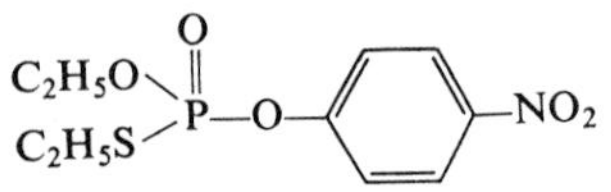

$$(C_2H_5O)(C_2H_5S)P(=O)\text{—O—}C_6H_4\text{—}NO_2$$

This is called *O*-ethyl *S*-ethyl *O*-*p*-nitrophenyl phosphorothiolate.

Virtually all the difficulties in naming organophosphates and, more importantly, in drawing a formula when given the chemical name, come in naming the side-chain alcohols. Fortunately the great majority of commercial compounds are *O,O*-diethyl and *O,O*-dimethyl types, and all the variety comes in the nature of the third alcohol, often known as the leaving group, for reasons which will become apparent. In other words, most organophosphates conform to the general structure $(RO)_2P(A)X$, where R is methyl or ethyl, A is sulfur or oxygen, and X can vary a great deal. The common and scientific names of several well-known organophosphates are given in Table 3.1.

The multiplicity of organophosphates frequently causes them to be victims of confusion between common and proprietary names. A proprietary name is the one usually allocated by the company which owns the compound; it should always be used with a capital letter, and is often followed by an ® to show that it is a registered trade mark. Examples are Rogor, Baytex, and Bidrin. If widely used, compounds frequently have common names allocated to them by national or international committees. Sometimes these are new names, but often the proprietary name is given approval. Thereafter, capitals are omitted, and so one has malathion, dichlorvos, and diazinon. Tables of common names are published from time to time in, for example, the *Bulletin of the Entomological Society of America*.*

Nonenzymic Reactions

Certain nonenzymic reactions (as distinguished from biochemical reactions) are central to the understanding of organophosphate biochemistry. The two most crucial are hydrolysis and isomerization, because both alter biological properties in important ways.

* A consolidated list was published in *Bull. Entomol. Soc. Am.* **9**, 189–197 (1963) and added to in *Bull. Entomol. Soc. Am.* **10**, 198 (1964).

TABLE 3.1

SOME COMMON ORGANOPHOSPHATES

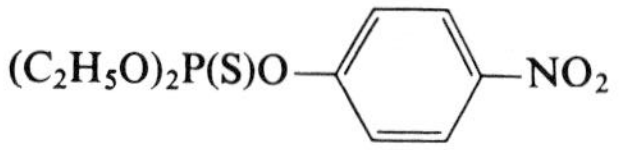

$(C_2H_5O)_2P(S)O-C_6H_4-NO_2$

Parathion
(Diethyl *p*-nitrophenyl phosphorothionate)

$(CH_3O)_2P(S)SCH(CH_2COOC_2H_5)COOC_2H_5$

Malathion
[*O*,*O*-dimethyl *S*-bis(carboethoxy)ethyl phosphorodithioate]

$(CH_3O)_2P(O)OCH{=}Cl_2$

Dichlorvos
(Dimethyl 2-dichlorovinyl phosphate)

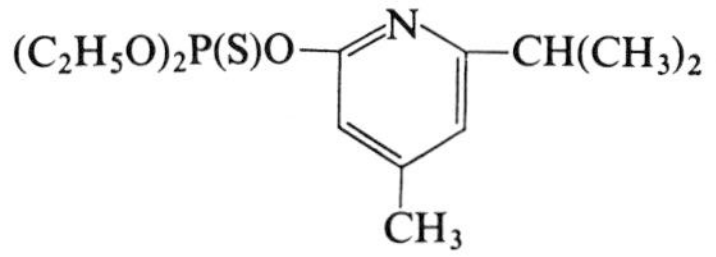

$(C_2H_5O)_2P(S)O-$ pyrimidinyl ($CH(CH_3)_2$, CH_3)

Diazinon
(Diethyl 2-isopropyl-4-methyl-6-pyrimidinyl phosphorothionate)

$(CH_3O)_2P(S)SCH_2N-$ (4-oxo-1,2,3-benzotriazinyl)

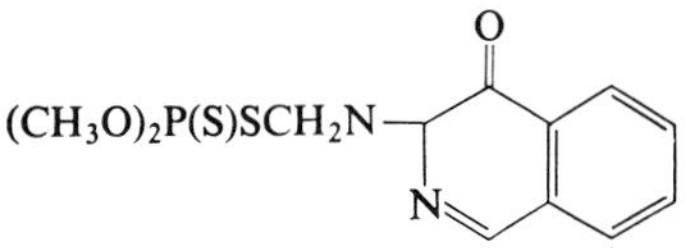

Azinphosmethyl (Guthion)
(*O*,*O*-dimethyl *S*-(4-oxo-1,2,3-benzotriazin-3(4*H*)ylmethyl phosphorodithioate)

$(CH_3O)_2P(O)OC(CH_3){=}C-C(O)N(CH_3)_2$

Bidrin
(Dimethyl 3-hydroxy-*N*,*N*-dimethyl-*cis*-crotonamide phosphate)

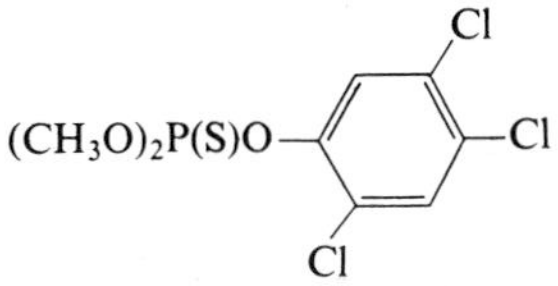

$(CH_3O)_2P(S)O-C_6H_2Cl_3$

Ronnel
(Dimethyl 3,4,6-trichlorophenyl phosphorothionate)

$(C_2H_5O)_2P(O)OP(O)(OC_2H_5)_2$

Tepp
(Diethyl phosphoric anhydride)

All the organophosphates can be hydrolyzed, and at a rate directly related to the alkalinity, because under all but very acid conditions it is the hydroxide ion which causes this hydrolysis. For example, with Sumithion:

$$(CH_3O)_2P(S)O-C_6H_3(CH_3)-NO_2 + OH^- \longrightarrow (CH_3O)_2P(S)O^- + HO-C_6H_3(CH_3)-NO_2$$

This formulation of the reaction does not tell the most important aspect of the story, that is, the mechanism of the hydrolysis. The mechanism involves an attack on the phosphorus by the OH^-. This is called a nucleophilic attack; it involves a negatively charged group, OH^-, attacking a relatively positive site, the phosphorus. The more positive the site, the more effective is the attack.* Consequently, the rate of hydrolysis is determined by the properties of the group attached to the phosphorus. Some groups are *electrophilic*, or electron withdrawing, and by withdrawing electrons make the phosphorus more positive and more subject to nucleophilic attack. Other groups are *nucleophilic*, or electron pushing, and tend to make atoms to which they are attached more negative. This simple electron pulling and pushing is called the *inductive effect*. Other effects can have the same consequences. The only other one that can be described here is the *field effect*: If a molecule is big enough that, for instance, a negative site can be brought up close to the phosphorus, then the electrophilic character of that phosphorus is reduced, and consequently the compound has lessened sensitivity to nucleophilic attack. (A fuller treatment of electronic effects is given in Chapter 1.) Consequently the malathion monoacid shown is far more stable to alkaline hydrolysis than its parent malathion.

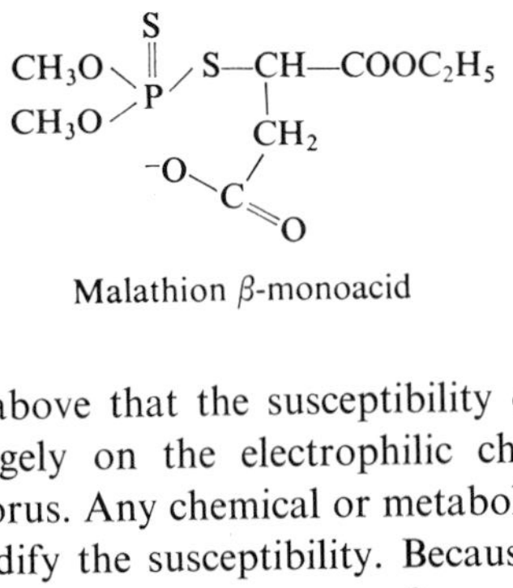

$(CH_3O)_2P(S)$—S—CH(CH_2—C(=O)—O^-)—$COOC_2H_5$

Malathion β-monoacid

It follows from the above that the susceptibility of organophosphate to hydrolysis depends largely on the electrophilic character of the groups attached to the phosphorus. Any chemical or metabolic change that modifies such character will modify the susceptibility. Because =O is more electrophilic than =S, the following common type of conversion greatly increases susceptibility to hydrolysis:

$(CH_3O)_2P(S)O-C_6H_4-NO_2 \longrightarrow (CH_3O)_2P(O)O-C_6H_4-NO_2$

Methyl parathion (a phosphorothionate) → Methyl paraoxon (a phosphate)

* The opposite is an electrophilic attack, in which a positively charged group, such as H^+, attacks a relatively negative site.

In fact the susceptibility is increased 22-fold (30). It is a general truth that phosphates are much more hydrolyzable than their corresponding phosphorothionates.

Naturally, one of the most potent electron-pushing groups is a negative ion. Consequently, if one hydrolyzes off one alcohol group from an organophosphate, the susceptibility to further hydrolysis is enormously reduced:

$$(C_2H_5O)_2P(O)O{-}C_6H_4{-}NO_2 \longrightarrow (C_2H_5O)_2P(O)O^-$$

Paraoxon — Diethyl phosphate

Whereas paraoxon has a half-life of 9.2 days at 25°C and pH 10, diethyl phosphate even at 100°C and pH 10 has a calculated half-life of 5 billion days (29,56).

An understanding of these hydrolysis phenomena is not only important in appreciating the stability of organophosphates, but provides a large part of the basis for understanding the problem of interaction of organophosphates with cholinesterase. Table 3.2 gives some typical half-lives of organophosphates at pH 7. Because their hydrolysis is primarily catalyzed by OH^-, one can roughly calculate the half-lives at higher pH's from the data of Table 3.2; each additional pH unit will decrease the half-life 10-fold because it increases the OH^- concentration 10-fold.

TABLE 3.2

HALF-LIVES OF ORGANOPHOSPHATES AT pH 8 AND 25° C[a]

Organophosphate	Half-life (hours)
Tepp	73
DFP	226
Thiolo-demeton	14,200
Paraoxon	22,200
Methyl parathion	50,200
Parathion	203,000
Thiono-demeton	1,250,000

[a] From Heath (29).

The above discussion has considered only the electronic factors which influence ease of hydrolysis. More precise thinking must take into account steric factors, such as the role of bulky groups in hindering access of hydroxyl ion. For instance, compound VII hydrolyzes 10^4 times more slowly than VIII in alkali:*

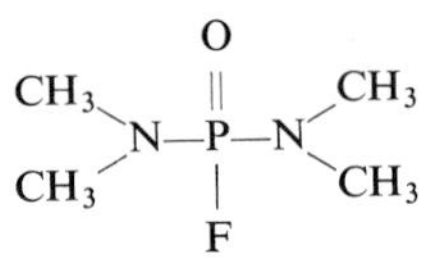

$$(CH_3)_2N-P(=O)(F)-N(CH_3)_2$$

(VII)

$$(C_3H_5)(H)N-P(=O)(F)-N(H)(C_3H_5)$$

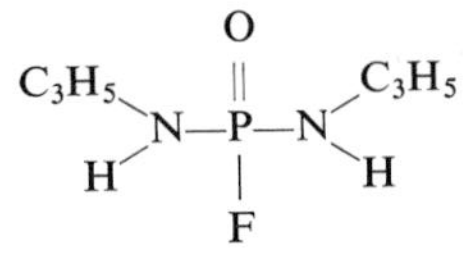

(VIII)

These steric factors will be found to play a far bigger role when we go beyond the relatively simple problem of interactions between organophosphates and the hydroxyl ion, whose small size minimizes steric effects, and turn to the very complex problem of interaction between organophosphates and the huge proteins of which enzymes are made.

Finally, it should be noted that a number of materials promote the hydrolysis of organophosphates. They include many amino acids, hydroxamic acids, chlorine, inorganic phosphates, and copper and molybdate ions (ref. 47, pp. 43–52).

The other nonenzymic process of major importance is isomerization. Prior to 1951 many conclusions were drawn, especially about the properties of phosphorothionates, which are now known to be invalid. For instance, it was believed that the common phosphorothionates could readily inhibit cholinesterase directly. As we shall see later, this is not true. The reason for the mistake was that virtually any sample of a phosphorothionate which has not been scrupulously purified contains isomers whose properties differ in important ways from those of the parent compound.

The commonest isomerization is the thiono–thiolo type, whereby a sulfur changes from the thiono (=S) form to the thiolo (—S—). A much-studied case is parathion (60) which isomerizes primarily to the *S*-ethyl derivative:

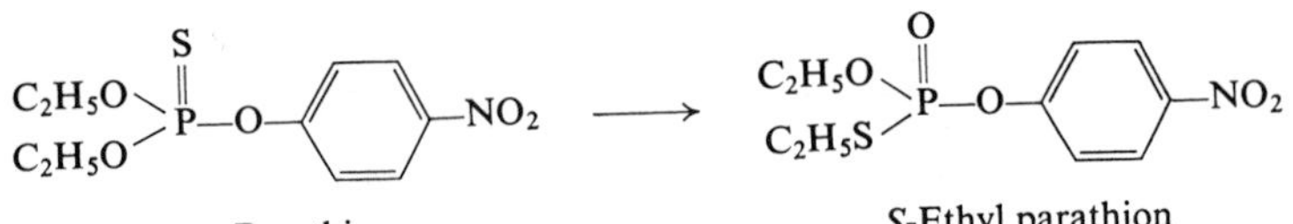

$$(C_2H_5O)_2P(=S)-O-C_6H_4-NO_2 \longrightarrow (C_2H_5O)(C_2H_5S)P(=O)-O-C_6H_4-NO_2$$

Parathion — *S*-Ethyl parathion

Similar *S*-alkyl isomerization occurs with malathion (26) and doubtless many other phosphorothionates. The process is very slow at room temperature, but occurs rapidly at high temperatures: good yields of isomer are common at 150°–200°C.

* Heath (29) first proposed this to be a steric effect, but has since had some doubts (31).

In principle, one would expect that not only the alkyl but the leaving groups should show thiono–thiolo changes, and this is the case. In fact, doubtless all crude preparations contain small amounts, e.g., of *S-p*-nitrophenyl parathion in the case of parathion samples. But extensive *S*-leaving group isomerization occurs in certain special instances, and when it does, occurs very readily even at room temperature. The reason is that a special condition can occur which enormously facilitates such isomerization: the condition is that some compound intermediate between the two isomers can be readily formed. Perhaps the best worked-out case (26) is for the thiono analog of Amiton (whose oxalate salt is called Tetram); it can form a cyclic immonium ion:

$$(C_2H_5O)_2P(S)OCH_2CH_2N(C_2H_5)_2 \rightleftharpoons (C_2H_5O)_2P(S)O^- + \begin{array}{l} CH_2 \\ | \\ CH_2 \end{array} \!\!\! \overset{+}{>} N(C_2H_5)_2$$

And because $(C_2H_5O)_2P(S)O^-$ rapidly equilibrates with the form $(C_2H_5O)_2P(O)S^-$, a large amount of the ammonium ion recombines with that form to give the *S*-side-chain isomer:

$$(C_2H_5O)_2P(O)SCH_2CH_2N(C_2H_5)_2$$

Amiton (thiolo isomer)

Because phosphorothionates, like other organophosphates, are usually manufactured at elevated temperatures, they commonly contain isomers, which are often responsible for the unpleasant odors, the direct anticholinesterase activity, and the rapidly hydrolyzed components of crude preparations. It will be evident in the light of the earlier discussion that such isomerizations, because they have the effect of converting P═S to P═O, greatly increase susceptibility to hydrolysis. It is for precisely parallel reasons, as we shall see, that they greatly increase potency against cholinesterase *in vitro*.

Reaction with Cholinesterase

Inhibition

We shall now consider the reactions of organophosphates with cholinesterase. This reaction is generally, but not universally, held to be the basis for their biological activity. The attack of OH^- upon organophosphates has been described above. In essence, a parallel reaction occurs when an OH of a vital serine molecule in the cholinesterase attacks an organophosphate. But because one is inclined to think of the organophosphate as the reagent, whereas the OH^- was the reagent in considering hydrolysis, it is more common to speak of the organophosphate attacking the cholinesterase. The serine involved is at the active site of cholinesterase, and is essential for the functioning of the enzyme. In the course of the attack, the leaving group of the organophosphate leaves and is replaced by the cholinesterase, which can be symbolized as EOH. Thus the *overall* reaction, for a phosphate of the type $(RO)_2P(O)X$, where X is the leaving group, is:

$$(RO)_2P(O)X + EOH \xrightarrow{k} (RO)_2P(O)OE + H^+ + X^-$$

The reaction therefore involves, *overall*, not merely a complex of enzyme and inhibitor, but a chemical reaction, a phosphorylation, with covalent bond formation between enzyme and inhibitor. It is a progressive reaction, i.e., the amount of reaction (inhibition) increases with time as discussed below. The equation above also shows that the nature of the inhibited enzyme, $EOP(O)(OR)_2$, is independent of the nature of the leaving group X. Thus, referring to Table 3.1, dichlorvos would yield a dimethyl phosphorylated enzyme $EOP(O)(OCH_3)$ and tepp would yield a diethyl phosphorylated enzyme $EOP(O)(OC_2H_5)_2$.

A reaction such as that pictured above involves two molecules (enzyme and inhibitor) and is therefore called "bimolecular." The rate at which the reaction occurs is determined by the nature of the particular cholinesterase and the particular organophosphate, and is described by a rate constant, the bimolecular rate constant, which we may symbolize as k_i. In most cases, the concentration of cholinesterase experimentally used is extremely small, often about 10^{-9} or $10^{-10}M$, because this is all that is needed to give a brisk hydrolysis of acetylcholine. Other practical considerations lead to use of inhibitor concentrations much higher than this, such as 10^{-5} or $10^{-6}M$. Under such conditions, the reaction between inhibitor and enzyme conform to so-called first-order kinetics, and the course of the reaction can be described (ref. 47, p. 76) by equations such as:

$$\log P = 2 - \frac{k_i I}{2.3} t \tag{1}$$

where P is the percent activity of enzyme remaining after incubation of I concentration of inhibitor for t time. A consequence of this equation, whose relevance to organophosphates was shown in 1950 by Aldridge (2), is that a plot of log P against t gives a straight line with a slope of $-k_i I/2.3$ and a y intercept of 2. From such plots one can therefore calculate k_i for any given enzyme and inhibitor. Figure 3.1 shows a set of such plots.

There are a number of cases on record where departures from first-order kinetics occur even when the above conditions are satisfied. Possible causes include breakdown of inhibitor by the enzyme preparation, and the unsuspected presence of two or more enzymes that can be inhibited and can act upon the substrate used for enzyme assay. The problem has been discussed thoughtfully by Krysan and Chadwick (41).

From Eq. (1) it can be seen that, for any fixed value of t, there is a concentration of inhibitor I which would reduce P to 50%. This concentration is called the I_{50}. Because its value is often small, the negative logarithm of the I_{50}, which is called the pI_{50}, is frequently used. Thus an I_{50} of $10^{-6}M$ can also be expressed as a pI_{50} of 6. It is often of interest to compare inhibitory potencies of a series of inhibitors against some enzyme; or of one inhibitor against a series of enzymes. The literature for this purpose uses sometimes the k_i value, sometimes the I_{50} (or pI_{50}). Clearly if the I_{50} is given, and one knows t, one

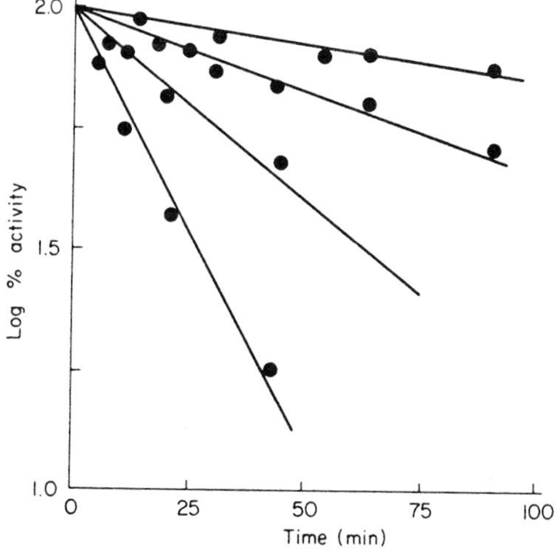

FIG. 3.1. Rate of inhibition of erythrocyte cholinesterase by various concentrations of purified diethyl *p*-chlorophenyl phosphate. From Aldridge and Davison (5).

may calculate k_i from Eq. (1), However, this calculation is meaningful only if, in fact, first-order kinetics are followed; in other circumstances, no k_i value exists and the I_{50} is an arbitrary value which combines information about inhibitory potency wrapped up inextricably with information about inhibitor breakdown (or other factors) in the particular preparation involved.

For almost 20 years of organophosphate research, it was customary, in comparing potency of inhibitors for a given enzyme, to compare their k_i values or I_{50} values, and to explain the observed differences in terms of electronic and steric factors. The earliest successful attempt was that of Aldridge and Davison (6), who showed in 1952 that, for ten differently substituted diethyl phenyl phosphates, there was a precise parallelism between their ease of alkaline hydrolysis and their potency against a cholinesterase. This is a specific quantitative statement of the general qualitative argument given above: positivity of the phosphorus promotes ability to attack OH^- and to attack the serine OH of cholinesterase. Since then, more elegant and complete evaluations of this type have been made (24,25,48). When sufficiently complete, such studies invariably encounter anomalous compounds, the commonest anomaly being that the compound is a better inhibitor than it "ought to be," in view of its susceptibility to alkaline hydrolysis. It has been customary to explain such deviations as indicating that some structural feature exists which promotes attack of inhibitor upon enzyme, while having little or no effect on the attack of inhibitor upon, for instance, OH^-.

In 1964, a simple kinetic treatment was introduced by Main which has enabled us to evaluate separately the affinity of the inhibitor for the enzyme molecule (which would be profoundly affected by, for instance, binding of the leaving group to the cholinesterase surface) and the ability to phosphorylate the enzyme once binding of the inhibitor has occurred. Main pointed out (43) that the reaction shown above from which Eq. (1) was deduced is only approximately accurate; a complete formulation should show the binding of inhibitor to enzyme prior to the phosphorylation reaction:

$$(RO)_2P(O)X + EOH \rightleftharpoons [(RO)_2P(O)X \cdot EOH] \rightarrow (RO)_2P(O)OE + H^+ + X^-$$

Let us symbolize this reaction as:

$$PX + E \underset{k_{-1}}{\overset{k_1}{\rightleftharpoons}} PXE \xrightarrow{k_2} PE$$

The overall reaction thus involves two aspects. First, there is the affinity of PX for E, which is described by the ratio of k_{-1} to k_1, and can be defined by the affinity constant $K_a = k_{-1}/k_1$. Second, there is ability of PX, after its binding to E, to phosphorylate it, an ability measured by the monomolecular rate constant k_2.

In order to compare this formulation with that of Aldridge, let us use k_i for the bimolecular constant of Aldridge as employed before; and define $k_x = k_3/K_a$. If we now use PX and E for the initial concentrations of inhibitor and enzyme, and PXE and PE for the concentrations of the reversibly and irreversibly inhibited forms at time t, Main points out that the rate of formation of PE is given by

$$d\,PE/dt = k_x(E - PE - PXE)PX$$

whereas the Aldridge treatment stated that

$$d\,PE/dt = k_i(E - PE)PX$$

Consequently when PXE, the reversible complex of enzyme and inhibitor, is at a very low concentration, the Main and Aldridge equations become almost identical, and k_x and k are numerically equal. However, k_i now stands revealed not as a simple bimolecular rate constant, but (since it is equivalent to k_3/K_a) as a combination of a unimolecular rate constant and an affinity constant.

Under conditions such that PXE achieves a significant concentration, the Aldridge treatment is wrong and Eq. (1) is not followed. Main has developed another equation which holds regardless of the concentration of PXE:

$$1/\mathrm{PX} = (tk_x/2.3\,\Delta \log V) - 1/K_a \qquad (2)$$

where $\Delta \log V$ is the change in the logarithm of the velocity of the hydrolysis of substrate, choosing assay conditions such that there is a large excess of substrate over inhibitor.* From a plot of 1/PX against $t/2.3\Delta \log V$ one can therefore find K_a and k_x, and consequently k_2.

Very few such measurements have yet been made. Main reports, for human serum cholinesterase, values of k_2 and K_a of about 30 min^{-1} and $10^{-5}M$, respectively, for DFP (diisopropyl phosphorofluoridate) and of 11 min^{-1} and $7.7 \times 10^{-4}M$, respectively, for malaoxon. From these values one can calculate the amount of inhibited enzyme at any given moment which is in the form PXE. Because of the high value for k_2 and relatively high value for K_a, it turns out that under familiar conditions of inhibition, which use low organophosphate concentrations and inhibition times of 15–30 minutes, the amount of PXE is extremely small, representing less than 1% of the total inhibited enzyme (PXE+PE). In order to measure k_2 and K_a, one has to use very high inhibitor concentrations and very short inhibition times. This fact accounts for the fact that the Aldridge formulation has for so many years seemed satisfactory. It also implies that the measurement of k_i in the traditional way affords a satisfactory measure of inhibitory potency for many purposes, although it is not really a bimolecular rate constant (Main suggests that it be called a bimolecular reaction constant). The value of the Main analysis is that we may now examine the effects of substituents separately upon affinity and phosphorylation; there is every reason to believe that the effects of any given substituent will not be the same on both factors.

Activation Products. If one were to examine all the common organophosphates, he would observe that the majority, perhaps 75% of them, were

* This is the usual condition when acetylcholine is the substrate. The requirement, to be more explicit, is that the assay be such that addition of a substrate leads to the disappearance of PXE by competitive displacement. Such displacement would not occur fully if one used low concentrations of a substrate having poor affinity, for instance, indophenyl acetate, whose low solubility and intensely colored hydrolysis product lead to the use of very low substrate concentrations.

rather poor inhibitors of cholinesterase *in vitro*, requiring as much as 10^{-3} or $10^{-4}M$ to inhibit 50% in periods of 15–30 minutes. The other compounds would prove to be potent inhibitors, typically requiring 10^{-5} to $10^{-9}M$ to inhibit 50%; these we may call *direct inhibitors*. Yet when comparisons are made of animals poisoned by the organophosphates, the differences between the direct inhibitors and the others would disappear. The explanation is that many organophosphates are *latent inhibitors*: They owe their potency *in vivo* to the fact that they are converted or "activated" in the body to give compounds which are direct inhibitors.

The commonest activation is conversion of a phosphorothionate, or P=S compound, to a phosphate, or P=O compound. Thus parathion is converted to paraoxon, malathion to malaoxon. This conversion is often called an oxidation, but in fact no change of valence state occurs, and "desulfuration" is therefore the correct term. Compounds which are already P(O) compounds are usually direct inhibitors and therefore do not require such activation: examples are tepp and dichlorvos (some exceptions will be discovered below). The reason that activation is required for most phosphorothionates is to be found in the electronic factors already discussed: =S is less electrophilic than =O, and consequently the P in most P=S compounds is inadequately positive to undergo rapid reaction with cholinesterase.

There are other important types of activation. One is found in certain phosphoroamidates, and has been best examined for schradan. It involves (32,53) hydroxylation of one of the *N*-methyl groups as follows:

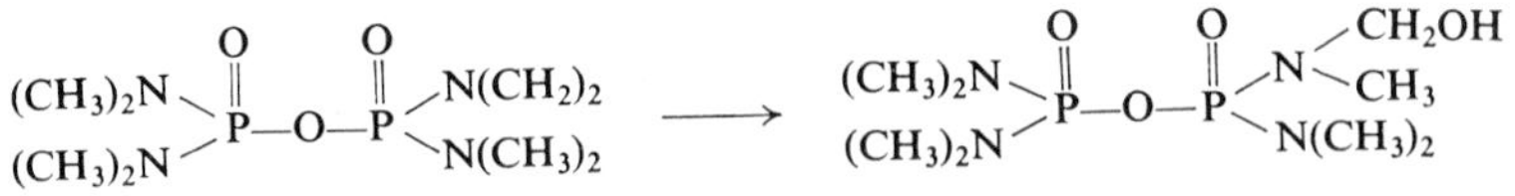

$$[(CH_3)_2N]_2P(=O)\text{—O—}P(=O)[N(CH_2)_2][N(CH_3)_2] \longrightarrow [(CH_3)_2N]_2P(=O)\text{—O—}P(=O)[N(CH_2OH)(CH_3)][N(CH_3)_2]$$

It should be noted that this view replaces the earlier opinion that the activation product is an *N*-oxide, containing —$N(O)(CH_3)_2$. One cannot rule out the possibility that this *N*-oxide is an intermediate in the formation of the above hydroxylated compound, but it is clear that the *N*-oxide has only a transient existence at best, and can be ignored except when the precise mechanism of hydroxylation is being considered:

The only other case for which evidence for a comparable hydroxylation has been obtained (11) is dimefox, for which one can suggest:

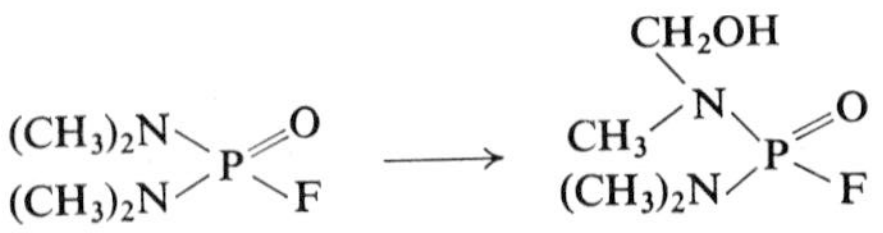

$$[(CH_3)_2N]_2P(=O)F \longrightarrow [N(CH_2OH)(CH_3)][(CH_3)_2N]P(=O)F$$

A most important activation occurs with thioethers. These are activated primarily by oxidation of the thioether sulfur to the sulfoxide and also to the sulfone, e.g., for phorate (15)

$$(C_2H_5O)_2P(S)SCH_2SC_2H_5 \rightarrow (C_2H_5O)_2P(S)SCH_2\overset{O}{\overset{\uparrow}{S}}C_2H_5 \rightarrow (C_2H_5O)_2P(S)SCH_2\underset{O}{\underset{\downarrow}{\overset{O}{\overset{\uparrow}{S}}}}C_2H_5$$

Phorate — Phorate sulfoxide — Phorate sulfone

It appears that oxidation of the thioether sulfur is the major activation pathway, even though desulfuration of the P(S) can and does occur to a small extent as an alternative activation. Thioether oxidation to the sulfone also occurs (13) when the parent molecule has a sulfoxide group attached to an aromatic group as in Bayer 25141:

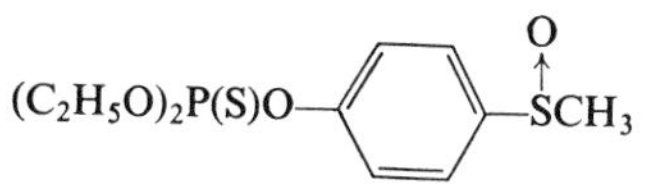

$$(C_2H_5O)_2P(S)O\text{—}C_6H_4\text{—}\overset{O}{\overset{\uparrow}{S}}CH_3$$

Recently, a most interesting activation has been shown for tri-*o*-cresyl phosphate. Since 1954, it has been known that this was a latent inhibitor, but only in 1961 was the activation reaction established (16). It involves hydroxylation followed by cyclization with elimination of one cresyl group:

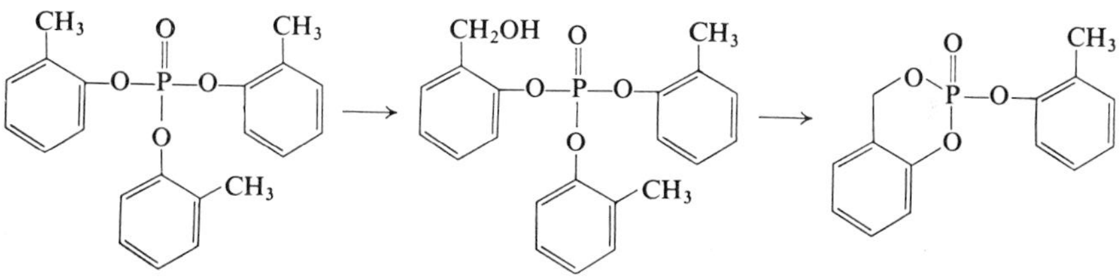

CH₃ O CH₃ / —O—P—O— / O / CH₃ → CH₂OH O CH₃ / —O—P—O— / O / CH₃ → O CH₃ / O—P—O— / O

The reasons why the above three reactions (*N*-methyl hydroxylation, sulfoxidation, cyclization) constitute activations are by no means clear. Attempts have been made to argue that, in the cases of hydroxylation and sulfoxidation, the added oxygen increases the positivity of the phosphorus by an inductive electrophilic effect. However, the inductive effect is very poorly transmitted through a chain of atoms, and the argument is therefore unsatisfactory. One alternative explanation would be that the molecule has a configuration such that the added oxygen lies close to the phosphorus and exerts a field effect. Another would be that the effects have nothing to do with alterations of the positivity of the phosphorus, and are instead concerned with improved binding to the cholinesterase. These, however, are mere speculations.

So far we have discussed metabolic activation. Precisely parallel arguments hold for these isomerizations described above which have the effect of converting P(S) to P(O). Such isomers are invariably far better anticholinesterases than their parents. Because any phosphorothionate preparation that has not been scrupulously purified always contains a certain amount of isomers, such preparations will inhibit cholinesterase directly. As mentioned above, the earlier workers, who (up to 1951) did not have highly purified materials available, did not recognize that phosphorothionates are latent inhibitors. The literature prior to 1951 must, therefore, be interpreted with care.

Degradation Products. Just as reactions which increase the positivity of the phosphorus will increase the anticholinesterase potency, so reactions which decrease its positivity will decrease anticholinesterase potency. Consequently, the hydrolysis products described above (p. 36) are extremely poor inhibitors of cholinesterase, and for the same reason that they are extremely insensitive to alkaline hydrolysis (i.e., attack by OH^-); hydrolysis introduces a negative ion, i.e., an anionic group, either close to the phosphorus or in a place such that the anionic group can lie near the phosphorus. Consequently, the positivity of the phosphorus is profoundly reduced, and the ability to attack cholinesterase is reduced or abolished.

There are a very few cases of organophosphates which can undergo a hydrolysis which does not introduce an anionic group. Such hydrolyses do not, therefore, reduce inhibitory potency. An example is acetyl trichlorfon. Its hydrolysis product, trichlorfon, is in fact a more potent inhibitor (10)

$$(CH_3O)_2P(O)CH(OC(O)CH_3)CCl_3 \rightarrow (CH_3O)_2P(O)CH(OH)CCl_3$$

Acetyl trichlorfon → Trichlorfon

The section on metabolism of organophosphates (p. 62) will make it clear that the conversions of parent compounds to activation and degradation products are of immense importance for toxicity, and differences in the rates of these reactions can be all-important in determining death or survival after treatment with an organophosphate.

Spontaneous Recovery

So far we have discussed the phosphorylation of cholinesterase and the factors which control its rate. We have spoken as if the reaction was irreversible, and indeed for most compounds in the course of experiments of a few hours duration, such is essentially the case. However, an important factor in many cases is dephosphorylation of the phosphorylated enzyme to give uninhibited enzyme plus hydrolyzed phosphate. This hydrolysis of phosphorylated enzyme PE (using the symbolism of p. 42) is perhaps analogous to hydrolysis of the parent phosphate PX, so that we may write:

$$PE + OH^- \rightarrow EH + PO^-$$

or in a particular case, such as that of dimethyl phosphorylated cholinesterase, and using normal chemical symbols:

$$(CH_3O)_2P(O)E + OH^- \rightarrow EH + \underset{\text{Dimethyl phosphate}}{(CH_3O)_2P(O)O^-}$$

That the reaction is hydroxyl catalyzed may be inferred from the effect of P-substituents upon recovery, especially in view of the aging reaction described below. But increasing the OH^- concentration does not increase the recovery rate indefinitely; there is a pH optimum above which recovery is actually slower, perhaps because some sort of promoted denaturation more than compensates for the extra OH^-. Alternatively, the dephosphorylation may be caused by a pair of groups in the enzyme surface, which act optimally when one group is protonated and the other is deprotonated. The pH optimum is dependent on salt concentration: for instance, in $1M$ NaCl it is pH 8.0, and in $0.02M$ NaCl it is 9.0, for dimethyl phosphorylated eel cholinesterase (18). The reaction is temperature dependent, as expected for a simple hydrolysis, having an energy of activation of 14,400 cal $mole^{-1}$ for dimethyl phosphorylated rabbit erythrocyte cholinesterase (3). Strangely enough, dephosphorylation of pseudocholinesterases is fastest under acid conditions (21).

As far as the enzyme is concerned, one might therefore say that the inhibitory reaction is slowly reversible, and this view is sometimes embodied by the use of the term "irreversible" in quotation marks when describing organophosphate inhibition. The term is better avoided, however, because the dephosphorylation is not truly a reversal, but rather an ongoing reaction; when one considers the fate of the inhibitor, the overall reaction involves hydrolysis of PX to PO^-, so that the overall reaction is no more reversible than is, for instance, the hydrolysis of sucrose.

This spontaneous recovery of inhibited enzyme was described in 1951 by Hobbiger (35) and Wilson (57) independently. The latter's results indicate how slow the reaction often is: Eel cholinesterase inhibited by tepp recovered 45% in 28 days at 7°C and pH 7.

Because the leaving group X has departed when PX has reacted with cholinesterase to give PE, the nature of X has no bearing on the reactivation rate,* but P and E have great importance. Thus pseudocholinesterase recovers more slowly than acetylcholinesterase (21) and brain pseudocholinesterase

* At least, it ought to have no effect. In view of the fact (36) that X paradoxically influences the aging rate (discussed below) one would like to see more experiments assuring one of the *universal* validity of the X independence of reactivation. It has been convincingly validated for dimethyl and diethyl phenyl phosphates (7).

recovers more slowly than other pseudocholinesterases, such as those of serum or heart (20). The substituent effect also varies with enzyme: For rabbit erythrocytes the effect of the alkyl substituent is that most often quoted as a general truth: methyl > ethyl > isopropyl (4). But with several rat pseudo-cholinesterases it has been said (21) that diethyl phosphorylated cholinesterase recovers fast (the half-life at pH 7.8 and 37°C was 5 hours) and the dimethyl and diisopropyl phosphorylated cholinesterases recovery extremely slowly (half-life over 200 hours). With human serum cholinesterase, dimethyl and diethyl phosphorylated enzymes recovered at the same rate, but diisopropyl derivative hardly at all (44). At least the reports all agree on the poor reactivation of diisopropyl phosphorylated enzymes.

A remarkable fact has been reported (12) and confirmed (44): housefly cholinesterase does not recover *in vitro* from any phosphate inhibitors, even though recovery *in vivo* is readily shown. This strange phenomenon has been shown for five different compounds. The two implications are: 1. that housefly cholinesterase is in some basic way unlike mammalian enzymes (see p. 283), and 2. that some mechanism operates *in vivo* that is lacking *in vitro*; and there is some evidence that a labile reactivating factor is present in whole flies (44) as has been claimed for mammalian sera (46).

Induced Recovery

The existence of the hydroxyl-catalyzed reactivation described above raised the possibility that reagents better than hydroxyl could be found. Like hydroxyl ion, they would probably be nucleophilic reagents (p. 7). Wilson has been especially prominent in the search for such reagents, beginning with hydroxylamine in 1951 (57) and terminating in the oximes (compounds containing CH=NOH) which are the present compounds of choice. Of the simple oximes, monoisonitrosoacetone (MINA) is perhaps best known.

$CH_3C{=}O$
|
CH=NOH

MINA

But more popular types are 2-PAM [announced in 1955 by American and English researchers (17,59)] and its derivative bis-4-PAM, often known as TMB4.

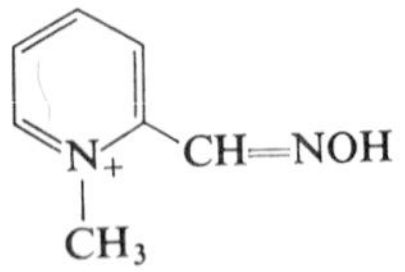

CH=NOH CH=NOH

N+ CH=NOH N+ N+

CH_3 $CH_2—CH_2—CH_2$

2-PAM 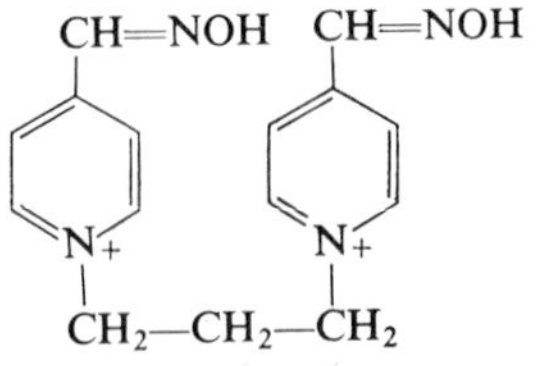 TMB4

The TMB4-type compounds were described in 1958, also by an American group (50) and a British group (38).

All these oximes accelerate the recovery rate of phosphorylated cholinesterase. The superiority of 2-PAM was believed to reside in its quaternary nitrogen, which is assumed to bind to the anionic site of the phosphorylated enzyme, coupled with a strategically located oxime group (which at pH 7 has the form —CH=N—O$^-$) to attack the P—O—enzyme bond (58). However, the fact that in the TMB4 type of compound it is the 4-position of the oxime substituent that is optimal, rather complicates the picture. The TMB4 type is commonly 20-fold better than the 2-PAM type, a finding which has no simple explanation, but revives the possibility that cholinesterase has two anionic sites per esteratic site.

The reactivation reaction is pH dependent, with an optimum at pH 7.8 for MINA acting on diethyl phosphorylated cholinesterase (19). The rate of reactivitation is proportional to oxime concentration and increases with temperature (19). There can be little doubt that the exact mechanism involves a transfer of the substituted-phosphate group from enzyme to oxime, often with subsequent rapid hydrolysis of the phosphorylated oxime,

$$R{=}N{-}OH + PE \rightarrow R{=}N{-}OP + EH$$

so that the initial step is attack upon the phosphorus by the N—O$^-$ group of the oxime. One would expect that an analogous attack by the oxime could be made on PX, the original inhibitor, and such is indeed the case; Hackley *et al.* (27) isolated just such a phosphorylated oxime in 1959 by reacting 2-PAM with sarin to give:

$$\text{(1-methylpyridinium-2-yl)}{-}CH{=}N{-}O{-}P(=O)(CH_3)(OC_3H_7)$$

The compound was easily hydrolyzed (half-life, 15 minutes at pH 7.4 and 38°C) and a rather better anticholinesterase than sarin itself!

The rate of reactivation by agents varies with enzyme and with the substituents on the phosphorus; thus with 2-PAM, diethyl phosphorylated eel cholinesterase is reactivated ten times faster than erythrocyte enzyme; and for both enzymes, the diisopropyl phosphorylated enzyme is reactivated ten times slower than the diethyl phosphorylated enzyme (37). There are some organophosphates which give rise to an inhibited enzyme which cannot be reactivated. In some cases this is because of rapid or instantaneous aging (see below), but in at least one case, described in 1958 by Tammelin and Enander (54), the probable reason is that the bulky side group, which is *not* the leaving group, prevents attack of the oxime on the inhibited enzyme.

$$(CH_3)(F)P(O)OCH_2CH_2\overset{+}{N}(CH_3)_3 + EOH \rightarrow (CH_3)(EO)P(O)OCH_2CH_2\overset{+}{N}(CH_3)_3 + H^+ + F^-$$

Some other agents than oximes can catalyze dephosphorylation. Heilbronn (33,34) first reported in 1965 that sodium fluoride is a potent reactivator when used at relatively high concentrations (of the order of $10^{-3}M$). In this case the efficiency of reactivation increases with decreasing pH (the range tested was pH 5–9) suggesting the possibility that HF and HF_2^- might be the effective species, for such a pH dependence is quite unlike that of oxime reactivation with its pH optimum at 7.8 (37). Under "physiological conditions" (pH 7.4, 37°C) fluoride is 45 times less active than 2-PAM,* as measured by reactivation of sarin-inhibited human erythrocyte cholinesterase.

Although housefly cholinesterase shows no spontaneous recovery from inhibition, recovery can be induced by 2-PAM (44). Such experiments have not been done for other insect cholinesterases.

AGING

In 1955 Hobbiger (36) noted that isopropyl phosphorylated serum cholinesterase could undergo almost total induced reactivation if the inducer was used promptly after the inhibition reaction, but if one delayed addition of inducer for an hour, very little induced reactivation was possible. This phenomenon, which is now very well established, has become known as "aging." Aging is therefore defined as the development of an inability to be reactivated. Aging is a temperature-dependent reaction, often negligible at 0°C, and is pH dependent, being rapid at low and slow at high pH (19).

At first it was believed that aging is caused by transphosphorylation: that the unaged enzyme was phosphorylated at a histidine group in the active site, and that the dialkyl phosphoryl group was transferred to a serine in the course of aging (see review in ref. 47). The current view is quite different, and is based on Dutch work (14,49) which showed in 1959 for pseudocholinesterase that aging was paralleled by conversion of the diisopropyl phosphoryl enzyme to a monoisopropyl form:

$$EO\overset{O}{\overset{\|}{P}}(OC_3H_7)_2 \rightarrow EO\overset{O}{\overset{\|}{P}}(OC_3H_7)(O^-)$$

* Officially, 2-PAM is the iodide salt of the structure shown on p. 48; Heilbronn used the sulfonate salt instead, a compound often called P2S. I have used 2-PAM as a generic name; this would be improper procedure if the different salts really behave differently, which seems implausible to me, though some evidence favors it.

Such an explanation for aging explains on electronic grounds why the aged form is insensitive to oximes and other nucleophilic agents, for the anionic charge on the aged form would confer negativity on the adjacent phosphorus, and make it insensitive to attack by nucleophilic agents.

For acetylcholinesterase, Harris *et al.* (28) in 1966 showed a similar effect in a very elegant set of experiments, in which rat brain cholinesterase was inhibited *in vivo* with P^{32}-sarin and in which aging was permitted *in vivo*, by removing brains at a variety of times and, at each time, measuring the amount of enzyme which could be reactivated by 2-PAM, the amount of P^{32} released by 2-PAM treatment (they showed that all this P^{32} was present as isopropyl methylphosphoric acid) and, after alkaline digestion, the amount of P^{32} retained in the enzyme (which, they showed, was present entirely as methyl phosphoric acid).

$$E{-}P(=O)(CH_3)(OC_3H_7) \xrightarrow{\text{Aging}} E{-}P(=O)(CH_3)(O^-) \xrightarrow{\text{Digestion}} {}^-O{-}P(=O)(CH_3)(O^-)$$

$$E{-}P(=O)(CH_3)(OC_3H_7) \xrightarrow{\text{2-PAM}} {}^-O{-}P(=O)(CH_3)(OC_3H_7)$$

Their data (Table 3.3) convincingly demonstrated that aging is paralleled by deisopropylation.

TABLE 3.3

AGING AND DEALKYLATION OF SARIN-INHIBITED RAT BRAIN CHOLINESTERASE *in Vivo*[a]

Time of aging (hours)	Reactivatable enzyme (%)	P^{32} released as $(OH)(OC_3H_7)P(O)CH_3$ (%)	P^{32} on enzyme as $(OH)_2P(O)CH_3$ (%)
0.5	92	91	9
3	74	72	21
6	46	55	45
9	32	36	70
14	17	23	77
24	8	9	91

[a] Data, rounded off, from Harris *et al.* (28).

The rate of aging should be independent of the organophosphate's leaving group, which has left prior to the aging reaction; and dependent on the nature of the alkoxy (or other nonleaving groups) and the enzyme. Hobbiger (37) reports for acetylcholinesterase the following approximate half-lives of aging (pH 7.4, 37°C) in hours: diethyl phosphoryl, 40; diisopropyl phosphoryl, 2.5; isopropyl methylphosphonyl, 2.5. Dimethyl phosphoryl enzyme is reported to age as fast as isopropyl (19). But with housefly cholinesterase, instead of the above order, methyl aged faster than ethyl which aged faster than isopropyl phosphoryl enzyme.

Some inhibitors give rise to what we might call "instantly aged" enzyme, that is, reactivators are ineffective regardless of the time between inhibition and addition of reactivator. Probably such instant aging falls into three classes. On the one hand are those compounds in which the phosphorylated enzyme in its initial form is unreactivatable. This is undoubtedly the reason why cholinesterase inhibited by phosphodiesters* cannot be reactivated by 2-PAM (1):

$$(^{-}O)(C_2H_5O)P(O)SCH_2CH_2N(C_2H_5)_2 + EOH \rightarrow (^{-}O)(C_2H_5O)P(O)OE$$

One thus obtains an anionic form directly. Another subclass, within this first class, is of compounds (such as the cholinyl phosphate described on p. 50) in which the initial form of inhibited enzyme defies dephosphorylation, not because of its anionic nature, but because of (presumably) steric interference with the approach of reactivator.

A second class is that in which dealkylation is exceptionally fast, of which tabun and soman are examples (22,23). Thus for soman the half-life for aging and for loss of the pinacoloxy group is about 2 minutes (22).

Finally, there are compounds of which one can only say that 2-PAM and other oximes do not reactivate them, but inadequate work has been done to establish to which of the above two classes they belong. The principal example is schradan, whose active form is the hydroxymethyl derivative (p. 44) and which probably gives rise to the following inhibited enzyme:

$$\begin{array}{c} HOCH_2 \\ \end{array}\!\!\searrow N{-}\overset{\overset{\displaystyle O}{\|}}{\underset{\underset{\displaystyle E}{\displaystyle O}}{P}}{-}N(CH_3)_2 \quad (CH_3 \text{ on } N)$$

Perhaps steric factors are involved in the unreactivatability which has been reported (39).

REFERENCES

1. Aharoni, A., and O'Brien, R. D., *Biochemistry* (in press, 1967).
2. Aldridge, W. N., *Biochem. J.* **46**, 451 (1950).
3. Aldridge, W. N., *Biochem. J.* **54**, 442 (1953).

* Monodealkylated organophosphates: most of them are virtually without anticholinesterase activity, but there are special exceptions (1).

4. Aldridge, W. N., *Chem. Ind.* (*London*) p. 473 (1954).
5. Aldridge, W. N., and Davison, A. N., *Biochem. J.* **51**, 62 (1952).
6. Aldridge, W. N., and Davison, A. N., *Biochem. J.* **52**, 663 (1952).
7. Aldridge, W. N., and Davison, A. N., *Biochem. J.* **55**, 763 (1953).
8. Anonymous, *Chem. Eng. News* **30**, 4515 (1952).
9. Anonymous, *J. Chem. Soc.* p. 5122 (1952).
10. Arthur, B. W., and Casida, J. E., *J. Agr. Food Chem.* **5**, 186 (1957).
11. Arthur, B. W., and Casida, J. E., *J. Econ. Entomol.* **52**, 20 (1959).
12. Asperen, K. van, and Dekhuijsen, H. M., *Biochim. Biophys. Acta* **28**, 603 (1958).
13. Benjamini, E., Metcalf, R. L., and Fukuto, T. R., *J. Econ. Entomol.* **52**, 99 (1959).
14. Berends, F., Posthumus, C. H., van der Sluys, I., and Deierkauf, F. A., *Biochim. Biophys. Acta* **34**, 576 (1959).
15. Bowman, J. S., and Casida, J. E., *J. Econ. Entomol.* **51**, 838 (1958).
16. Casida, J. E., Eto, M., and Baron, R. L., *Nature* **191**, 1396 (1961).
17. Childs, A. F., Davies, D. R., Green, A. L., and Rutland, J. P., *Brit. J. Pharmacol.* **10**, 462 (1955).
18. Cohen, J. A., and Oosterbaan, R. A., *in* "Cholinesterase and Anticholinesterase Agents", Handbuch der Experimentellen Pharmakologie (G. B. Koelle, ed.), Vol. 15, Chapt. 7. Springer, Berlin, 1963.
19. Davies, D. R., and Green, A. L., *Biochem. J.* **63**, 529 (1956).
20. Davison, A. N., *Biochem. J.* **54**, 583 (1953).
21. Davison, A. N., *Biochem. J.* **60**, 339 (1955).
22. Fleisher, J. H., and Harris, L. W., *Biochem. Pharmacol.* **14**, 641 (1965).
23. Fleisher, J. H., Michel, H. O., Yates, L., and Harrison, C. S., *J. Pharmacol. Exptl. Therap.* **129**, 31 (1960).
24. Fukuto, T. R., and Metcalf, R. L., *J. Agr. Food Chem.* **4**, 930 (1956).
25. Fukuto, T. R., Metcalf, R. L., Frederickson, M., and Winton, M. Y., *J. Agr. Food. Chem.* **12**, 231 (1964).
26. Fukuto, T. R., and Stafford, E. M., *J. Am. Chem. Soc.* **79**, 6083 (1957).
27. Hackley, B. E., Steinberg, G. M., and Lamb, J. C., *Arch. Biochem.* **80**, 211 (1959).
28. Harris, L. W., Fleisher, J. H., Clark, J., and Cliff, W. J., *Science* **154**, 404 (1966).
29. Heath, D. F., *J. Chem. Soc.* p. 3796 (1956).
30. Heath, D. F., *J. Chem. Soc.* p. 3804 (1956).
31. Heath, D. F., "Organophosphorus Poisons," 403 pp. Macmillan (Pergamon), New York, 1961.
32. Heath, D. F., Lane, D. W. J., and Park, P. O., *Phil. Trans. Roy. Soc. London* **B239**, 191 (1955).
33. Heilbronn, E., *Acta Chem. Scand.* **18**, 2410 (1964).
34. Heilbronn, E., *Biochem. Pharmacol.* **14**, 1363 (1965).
35. Hobbiger, F., *Brit. J. Pharmacol.* **6**, 21 (1951).
36. Hobbiger, F., *Brit. J. Pharmacol.* **10**, 356 (1955).
37. Hobbiger, F., *in* "Cholinesterase and Anticholinesterase Agents," Handbuch der Experimentellen Pharmakologie (G. B. Koelle, ed.), Vol. 15, Chapt. 21. Springer, Berlin, 1963.
38. Hobbiger, F., O'Sullivan, D. G., and Sadler, P. W., *Nature* **182**, 1498 (1958).
39. Kewitz, H., *Arch. Biochem.* **66**, 263 (1957).
40. Koelle, G. B., ed. "Cholinesterases and Anticholinesterase Agents," Handbuch der Experimentellen Pharmakologie (O. Eichler and A. Farah, gen. eds.), Vol. 15, 1220 pp. Springer, Berlin, 1963.
41. Krysan, J. L., and Chadwick, L. E., *Entomol. Exptl. Appl.* **5**, 179 (1962).

42. Larsson, L., Holmstedt, B., and Tjus, E., *Acta Chem. Scand.* **8**, 1593 (1954).
43. Main, A. R., *Science* **144**, 992 (1964).
44. Mengle, D. C., and O'Brien, R. D., *Biochem. J.* **75**, 201 (1960).
45. Metcalf, R. L., *Bull. Entomol. Soc. Am.* **5**, 3 (1959).
46. Neubert, D., Schaefer, J., and Kewitz, H., *Naturwissenschaften* **45**, 290 (1958).
47. O'Brien, R. D., "Toxic Phosphorus Esters," 434 pp. Academic Press, New York, 1960.
48. Ooms, A. J. J., De Reactiviteit van Organische Fosforverbindingen ten Opzichte van ee Aantal Esterasen. Ph.D. Thesis, Univ. of Leiden, 1961.
49. Oosterbaan, R. A., Warringa, M. G. P. J., Jansz, F. B., and Cohen, J. A., *Proc. 4th Intern. Congr. Biochem., Vienna*, 1958 Abstr. 4–12, p. 38 (1959).
50. Poziomek, E. J., Hackley, B. E., and Steinberg, G. M., *J. Org. Chem.* **23**, 714 (1958).
51. Rosival, L., Vrbovsky, L., and Selecky, F. V., "Toxikologia a Farmakobiocynamika Organofosforvych Zlucenin," 299 pp. Slovenska Akad. Vied, Bratislava, Czechoslovakia, 1959.
52. Schrader, G., "Die Entwicklung Neuer Insekitizider Phosphorsäure-Ester," 3rd ed., 444 pp. Verlag Chemie, Weinheim, 1963.
53. Spencer, E. Y., O'Brien, R. D., and White, R. W., *J. Agr. Food Chem.* **5**, 123 (1957).
54. Tammelin, L. E., and Enander, I., *Proc. 4th Intern. Congr. Biochem., Vienna*, 1958 Abstr. 4–10 (1959).
55. Various authors, *Advan. Chem. Ser.* **26**, 100 pp. (1960).
56. Vernon, C. A., *Chem. Soc. (London) Spec. Publ.* **8**, 17 (1957).
57. Wilson, I. B., *J. Biol. Chem.* **190**, 111 (1951).
58. Wilson, I. B., *Discussions Faraday Soc.* **20**, 119 (1955).
59. Wilson, I. B., and Ginsburg, S., *Biochim. Biophys. Acta* **18**, 168 (1955).
60. Woodcock, D., and Stringer, A., *Ann. Appl. Biol.* **38**, 111 (1951).

CHAPTER 4

Organophosphates: Action, Therapy, and Metabolism

Mode of Action

It is widely accepted that organophosphates kill animals, both vertebrate and invertebrate, by inhibiting cholinesterase with consequent disruption of nervous activity caused by accumulation of acetylcholine at nerve endings (see p. 17 for a description of normal functioning). The most convincing evidence for this belief (reviewed at length in ref. 66) is (1) that cholinesterase is a vital enzyme, judged by the fact that its severe inhibition is usually associated with death, (2) that the organophosphates kill by affecting the nervous system, since convulsions and excessive parasympathetic activity, such as lachrymation and salivation, are normally observed, (3) that the organophosphates, or their activation products, are extremely potent inhibitors of cholinesterase, and poor inhibitors of other vital enzymes which have been studied, (4) that, in general, very good inhibitors of cholinesterase are very toxic and very bad inhibitors are not.*

Although the above is the most generally received view, certain eminent authorities disagree with it. Chadwick (15) in particular points to the several anomalies in our knowledge of organophosphate action in mammals, and the shockingly inadequate status of our knowledge of cholinergic mechanisms in insects, and concludes that for invertebrates "toxicity is rarely exercised through what is ordinarily understood as a cholinergic mechanism." My view is that such an opinion reflects the inadequacy of our knowledge rather than

* The term "toxic" is sometimes misused in at least two ways. Some use it when they mean "has antienzyme activity." Others use it when they mean "is toxic to warm-blooded vertebrates."

any strong data to the contrary. Certainly no *more* convincing mechanism of action has been postulated than that given above.

The symptoms of poisoning in vertebrates and insects are what one would expect from cholinesterase inhibition, leading at first to excessive activity at the synapse, but subsequently (in severe poisoning) to blockade.

VERTEBRATES

The clearly visible early symptoms are those of parasympathetic stimulation (see p. 19), especially defecation, urination, lachrymation, contraction of the pupil (myosis), slowing of the heart (bradycardia), and consequent drop in blood pressure (hypotension). These effects are the so-called muscarinic effects (p. 20), which may be antagonized by atropine. In addition, nicotinic effects (p. 20) involving the neuromuscular junction are seen, at first excitatory, leading to twitching of the muscles, then inhibitory, leading to paralysis. These nicotinic symptoms may be treated by oximes. Convulsions are usual in severe poisoning, and are primarily clonic, that is, with rapid repetitive movements. Convulsions, since they involve much of the nervous system, must be central in origin. Another important central effect is inhibition of the respiratory center of the brain.

Death is due to asphyxiation because of respiratory failure; the failure may be caused centrally, via the respiratory center, or peripherally, via the respiratory muscles. The relative contribution of central effects (against which atropine is effective) and peripheral effects varies both with compound and with species (23,66). Thus, in a cat poisoned by tepp, the central effect predominates, but in rabbits poisoned by tepp, peripheral effects cause death. Usually central effects predominate, and the peripheral effects contribute little or (for instance, in the monkey) nothing.

Cholinesterase declines profoundly, with death usually occurring when brain acetylcholinesterase is 95% inhibited (60). Other cholinesterases may or may not reflect the brain inhibition. Erythrocyte cholinesterase is quite a good index, but is inaccurate for compounds that penetrate brain poorly, such as ionic or amidic organophosphates. Serum cholinesterase is a worse index, for not only does it suffer from the distributional problem just mentioned, but many organophosphates inhibit it markedly more (or less) than brain or erythrocyte acetylcholinesterase; thus with eight organophosphates (most of them insecticides) taken at random (68), the relative potencies for human plasma compared with human erythrocyte cholinesterase were 2.6, 8, 159, 0.1, 0.5, 4, 2.5, and 0.8. Obviously, results on plasma enzyme would only be relevant in the last compound.

Acetylcholine in blood and brain rises to the extent of 2- to 3-fold in organophosphate poisoning of cats, dogs, rabbits (66), and doubtless in other animals.

INSECTS

The pharmacology of insects is very poorly understood in comparison with that of mammals, and the details of poisoning must be correspondingly less precisely known. Poisoning leads to symptoms of excitability, followed by tremors that are especially noticeable in the extremities, and finally paralysis

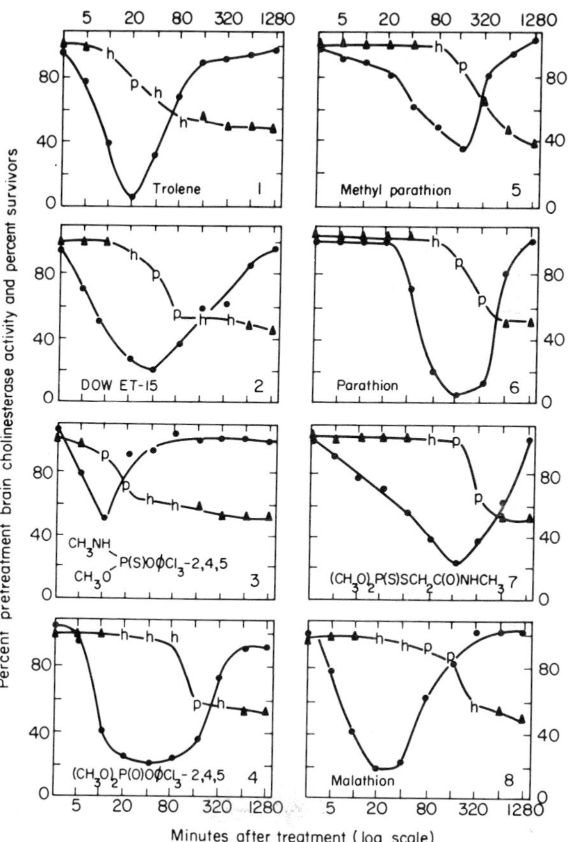

FIG. 4.1. Cholinesterase inhibition in survivors and mortality of houseflies treated with the LD_{50} of organophosphates: h, hyperactive; p, paralyzed (refer to survivors). From Mengle and Casida (48).

and death. These symptoms may take many hours to develop, especially with latent inhibitors (p. 44), and death usually takes about a day when the LD_{50} is applied.

Cholinesterase declines steadily for about an hour after treatment by direct inhibitors, and then recovers steadily in survivors to about normal (48) (Fig. 4.1). In dead flies also, a little recovery occurs (67). Studies such as these are fraught with problems. For instance, with direct (but not with latent) inhibitors there may be a "homogenization artifact," arising when inhibitor which *in vivo* was kept away from cholinesterase (for instance, in fat body) is brought into contact with cholinesterase during homogenization. The artifact can be prevented by homogenizing in substrate, which protects the enzyme (7).* Another problem is that the LD_{50} of organophosphates is the same for normal and for decapitated houseflies (49), so that it is improbable that the cholinesterase of the head is crucial; yet the head, being the richest source of cholinesterase, is commonly used, as in Fig. 4.1. Happily, results with whole houseflies show similar trends (67) except for a less complete enzyme recovery in survivors.

One might well argue that if one is interested in lethal mechanisms, one should study the victims of organophosphate poisoning, not the survivors. This has been done in the course of an attempt to settle what was once a very fierce argument: is the inhibition of other esterases than cholinesterase important for poisoning? Particularly, aliesterase, an enzyme or group of enzymes that hydrolyzes aliphatic compounds such as methyl butyrate, was under study. The debate has been fully reviewed (66) and seems now to be settled in favor of the unimportance of aliesterase; a turning point in the battle was the demonstration by Stegwee that by using TOCP one can specifically inhibit the aliesterase of houseflies with no ill effects (82). Furthermore, in houseflies killed by organophosphates, cholinesterase in the whole insect was usually the most inhibited esterase; for example, 99% inhibition for parathion, 74% for malathion, 83% for diazinon, and 98% for coumaphos. All these compounds were applied at the LD_{50} 5 hours before assay (67).

Acetylcholine levels in poisoned insects rise sharply in organophosphate poisoning (79). This and the above facts have convinced the majority that cholinesterase inhibition is the biochemical lesion in insects. But whereas for the vertebrate one can trace the physiological consequences of the lesion, no such consequence has been traced in insects. The *immediate* cause of death is completely unknown.

DEMYELINATION

In addition to the direct toxicant action of organophosphates, a few of them exert in vertebrates a specific action which shows itself grossly as a flaccid paralysis, especially of the legs (in man and birds) or hind limbs (of quadrupeds). Microscopically, this action is associated with damage to the myelin sheath surrounding most nerves. Both symptoms occur only about 2 weeks after poisoning, and recovery is common. An extensive review of this phenomenon has been written (20).

* The experiments of Fig. 4.1 did not employ protection, but are probably correct because the insects were treated on the abdomen and the heads only were assayed.

There have been two cases of widespread poisoning of humans; one in the 1930's in the United States, when a contaminated cargo of ginger, which was used primarily for preparing illicit alcohol drinks in prohibition days, caused several thousand people to suffer "ginger Jake paralysis" (81); and another in Morocco in the 1950's, when motor oil was sold for cooking purposes (80).

Demyelination is observed only in some species, and only with some compounds. The monkey, dog, and rat are insensitive, but man, the chicken, the calf, the cat, the lamb, and the rabbit are susceptible (22). There have been 40,000 cases in man alone (20). Only in the chicken and the cat are the symptoms closely similar to those seen in man (20). The demyelinating compounds include TOCP, diisopropyl phosphorofluoridate (DFP), mipafox, diethyl phosphorofluoridate, and tri(ethylphenyl) phosphate. The following do not cause demyelination: diazinon, dichlorvos, demeton, chlorthion, sarin, soman, tabun, EPN (ethyl *p*-nitrophenyl benzenephosphonothionate), malathion, schradan, tri-*m*-cresyl phosphate, and tri-*p*-cresyl phosphate (66). In general, then, phosphorofluoridates and some substituted triphenyl phosphates are the types of compound in which one may expect demyelinating effects.

The cause of demyelination remains unknown. In the 1940's, an effect upon cholinesterase at the neuromuscular junction was suspected, but this view fails to explain the subsequent finding that many potent anticholinesterases do not demyelinate. Similarly, a theory in the 1950's held that inhibition of pseudocholinesterase was crucial; and indeed most demyelinators are specific for that enzyme, which is high in myelinated tracts of the nervous system. But subsequently, potent inhibitors of pseudocholinesterase were found which were not demyelinating (66).

More recently, an older theory which Meunier *et al.* (55) proposed in 1947 has received new attention: a connection between vitamin E and demyelination. The best evidence was the demonstration that vitamin E-deficient lambs were abnormally sensitive to demyelination by TOCP. But subsequent work has not given support: vitamin E is not therapeutic for TOCP poisoning (59). The corollaries of other theories have been examined (9) without success. Thus thiamine and analogs of it were tested, and were inactive or detrimental; cortisone acetate, but not cortisone, gave improved physical condition, but was not specifically antidotal; various 2-PAM salts and analogs of it were inactive, as were nonionic reactivators such as monoisonitrosoacetone and diacetyl monoxime; and such agents as BAL, SKF 525A (p. 221), saponin, and pilocarpine were ineffective.

Along different lines, Davies *et al.* (21) suggested in 1960 that fluoride ion, released strategically when DFP and related compounds reacted with cholinesterase, was responsible. Clearly this view has no relevance for the non-fluorinated demyelinators. Fleisher and O'Brien (unpublished) are exploring the possibility that demyelination is an autoimmune phenomenon, in which animals make antibody to their own myelin.

In short, the mechanism of demyelination remains unknown.

Therapy

The treatment of organophosphate poisoning, in so far as it is accomplished by drugs, represents a particular case of antagonism, i.e., between the organophosphate and the drug, and as such might be dealt with in Chapter 14. However, as it is a rather specialized topic, only those parts have been relegated to Chapter 14 which deal with microsomal mechanisms operating either through prior induction of microsomes, or inhibition by general "microsome inhibitors," for in these effects, the organophosphates are but one of many groups influenced by such treatments. Although these microsomally mediated actions can affect organophosphate toxicity, they have not been used in practical therapy, in part because those actions are rather compound specific.

Two principles have been employed in therapy: attempts to reactivate the inhibited cholinesterase and so repair the biochemical lesion, and attempts to compensate for the excess acetylcholine resulting from cholinesterase inhibition by using acetylcholine antagonists.

Acetylcholine Antagonism

The antagonism between atropine and eserine (the carbamate anticholinesterase) was known in 1864 (35), so there can be no doubt that atropine is the oldest successful antidote for anticholinesterases. It remains the best known and the most used. Atropine is a complex alkaloid derived from *Atropa belladonna*, and competively blocks acetylcholine, but only at muscarinic receptors (see p. 20). Consequently, to the extent that organophosphate poisoning involves action at muscarinic sites, atropine is an excellent antagonist. Its effectiveness varies greatly with compound and species, however, as Table 4.1 shows; for instance, it is at its best against sarin poisoning of the monkey, and at its worst, almost useless, in sarin poisoning of the mouse. Presumably these variations represent, in large part, a measure of the variations in the contributions of muscarinic effects to the poisoning process.

For its use in poisoning of humans, there is an excellent review by Grob (30), in which the high points are that large quantities are needed, e.g., 2 mg at half-hour intervals, and the efficacy is measured by the appearance of symptoms of mild atropinization in the form of dry mouth and skin, but not of dilated pupil; the latter response is an inadequate index for systemic atropine. The dose commonly needs much repetition: half-hourly in mild cases, or every 3–8 minutes in severe cases. Atropine by itself is of course a very poisonous compound; if the patient has *not* been poisoned by an anticholinesterase, several doses of 2 mg administered in an hour or two are

TABLE 4.1
PROTECTION BY ATROPINE[a]

Animal	Ratio of LD_{50} with atropine/LD_{50} alone	
	Sarin	Paraoxon
Monkey	1000	50
Dog	150	10
Cat	10	2.5
Rabbit	3	3
Mouse	1.1	2.1

[a] Data of De Candole and McPhail (24).

severely incapacitating, leading to dryness of the mouth, dilated pupils with blurring of vision, disorientation, and hallucinations.

In an attempt to help those nicotinic sites affected by organophosphates, as well as the muscarinic sites, a variety of adjuvants (i.e., added compounds) have been tried with atropine, often with great success. Thus pentamethonium, $(CH_3)_3N^+(CH_2)_5N^+(CH_3)_3$, plus atropine increased the LD_{50} of sarin for mice 6.6-fold, compared with a 1.1-fold increase for atropine alone (24). Other effective adjuvants include magnesium (47), benzoquinonium, tubocurarine, hexamethonium, and nikethamide (an anticonvulsant) (66). All of these looked effective in the experiments reported, but have not found general acceptance in medical practice, in which simple atropine treatment remains favored.

CHOLINESTERASE RESTORATION

If one could restore cholinesterase to its uninhibited form, the poisoning would disappear. The effectiveness of various oximes *in vitro* has been described on p. 48, and of course the reason these compounds were developed was the interest in finding therapeutic agents. And indeed the compounds described, and many other oximes and a few related compounds, are quite good therapeutic agents.

With 2-PAM alone, the increases in LD_{50} are not so spectacular as those shown in Table 4.1 for atropine. Thus in mice, increases in LD_{50} of between 1.0- and 4.0-fold have been reported for five different organophosphates (Table 6.3 of ref. 66). However, if used in combination with atropine, quite spectacular effects have been reported. Thus given prophylactically* in mice,

* Prophylaxis involves giving the protective agent before the poison; therapy involves giving it after the poison.

atropine alone or 2-PAM alone protected against tepp or paraoxon or DFP, increasing the LD_{50} 2- or 4-fold. But used together, the increases were 24-fold for DFP, 32-fold for tepp, and a huge 128-fold for paraoxon. These findings suggest that both nicotinic and muscarinic sites are vitally involved in poisoning of mice, and massive protection requires treatment of both sites. For just as atropine works primarily on muscarinic sites, the ionized oximes work primarily on nicotinic sites. Probably a major factor is the ionization of 2-PAM which precludes easy penetration of the blood-brain barrier, through which atropine can pass.

The bis-PAM type of compounds, such as TMB4, appear experimentally far better than 2-PAM, although they have not yet come into general use. Thus TMB4 increased the LD_{50} of tepp to mice 100-fold, compared with 5-fold for 2-PAM (11).

The oximes, of course, are not therapeutic for those few compounds, such as soman or schradan (p. 52), which give rise to an unreactivatable cholinesterase. The phrase "of course" is dangerous, for several pieces of evidence (32) cast doubt on the assumption that the therapeutic excellence of 2-PAM and TMB4 is due entirely to their reactivating ability. However, the consensus is that reactivation is the major factor, even though some direct effects on the receptor (primarily a partial blockade analogous to atropine's effect) may play a part.

In insects, oximes such as 2-PAM or diisonitrosoacetone have little effect upon poisoning; the maximum effect reported was a 1.5-fold increase in the LD_{50} of DFP caused by 2-PAM (50, 87).

Metabolism

The metabolism of organophosphates has become such a large field that, in this chapter, I must attempt to offer only major generalizations, illustrated with some specific examples, without pretending to a comprehensive coverage. More detailed reviews of the literature prior to 1960 may be found in ref. 66, and of later work, in the regular bibliographies on "Radioisotopes and Ionizing Radiations in Entomology" published by the International Atomic Energy Agency.

On grounds of convenience and toxicological significance (rather than by reason of correct biochemical systematics), the topic can be divided into activative and degradative metabolism. Activative metabolism is that which converts from a poorer to a stronger anticholinesterase. Degradative metabolism is the reverse. At first thought, such a classification may seem a petty one; but in fact, in the great majority of cases the activating step is absolutely crucial to conversion of latent to direct inhibitors; and the degradative step commonly effects a conversion from a noxious to a harmless compound; so the two types are utterly opposite in toxicological significance.

Activation

The activative reactions have been listed in Chapter 3. The major ones are: P(S) to P(O) conversion (desulfuration); hydroxylation (found only in phosphoramides); thioether oxidation; and cyclization. All four reactions occur in intact vertebrates and insects, and the first three certainly occur in plants. In mammals, the catalytic system is the microsomes* of liver, which when isolated require reduced pyridine nucleotide (sometimes $NADH_2$, sometimes $NADPH_2$; both are often usable) and in many cases are aided by the presence of Mg^{++} and nicotinamide, added to inhibit nucleotide hydrolysis, and of more importance in crude than "pure" systems.

This same fortified microsome preparation can accomplish an extraordinary number of other reactions, many of which involve conversion of drugs and other exotic compounds to oxidized or hydroxylated forms (see Table 14.1). It has been postulated that the increase in polarity of the products is the valuable feature for the body, for only polar compounds are excreted through the kidney. The reason for the evolution of these microsomal mechanisms is therefore protective; yet, paradoxically, many organophosphates would be almost completely nontoxic were it not for microsomal activation. The increase in anticholinesterase potency is about 10,000-fold for parathion, methyl parathion, thiono-demeton, and malathion (66), so that, in these typical compounds, activation is an absolute prerequisite for toxicity. A few compounds do exist, however, for which P(S) activation produces only a small increase in anticholinesterase activity. Some are compounds which are "already activated," like the sulfoxide and sulfone of thiono-demeton, which are improved only 3-fold and 6-fold, respectively, by P(O) activation (29).

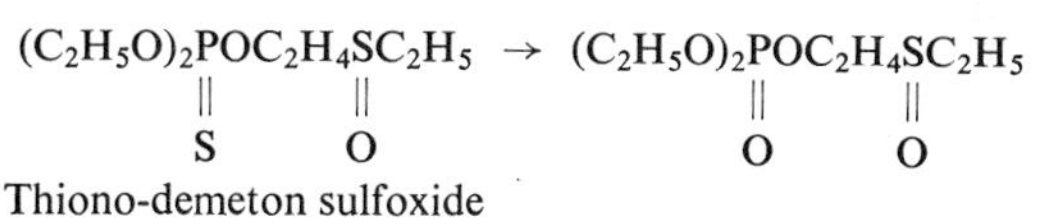

$$\underset{\text{Thiono-demeton sulfoxide}}{(C_2H_5O)_2\underset{\underset{S}{\|}}{P}OC_2H_4\underset{\underset{O}{\|}}{S}C_2H_5} \rightarrow (C_2H_5O)_2\underset{\underset{O}{\|}}{P}OC_2H_4\underset{\underset{O}{\|}}{S}C_2H_5$$

There is an indication (J. B. Lovell, American Cyanamid Company, unpublished data) that one compound is actually decreased in anticholinesterase potency by conversion to its P(O) analog:

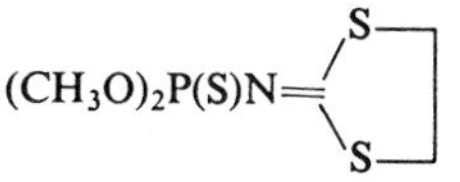

$$(CH_3O)_2P(S)N{=}C\langle{}^{S-CH_2}_{S-CH_2}\rangle$$

2-(Dimethoxyphosphinothioylimino)-1,3-dithiolane

* Microsomes may be defined as that fraction of a broken-cell preparation which precipitates only at very high centrifugal forces, such as 50,000–100,000 *g*. They are heterogeneous, and consist of fragments of the netlike endoplasmic reticulum, to which the ribosomes, the RNA-rich protein-synthesizing particles, are attached.

But such oddities do not deny the generality of the rule that weak cholinesterases are profoundly activated by desulfuration.

Activation by liver preparations *in vitro* has been studied only in a few preparations, but because it has been observed whenever looked for, the present trend is to look for it *in vivo* as part of an overall metabolic study, but not to perform *in vitro* studies. For instance, cyclization of TOCP (p. 45) has only been specifically shown in whole rats (25), not in liver preparations, although the early work in 1954 did show that liver slices increased the anticholinesterase potency of TOCP (4), and it seems almost certain now that cyclization was involved.

The microsomal fraction of whole insects, like that of the vertebrate liver, is the source of activating enzymes. But whereas in the vertebrates activating ability is found almost exclusively in liver [although lung, heart, and testes have a little activity (64)], in insects a variety of tissues are effective. In the American cockroach, all parts of the gut, and also nerve cord and especially fat body, have been shown to be potent in activating methyl parathion (54), parathion (39), and schradan (71), whereas muscle is inactive. A variety of inhibitors will block the activation if used at the fairly high concentrations of $10^{-3}M$; these include chloropicrin and iodoacetate, which inhibit sulfhydryl enzymes, and cyanide and azide, which inhibit metalloenzymes. Inhibitors of carbohydrate metabolism, malonate and fluoroacetate, are ineffective.

Just as in liver, homogenization of insect tissues virtually destroys the ability to activate, but the ability can (at least in some cases) be restored by adding a nucleotide such as NAD. If one removes the soluble enzymes, one must add $NADH_2$ or $NADPH_2$, which are the forms actually required for the activation, and which can be generated from their oxidized forms by the soluble enzymes. For unknown reasons, homogenates of cockroach gut do not activate schradan even when nucleotides are added (72), and in this way differ from liver homogenates. Activation of thioethers, both aromatic (10) and aliphatic (45), has also been shown with cockroach gut preparations. Activation by cyclization has not been shown with insect preparations *in vitro*, but has been observed in whole houseflies when 2000 houseflies were treated with methyl di-*o*-tolyl phosphate (26):

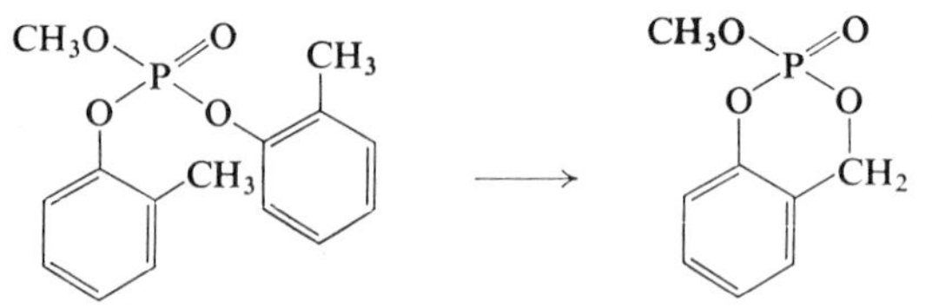

CH_3O, O, P, O, O, CH_3, CH_3 ⟶ CH_3O, O, P, O, O, CH_2

Methyl di-*o*-tolyl phosphate   Methyl saligenin cyclic phosphate

One insect preparation comparable to liver microsomes in its effectiveness and cofactor requirement is the microsomal preparation of whole houseflies. This preparation requires reduced nucleotide and nicotinamide, and has been studied in detail for its naphthalene-hydroxylating activity (76), and to a lesser extent for parathion activation. More extensive studies on parathion activation have been made with microsomes from cockroach fat-body, and the optimal conditions for this system have been explored (61).

In plants, no *in vitro* preparation has been described which can accomplish desulfuration, but desulfuration products are common in intact plants, e.g., dimethoate in peas, corn, cotton, and potato, in which the principal metabolite was a hydrolysis product of the P(O) compound (19):

$$\underset{\text{Dimethoate}}{(CH_3O)_2P(S)SCH_2C(O)NHCH_3} \rightarrow \underset{\text{Dimethoxon acid}}{(CH_3O)_2P(O)SCH_2COOH}$$

Another plant system in which activation products are prominent is that of the thioethers. The oxidation to sulfoxide was rapid in all cases, but extraordinarily so for disulfoton, which was almost instantly converted to its sulfoxide, which in turn was quite rapidly converted (50% in 100 hours) to its P(O) analog and equally to its sulfone, both of which were converted fairly readily to the P(O) sulfone. If we may write disulfoton, $(C_2H_5O)_2P(S)SC_2H_4SC_2H_5$, as P(S) ··· S, then we can diagram these complicated interrelations as

$$P(S)\cdots S \longrightarrow \underset{\text{Sulfoxide}}{P(S)\cdots S{=}O} \;\begin{matrix} \nearrow \underset{\text{Sulfone}}{P(S)\cdots S(=O)_2} \searrow \\ \searrow \underset{\text{Phosphate sulfoxide}}{P(O)\cdots S{=}O} \nearrow \end{matrix}\; \underset{\text{Phosphate sulfone}}{P(O)\cdots S(=O)_2}$$

This sequence has been shown in beans, lemons, and alfalfa (53). The existence of similar sulfoxidation products has been seen in beans with aromatic thioethers such as Lebaycid (63):

$(C_2H_5O)_2P(S)O$—[benzene ring]—SCH_3, with CH_3 on the ring

In mammals, the existence of activation products is hard to show in whole organisms, for it represents only a small percentage of the applied dose, which in turn is small. Nevertheless, several such cases exist, a few examples being P(O) products of dimethoate, parathion, diazinon, and acethion in houseflies, cockroaches, and mice (43), and of famphur in mice, cockroaches, and milkweed bugs (69).

$(C_2H_5O)_2P(S)SCH_2COOC_2H_5$

Acethion

$(CH_3O)_2P(S)O-C_6H_4-S(=O)_2N(CH_3)_2$

Famphur

The precise mechanism of these activations has never been elucidated, nor has the mechanism of the numerous other reactions catalyzed by microsomes (p. 210). It is particularly odd that these oxidative reactions, which require gaseous O_2, should also need *reduced* nucleotide. The paradox could be resolved by assuming a peroxidative mechanism, first suggested in 1956 for schradan activation (64) and supported by the finding that H_2O_2 is produced when $NADH_2$ is added to liver microsomes (65), but not by much other evidence.

$NADH_2 \rightarrow NAD$; $O_2 \rightarrow H_2O_2$; $H_2O_2 \rightarrow H_2O$; $XH \rightarrow XOH$

DEGRADATION

Degradation occurs primarily by hydrolytic routes, which leave an anionic group attached to or capable of approaching the phosphorus, thereby reducing its positivity. Some rather special reductive and dealkylative routes will also be commented upon, but are of minor importance.

Phosphatases. By far the commonest hydrolysis is by phosphatases, which for present purposes we can define as enzymes hydrolyzing any phosphorus ester or anhydride bond, including P—O—C, P—S—C, P—F, and others. Unfortunately for the insecticidal organophosphates, although a great deal of valuable work has been done describing the hydrolysis of numerous compounds, there has never been any broadly based study which has attempted to define the spectrum of activity of these phosphatases. Indeed, in very few cases has the relation of these phosphatases (which, because they hydrolyze triesters, might be called phosphotriesterases) to the well-known phosphatases been worked out. One report, an exception, shows that serum parathionase is *not* alkaline phosphatase (34), and indeed the pH optima of the phosphotriesterases usually rule out both alkaline and acid phosphatase. But in addition, the relationships between paraoxonase, and the phosphatases acting on dichlorvos, famphur, and dimethoate (taking examples at random), have never been examined. One generalization can safely be made: all the organophosphates can be hydrolyzed, in mammals, insects, and plants, by phosphatases; commonly, this is the major metabolic route.

The phosphatases, as judged by their metabolic products, can be divided into the more common ones, which hydrolyze off the leaving group (side group), and the less common, which dealkylate. An example of the latter was first described for ronnel in 1958 by Plapp and Casida (74):

$$(CH_3O)_2P(S)O\text{—}C_6H_2Cl_3 \longrightarrow (CH_3O)(HO)P(S)O\text{—}C_6H_2Cl_3$$

Ronnel

This dealkylation product was as common in rat urine as a more familiar product, $(CH_3O)_2PSOH$, derived from leaving-group hydrolysis.

Two excellent studies by Fukami and Shishido (28,78) have shown (see Table 4.2) that in rat liver, but not in various insect preparations, there is a

TABLE 4.2

LOCALIZATION OF PHOSPHATASES[a]

	Hydrolysis proceeding by dealkylation (%)					
	Rat liver			Rice stem borer		
	Mito-chondria	Micro-somes	Super-natant	Mito-chondria	Micro-somes	Super-natant
Methyl parathion	42	17	84	23	22	27
Methyl paraoxon	20	8	90			
Sumithion	44	8	80	9	10	19
Ethyl sumithion	11	3	19	—	—	—

[a] The balance of the hydrolysis proceeded through routes involving hydrolytic removal of leaving group. From Shishido and Fukami (78).

soluble dealkylating phosphatase, separable from mitochondrial and microsomal phosphatases, which cleave quite differently. The fact that ethyl sumithion is poorly dealkylated suggests that the enzyme is a demethylase with little de-ethylase activity.

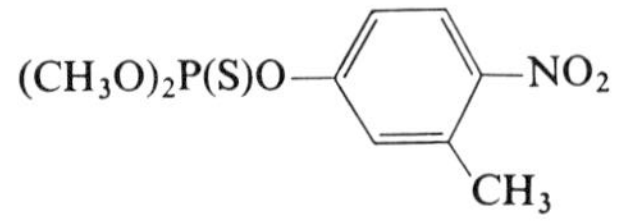

$(CH_3O)_2P(S)O$–[3-methyl-4-nitrophenyl] (CH_3, NO_2)

Sumithion

$(C_2H_5O)_2P(S)O$–[3-methyl-4-nitrophenyl] (CH_3, NO_2)

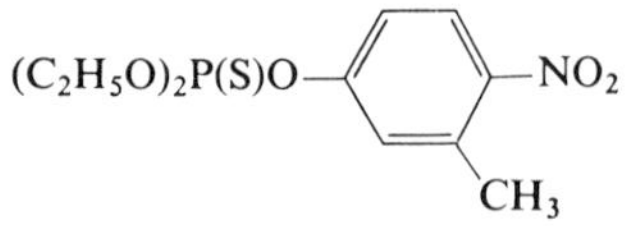

Ethyl sumithion

The soluble demethylase was found in all livers studied including those of rat, guinea pig, and rabbit, but not in insect preparations. It was sensitive to Cu^{++} (91% inhibition at $10^{-3}M$) and SH reagents, but had no requirement for oxygen or reduced nucleotide, and so is not related to the microsomal enzymes. Demethylase activity against dichlorvos has been shown in the soluble fraction of rat liver (33).

The existence of a demethylase also shows itself in metabolic studies, in which dimethyl organophosphates in particular give rise to their demethyl metabolites in urine. Thus with dimethoate, $(CH_3O)_2P(S)SCH_2C(O)NHCH_3$, 12% of the metabolites in rat urine (2 hours after treatment) were demethyl compounds (18). With malathion, the total urinary output contained 7% of demethyl malathion in the cow, 11% in the rat, and 21% in the dog (36,70).

$(CH_3O)_2P(S)SCHCOOC_2H_5$ with $CH_2COOC_2H_5$ on the CH

Malathion

$(CH_3O)(HO)P(S)SCHCOOC_2H_5$ with $CH_2COOC_2H_5$ on the CH

Demethyl malathion

With Azodrin (p. 77), demethylation provides 75% of the metabolites in boll weevils, 25% in houseflies or rats, and a major portion of metabolism in cotton seedlings (13). For the compound Bidrin (p. 35), demethylation (or, as perhaps we should call it in this case, *O*-demethylation, to distinguish the *O*-methyl from the *N*-methyl groups) is a major route in cotton seedlings, bollworm larvae, and boll weevil adults (12).

De-ethylation also occurs in many cases. Thus coumaphos is de-ethylated in rats (41), but the extent varies greatly with route of administration: 15% of urinary metabolites are de-ethylated compounds after an oral dose, but only 5% after a subcutaneous, and none after a dermal dose. Presumably the liver is the primary site of de-ethylation, and plays a minor role when the compound is delivered in such a way that many other tissues act first upon the compound.

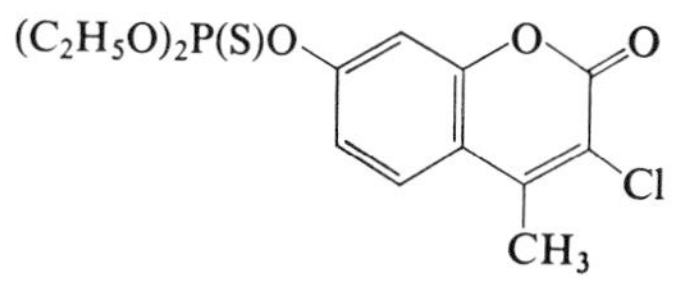

$(C_2H_5O)_2P(S)O$ — Cl — CH_3

Coumaphos

It is probable that all organophosphates can be dealkylated to some extent by all organisms, but usually dealkylation is a minor route and even in dimethyl phosphates one does not expect to find much dealkylation; for instance, it is a very minor route in dichlorvos metabolism by rat and rabbit tissues (33).

Let us now consider the commoner phosphatases, which cleave leaving groups. In view of the fact that the leaving group is defined as that which leaves during cholinesterase phosphorylation, it is to be expected that the same group would usually leave during phosphorylation of a phosphatase, which is presumably the first step that occurs when a phosphatase acts on an organophosphate.

Since these are the commonest phosphatases, it follows that the principal metabolite from dimethyl compounds is dimethyl phosphate, and for diethyl compounds is diethyl phosphate. These statements are not necessarily true if other, nonphosphatase routes of hydrolysis are available, as discussed below. And in the case of phosphorothionates, phosphorothiolates, and phosphorodithioates, one commonly gets a mixture of dialkyl phosphates and various thio analogs. Thus after treatment of rats with dioxathion, 83% of the urinary metabolites was diethyl phosphorothioate, $(C_2H_5O)_2PSOH$, 6% was the dithioate, $(C_2H_5O)_2PSSH$, and 11% was diethyl phosphate (6).

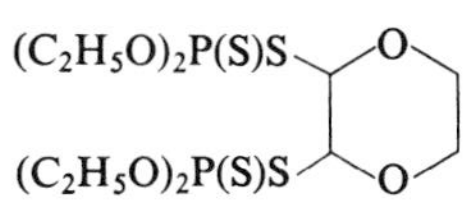

$(C_2H_5O)_2P(S)S$ — O
$(C_2H_5O)_2P(S)S$ — O

Dioxathion

One cannot say whether these findings imply that there is a phosphatase acting on dioxathion which can attack either P—S (to yield the POH product) or S—C (to yield the PSH product).

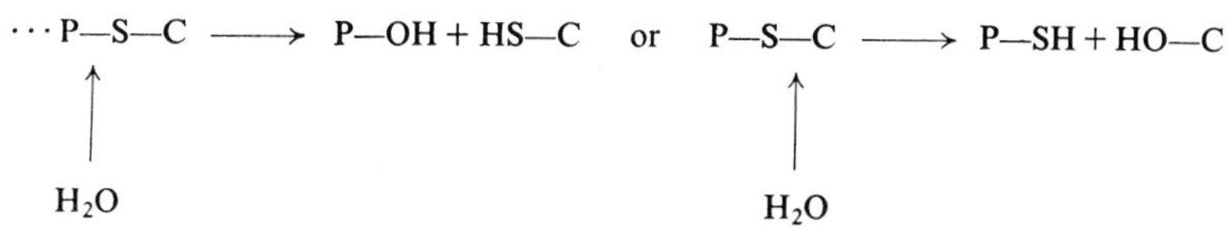

$$\cdots P\text{—}S\text{—}C \xrightarrow{} P\text{—}OH + HS\text{—}C \quad \text{or} \quad P\text{—}S\text{—}C \longrightarrow P\text{—}SH + HO\text{—}C$$

(In each case an arrow points from H_2O up to the bond attacked: the P—S bond in the first reaction, the S—C bond in the second.)

Alternatively, and more plausibly, there are at least two phosphatases specific for P—S and S—C, respectively.

It is clear from the fact that diethyl phosphorodithioate is a common metabolite that phosphorothionates can be hydrolyzed directly without prior oxidation of P(S) to P(O). There is the question whether there is a class of phosphatases which is *specific* for hydrolysis of phosphorothionates; one study suggests that there is a parathion-hydrolyzing enzyme in liver microsomes which requires $NADPH_2$, and is inactive against paraoxon (62).

The leaving-group phosphatases which have been studied in most detail are those which degrade warfare agents, most of which are fluoro compounds;

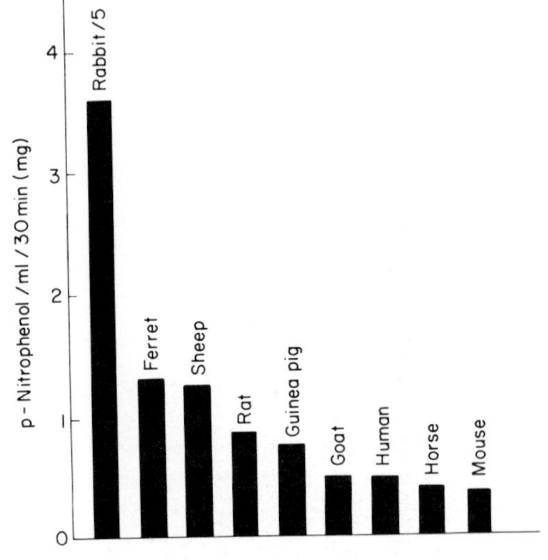

FIG. 4.2. Hydrolysis of paraoxon by sera of mammals. The value for rabbit has been reduced to one-fifth in the figure. Redrawn from Aldridge (3)

the enzyme(s) may therefore be called fluorophosphatase, although the term phosphorylphosphatase has also been used, for reasons obscure to me. Because no insecticidal organophosphates are fluoro compounds, we will not discuss fluorophosphatases in any detail, but only point out some features which, if we can judge by the skimpier data available for other phosphatases, appear generally applicable (57,66). The fluorophosphatases are present in virtually every tissue and organism studied, including microorganisms. There is a variety of enzymes which can, for instance, hydrolyze DFP [$(isoC_3H_7O)_2POF$], and they are separable by virtue of their source, ion sensitivity, solubility, specificity, and ability to be activated by agents such as dipyridyl. For instance, in hogs and rats, one can obtain a soluble, cobalt-activated, dipyridyl-activated enzyme from kidney, which hydrolyzes DFP and DBF [$(C_4H_8O)_2POF$] equally well; also a soluble liver enzyme with similar properties, except that it is insensitive to dipyridyl; and also a particulate, cobalt-inhibited, dipyridyl-insensitive enzyme from liver which hydrolyzes DBF ten times faster than DFP.

The only comparably intense studies with organophosphates of insecticidal interest have concerned paraoxon and dichlorvos. Aldridge published in 1953 two classical studies (2,3) in which he introduced the terms A- and B-esterases. A-esterase is the serum enzyme which hydrolyzes *p*-nitrophenyl acetate and paraoxon; B-esterase is the serum enzyme which hydrolyzes *p*-nitrophenyl

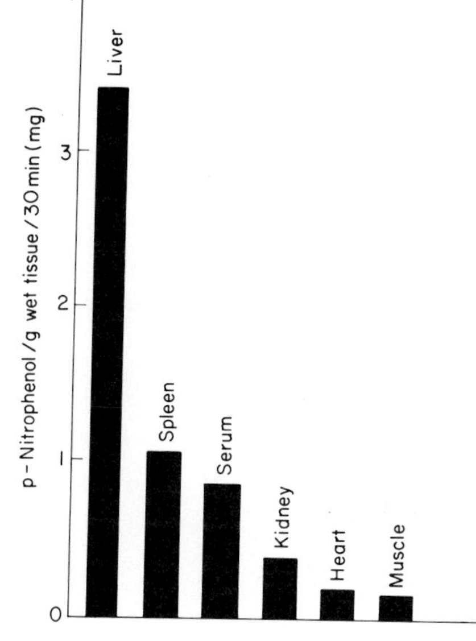

FIG. 4.3. Hydrolysis of paraoxon by homogenates of various rat tissues. Activity was not detectable in pancreas, brain, and submaxillary gland. Redrawn from Aldridge (3).

acetate but is inhibited by paraoxon ($10^{-8}M$). As Fig. 4.2 shows, the A-esterase activity of sera varies greatly with species, and is about 17 times higher in rabbits than in most other organisms.

Serum is by no means the only source of paraoxon-hydrolyzing enzyme. As Fig. 4.3 shows, rat liver is three or four times more active that rat serum. Within liver, there are several paraoxon-hydrolyzing enzymes (paraoxonases), implied in the data of Table 4.2, and shown specifically by Kojima and O'Brien (38), who found three liver paraoxonases with different pH optima and ion sensitivities. Undoubtedly, similarly complex conditions hold for other phosphatases, but the full story has not yet emerged.

An extensive study on dichlorvos phosphatase (33) revealed a picture differing enough in detail from paraoxon phosphatase to suggest different enzymes were at work. For instance, the order of activity of tissues was liver > kidney > spleen > serum, instead of liver > spleen > serum > kidney. The dichlorvos phosphatase activity in liver was caused by at least three enzymes: a Ca^{++}-stimulated mitochondrial system which cleaved only P—O—methyl, and two soluble enzymes, one which hydrolyzed P—O—methyl and was stimulated by Mn^{++}, and another which hydrolyzed P—O—vinyl and was insensitive to Ca^{++} or Mn^{++}.

Serum phosphatases are not effective against all organophosphates. Rabbit, rat, or human sera will hydrolyze, among other compounds, DFP, tabun, tepp, paraoxon, dichlorvos, butonate, naled, and chlorophan, but not schradan, chlorthion, demeton, mevinphos, malathion, trichlorfon, or diazinon (8, 33,56). There is some evidence for rabbit serum that DFP, tepp, and paraoxon are all hydrolyzed by the same enzyme (56), but for sheep serum there is excellent evidence that paraoxonase which has been purified hydrolyzes DFP but not tepp (44).

In intact houseflies, and to a great extent in other insects, phosphatase action is vigorous, and the half-life of applied organophosphates is but a few hours (43,49,69,86). Yet homogenates of insects are extremely inactive in such degradations (40,86). The most likely explanation is that a cofactor is required, and is diluted away in homogenization. In particular, the existence of microsomal systems requiring reduced nucleotides is an attractive possibility, but has never been shown experimentally. The problem is particularly severe in the study of resistant insects, for which small differences in phosphatase activity of homogenates has been made the basis for an explanation of resistance (p. 243).

The most complete study on insect phosphatases *in vitro* is that of Krueger and Casida (40) who worked with five insects and a mite, and studied ten organophosphates. In seven compounds, hydrolysis by insect homogenates was undetectable in most cases, although several of these compounds, e.g., paraoxon, malathion, and mevinphos, are known to be degraded rapidly in insects. Consequently the detailed work was performed on DFP, tepp, and dichlorvos, whose hydrolysis was brisk. Mn^{++} at $10^{-3} M$ was a potent activator, increasing hydrolysis by 4-fold for tepp and DFP, and by 19-fold for dichlorvos. Activity was inhibited by some SH inhibitors at $10^{-4} M$, including *p*-chloromercuribenzoic acid and mercuric and cupric ions. All these enzyme activities were in the soluble fraction. However, the manometric method was used in this work, and undoubtedly more sensitive procedures would reveal additional enzymes.

Studies on metabolism of insecticidal phosphonates have been few. One important compound, trichlorfon, has been the subject of some dispute because it quite readily rearranges, with loss of HCl, to give another well-known insecticide, dichlorvos. The reaction goes fastest under alkaline conditions.

$$\underset{\text{Trichlorfon}}{(CH_3O)_2P(O)CH(OH){-}CCl_3} \rightarrow \underset{\text{Dichlorvos}}{(CH_3O)_2P(O)OCH{=}CCl_2} + HCl$$

There was thus room for doubt whether metabolism would occur before or after rearrangement. Some evidence, incompletely published (5), suggests that direct P—C cleavage of the parent compound occurs, for the glucuronide of trichloroethanol was excreted by treated mammals. If this is confirmed, the overall reaction is presumably

$$\underset{\text{Trichlorfon}}{(CH_3O)_2P(O)CH(OH){-}CCl_3} \xrightarrow{H_2O} (CH_3O)P(O)OH + CH_2OHCCl_3$$

Phosphonates in which an alkyl group, rather than the leaving group, is attacked by a C—P bond are very probably metabolized by phosphatase cleavage of P—O—C; that is to say, the C—P bond does not play a special role. For instance, the warfare agent soman is metabolized in rat tissues thus (31):

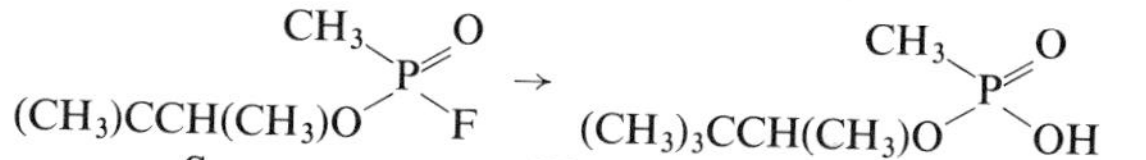

$$\underset{\text{Soman}}{(CH_3)CCH(CH_3)O{-}P(=O)(CH_3){-}F} \rightarrow \underset{\text{Pinacolyl methylphosphonic acid}}{(CH_3)_3CCH(CH_3)O{-}P(=O)(CH_3){-}OH}$$

The data on Colep are compatible with an analogous metabolism in plants (apples, cotton) and in rats, although the data for rats is doubtful (46).

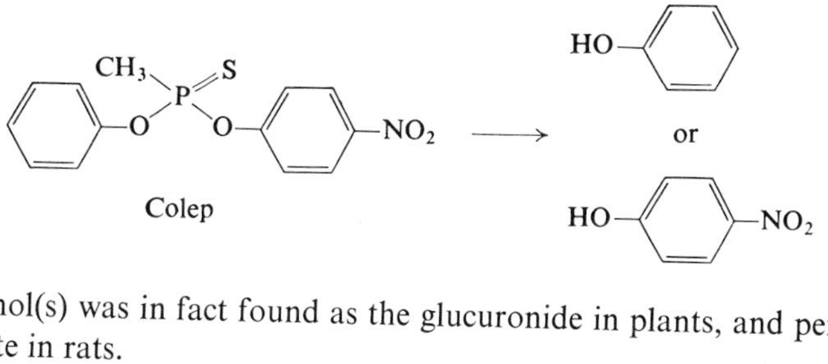

$$\underset{\text{Colep}}{C_6H_5O{-}P(=S)(CH_3){-}OC_6H_4NO_2} \longrightarrow HO{-}C_6H_5 \text{ or } HO{-}C_6H_4{-}NO_2$$

The phenol(s) was in fact found as the glucuronide in plants, and perhaps as the sulfate in rats.

We have discussed only phosphatase action upon triesters, that is to say, on parent compounds and their unhydrolyzed metabolites. But it is quite certain that the initial hydrolysis products are further hydrolyzed, for phosphoric acid and monoalkyl phosphoric acids are always found as metabolic products, although usually representing a small percentage. Very little work has been done on such "secondary phosphatases" as we might call them. The reason for the lack of interest is that the first hydrolysis almost always constitutes a detoxication, so that, from the toxicological viewpoint, further cleavage is of minor importance. One study showed that in liver, kidney, and spleen of rats and rabbits, demethyl dichlorvos was hydrolyzed as readily as dichlorvos; but in plasma, only dichlorvos was readily hydrolyzed. By contrast, methyl phosphate, which is very probably the product of demethyl dichlorvos hydrolysis, was hydrolyzed only very slowly by a soluble enzyme of rat liver. Putting together the various facts about dichlorvos described above, the complete hydrolysis picture in, for instance, rat liver, can be pictured as:

$(CH_3O)_2P(O)OCH{=}CCl_2$ (Dichlorvos) $\xrightarrow{\text{Fast}}$ $(CH_3O)_2P(O)OH$ (Dimethyl phosphate)

Dichlorvos $\xrightarrow{\text{Slow}}$ $(CH_3O)(HO)P(O)OCH{=}CCl_2$ (Demethyl dichlorvos) $\xrightarrow{\text{Fast}}$ $(CH_3O)(HO)P(O)OH$ (Methyl phosphate) $\xrightarrow{\text{Slow}}$ $(OH)_3P(O)$ (Phosphoric acid)

That the demethyl dichlorvos was hydrolyzed at its P—O—vinyl rather than its P—O—methyl bond was shown experimentally. Dimethyl phosphate was said to be unmetabolized (33).

Carboxyesterases. Phosphatase cleavage is universal in the organophosphates. But in those compounds containing a carboxyester group, COOR, cleavage of it also occurs, and in some cases may constitute the predominant degradative pathway.

The most clear-cut case is that of malathion, for which carboxyesterase activity predominates in mammals, and phosphatase and carboxyesterase activity are about equal in insects.

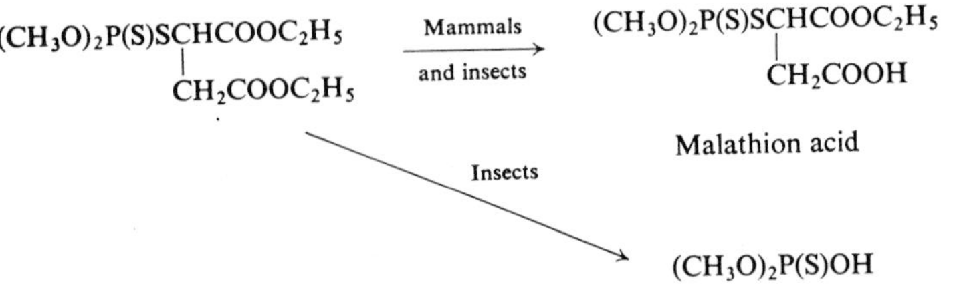

Thus of the total identified products, the percentage of carboxyesterase products at 30 minutes was 57% in American cockroach, 49% in German cockroach, 36% in housefly, and 77% in mice (42). The consequences of this difference for toxicity are most important, as discussed on p. 263.

Further carboxyesterase action can cleave the second $COOC_2H_5$ group from malathion acid to yield malathion diacid, and indeed this is a notable urinary metabolite. The percent of total urinary products present as malathion acid and diacid, respectively, are 63 and 17 in the cow; 12 and 48 in the rat; and 40 and 21 in the dog (36,70).

$$(CH_3O)_2P(S)SCHCOOH \quad (\text{with } CH_2COOH \text{ on the CH})$$

Malathion diacid

Several studies have described the effectiveness of various tissues in degrading malathion and its P(O) analog, malaoxon (37,58,77). Activity is ubiquitous, and was found in the liver, kidney, spleen, serum, lung, ileum, muscle, and brain of all mammals studied. There is variation among species, but only 10-fold at the most; e.g., serum of rat is 10 times more effective than that of dog (58). The ratio of malathion to malaoxon hydrolysis varies greatly (37), suggesting that different enzymes are involved; for instance, mouse brain hydrolyzes malathion, but not malaoxon.

In insects, all parts of the gut are active in hydrolyzing malathion, but not malaoxon. Fat body has less activity, hemolymph and nervous tissue have none. Whole insect homogenates vary greatly in activity; those of white peach scale are very active, and those of the lady beetle are inactive (37). Insect and mammalian carboxyesterase differ greatly in their susceptibility to inhibition; for example, that of American cockroach gut is 2500 times more susceptible to inhibition by malaoxon or acetoxon than that of mouse liver.*

The fact that malathion is hydrolyzed by mammals primarily at the carboxyester group does not imply that all carboxyester-containing organophosphates are similarly degraded. Mevinphos in cows is degraded entirely by phosphatase (14).

$$(CH_3O)_2P(O)OC(CH_3){=}CHCOOCH_3 \rightarrow (CH_3O)_2P(O)OH$$

Mevinphos — Dimethyl phosphate

The compound acethion is closely related to malathion, and was in fact prepared (73) in the hope that its metabolism, and hence its selectivity, would

* Acetoxon and malaoxon are both substrates and inhibitors for carboxyesterases; when their carboxyl end is attacked, they are substrates, but when their phosphoryl end is attacked, they are inhibitors. No doubt this explains the poor ability of many tissues to hydrolyze these compounds.

resemble malathion (see p. 265). Mouse liver preparations hydrolyze acethion almost exclusively by carboxyesterase action, to give acethion acid (73).

$$\underset{\text{Acethion}}{(C_2H_5O)_2P(S)SCH_2COOC_2H_5} \rightarrow \underset{\text{Acethion acid}}{(C_2H_5O)_2P(S)SCH_2COOH}$$

Nevertheless there is good evidence (37) that in both mice and American cockroaches, different enzymes are involved in hydrolysis of malathion and acethion. Thus the order of tissue activity in mice for malathion is liver > kidney > lung > brain > blood; for acethion it is liver = kidney > blood > lung > brain. Acetoxon, the P(O) analog of acethion, is degraded by enzyme(s) other than those acting on acethion; for instance, kidney and blood hydrolyze acethion excellently, acetoxon hardly at all. Insect tissues, which are almost inactive on malaoxon or acetoxon, also hydrolyze malathion and acethion by different enzymes, judged by the above criterion; thus cockroach nerve cord hydrolyzes acethion, but not malathion.

It is clear why cleavage of a P—O—R group, which in effect creates a P—O$^-$ group, causes degradation, for the positivity of the phosphorus is severely reduced by the neighboring anion (p. 46). But why is the P(O) derivative of malathion acid a poor anticholinesterase? The answer is probably that the field effect (p. 12) is operating, and the carboxylate ion reduces the positivity of the phosphorus.

$$\begin{array}{l} \qquad\quad\;\; O \\ \qquad\quad\;\; \| \\ (CH_3O)_2P{-}S{-}CHCOOC_2H_5 \\ \qquad\quad\;\; \vdots \qquad\quad | \\ \qquad\;\; {}^-O{-}C{-}CH_2 \\ \qquad\qquad\;\; \| \\ \qquad\qquad\;\; O \end{array}$$

Malaoxon acid

Amidases. Whenever a carboxyamide group, $CONR_2$ (where R is hydrogen or an alkyl group), exists in an organophosphate, there is a possibility of its cleavage by carboxyamidase (or amidase as we shall abbreviate it) as, for instance, in dimethoate:

$$\underset{\text{Dimethoate}}{(CH_3O)_2P(S)SCHC(O)NHCH_3} \rightarrow \underset{\text{Dimethoate acid}}{(CH_3O)_2P(S)CHCOOH}$$

Phosphatase action invariably occurs as well. The relative contributions of the phosphatase and the amidase routes varies widely in both insects and mammals. In five insect species studied (85), the phosphatase to amidase ratio for dimethoate was typically 2:1. In the mouse, the ratio was about 1:1, and in the guinea pig, about 7:3 (86). There is evidence that these various amidases differ a little, at least in their sensitivity to inhibition by EPN (ethyl *p*-nitrophenyl phosphorothionate) *in vivo*: dimethoate amidase was insensitive to

EPN in houseflies or milkweed bugs, was rather sensitive in mice, and was extremely sensitive in guinea pigs (86).

Dimethoate metabolism in vertebrates occurs almost exclusively in the liver (83), and the *in vitro* rate appears to parallel that *in vivo* because an excellent (inverse) correlation was found between toxicity and dimethoate degradation in liver homogenates for six vertebrates (83,84), a finding which encouraged us to predict, somewhat tentatively, the LD_{50} of dimethoate for humans, by studying dimethoate degradation in human liver (84). The dimethoate amidase of sheep liver was studied in more detail, and found to be primarily (60%) in the microsomes, and to have rather ordinary properties: a pH optimum of 8.0, stability up to 50°C, and a K_m of $2 \times 10^{-4} M$ (83).

An interesting amidase cleavage occurs in rats (51), steers (16), and cotton plants (27) acting upon Imidan; in all cases the major product is phthalamic acid:

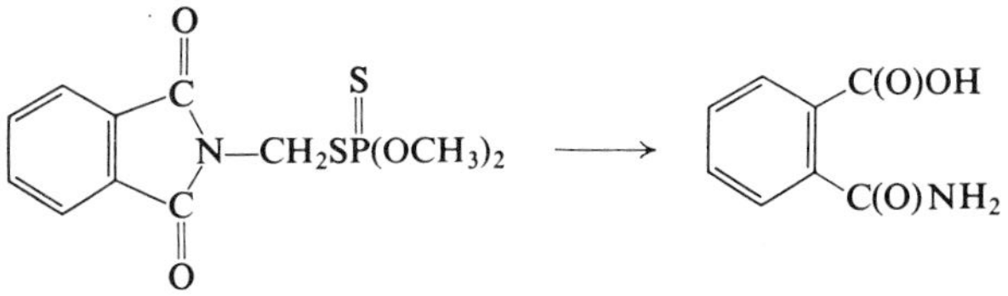

$$\text{C}_6\text{H}_4(\text{C=O})_2\text{N—CH}_2\text{S}\overset{\text{S}}{\overset{\|}{\text{P}}}(\text{OCH}_3)_2 \longrightarrow \text{C}_6\text{H}_4(\text{C(O)OH})(\text{C(O)NH}_2)$$

Imidan Phthalamic acid

This metabolism therefore involves a hydrolytic step (amidase cleavage) and removal of the phosphorus-bearing *N*-substituent by an unknown mechanism.

Amidase cleavage does not occur in all amidic organophosphates; it was not observed in the metabolism of Azodrin by bollworms, tobacco budworms, American cockroaches, or rats (13).

$$(\text{CH}_3\text{O})_2\text{P(O)O}\underset{\underset{\text{CH}_3}{|}}{\text{C}}\text{=CHCONHCH}_3$$

Azodrin

Nor was the closely related compound Bidrin (p. 35) cleaved by an amidase in adult boll weevils, larvae of the bollworm, rats, or cotton plants (12).

Reductive Degradation. As pointed out on p. 46, degradative reactions are usually those which result in a severe lessening of positivity on the phosphorus. The commonest mechanisms are hydrolytic, and introduce an anion. But under the right circumstances, the reduction of a nitro to an amino group has the same effect, as explained on p. 15. This reduction has been demonstrated to occur in rumen juice (17) and in the cow's rumen (1); 6 hours after oral parathion administration, the percentage of parathion plus metabolites represented by aminoparathion was 53% in rumen juice and 41% in urine, with lesser values for milk (7%) and blood (1%).

The reduction of nitrophenyl-containing organophosphates by rumen juice appears to be a general phenomenon, observed in all six cases studied. But only in one case, American Cyanamid 4138, did reduction outstrip hydrolysis as a degradation route; in this case, after one day, 75% was converted to the amino derivative, and only 20% was hydrolyzed to dimethyl phosphate (1).

$$(CH_3O)_2P(O)O\text{—}C_6H_3(Cl)\text{—}NO_2 \longrightarrow (CH_3O)_2P(O)O\text{—}C_6H_3(Cl)\text{—}NH_2$$

American Cyanamid 4138

N-Dealkylation and N-Hydroxyalkylation. For reasons which have no simple electronic explanation, the various *N*-derivatives of amino or amidic organophosphates differ considerably in anticholinesterase activity. Consequently, the removal or modification of the *N*-substituents can constitute an activation, a degradation, or neither (Table 4.3). *N*-Dealkylation is one of the many metabolic reactions catalyzed by liver microsomes (p. 63) and is probably oxidative, proceeding by hydroxylation of the alkyl group, followed by splitting out of an aldehyde, specifically formaldehyde if *N*-demethylation occurs:

$$\equiv N\text{—}CH_3 \rightarrow \equiv N\text{—}CH_2OH \rightarrow \equiv N\text{—}H + CH_2O$$

N-Methyl — *N*-Hydroxymethyl — *N*-Demethyl

TABLE 4.3

EFFECT OF *N*-SUBSTITUENTS IN BIDRIN ANALOGS: $(CH_3O)_2P(O)OC(CH_3){=}CHC(O)R$[a]

	LD_{50} (mg/kg)		pI_{50}	
R	Mouse	Housefly	Fly ChE	Plasma ChE
$N(CH_3)_2$ (Bidrin)	14	38	7.2	6.8
$N(CH_2OH)CH_3$	18	14	7.0	6.5
$NHCH_3$ (Azodrin)	8	6	6.8	6.5
$NHCH_2OH$	12	30	6.9	5.9
NH_2	3	1	6.5	5.6

[a] Conclusion: Variations in housefly toxicity are large compared with those for mice. Total dealkylation increases toxicity profoundly, but reduces anticholinesterase activity substantially. Probably the variations in toxicity are a reflection of differences in susceptibility to metabolism rather than in anticholinesterase activity. Data of Menzer and Casida (52).

In some cases the final step may be slow, so that hydroxymethylation is an important reaction. Such is the case for Azodrin (p. 77), in which hydroxymethylation is about as important as phosphatase hydrolysis in metabolism by rats; the *N*-demethylated compound occurs in urine at only about one-half the level of the hydroxymethylated compound until several hours after treatment, when both occur at similar levels. In bollworms, tobacco budworms, and American cockroaches, a rather similar pattern is found (13). The same is essentially true for the closely related compound Bidrin, when metabolized by rats or cotton plants. In adult boll weevils and larvae of bollworms, the

$$(CH_3O)_2P(O)OC(CH_3){=}CHC(O)N(CH_3)_2$$

Bidrin

N-hydroxymethyl and *N*-demethyl derivatives were virtually absent, and metabolism was by phosphatase action only (12). But in houseflies, measurable amounts (of the order of 1%) of *N*-hydroxymethyl and *N*-demethyl derivatives were found (52).

For famphur, *N*-demethylation is a significant pathway in insects, but not in mice (69). An hour after injection of famphur, milkweed bugs have demethylated 3% of the dose, cockroaches 1.2%, and mice only 0.01%. (It is, however, possible that the low yield in the mouse was due to its ability to hydrolyze the *N*-demethyl famphur rapidly.)

$$(CH_3O)_2P(S)O{-}C_6H_4{-}S(O)_2N(CH_3)_2 \longrightarrow (CH_3O)_2P(S)O{-}C_6H_4{-}S(O)_2NHCH_3$$

Famphur

Most of these metabolic alterations of *N*-substituents have been observed *in vivo*. Probably the earliest *in vitro* study was that (75) of Scaife and Campbell in 1959. They reported on the degradation of Amiton by liver homogenates and showed that the activity resided in microsomes, and required oxygen and supplementation with $NADH_2$. In other words, it was precisely the liver microsome system best known for its ability to degrade drugs (p. 210) and activate phosphorothionates (p. 63). Although they did not identify the breakdown product(s), it now seems likely that *N*-de-ethylation was occurring, in this case with an amine rather than an amide:

$$(C_2H_5O)_2P(O)SCH_2CH_2N(C_2H_5)_2 \rightarrow (C_2H_5O)_2P(O)SCH_2CH_2NHC_2H_5$$

Amiton

They noted that the enzyme activity was high in pig, dog, cow, and frog liver, but almost absent in human or cat liver.

REFERENCES

1. Ahmed, M. K., Casida, J. E., and Nichols, R. E., *J. Agr. Food Chem.* **6**, 740 (1958).
2. Aldridge, W. N., *Biochem. J.* **53**, 110 (1953).
3. Aldridge, W. N., *Biochem. J.* **53**, 117 (1953).
4. Aldridge, W. N., *Biochem. J.* **56**, 185 (1954).
5. Arthur, B. W., and Casida, J. E., *Proc. Entomol. Soc. Am. 3rd Ann. Meeting, Cincinatti,* 1955.
6. Arthur, B. W., and Casida, J. E., *J. Econ. Entomol.* **52**, 20 (1959).
7. Asperen, K. van, *Nature* **181**, 355 (1958).
8. Augustinsson, K. B., and Heimburger, G., *Acta Chem. Scand.* **8**, 1533 (1954).
9. Baron, R. L., and Casida, J. E., *Biochem. Pharmacol.* **11**, 1129 (1962).
10. Benjamini, E., Metcalf, R. L., and Fukuto, T. R., *J. Econ. Entomol.* **52**, 99 (1959).
11. Berry, W. K., Davies, D. R., and Green, A. L., *Biochem. J.* **71**, 150 (1959).
12. Bull, D. L., and Lindquist, D. A., *J. Agr. Food Chem.* **12**, 310 (1964).
13. Bull, D. L., and Lindquist, D. A., *J. Agr. Food Chem.* **14**, 105 (1966).
14. Casida, J. E., Gatterdam, P. E., Knaak, J. B., Lance, R. D., and Niedermeier, R. P., *J. Agr. Food Chem.* **6**, 685 (1958).
15. Chadwick, L. E. *In* "Cholinesterases and Anticholinesterase Agents," Handbuch der Experimentellen Pharmakologie (G. B. Koelle, ed.), Vol. 15, Chapt. 16. Springer, Berlin, 1963.
16. Chamberlain, W. F., *J. Econ. Entomol.* **58**, 51 (1965).
17. Cook, J. W., *J. Agr. Food Chem.* **5**, 859 (1957)
18. Dauterman, W. C., Casida, J. E., Knaak, J. B., and Kowalczyk, T., *J. Agr. Food Chem.* **7**, 188 (1959).
19. Dauterman, W. C., Viado, G. B., Casida, J. E., and O'Brien, R. D., *J. Agr. Food Chem.* **8**, 115 (1960).
20. Davies, D. R., *In* "Cholinesterases and Anticholinesterase Agents," Handbuch der Exterimentellen Pharmokologie (G. B. Koelle, ed.), Vol. 15, Chapt. 19. Springer, Berlin, 1963.
21. Davies, D. R., Holland, P., and Rumens, M. J., *Brit. J. Pharmacol.* **15**, 271 (1960).
22. Davison, A. N., *Chem. Ind.* (*London*) p. 895 (1954).
23. De Candole, C. A., Douglas, W. W., Evans, C. L., Holmes, R., Spencer, K. E. V., Torrance, R. W., and Wilson, K. M., *Brit. J. Pharmacol.* **8**, 466 (1953).
24. De Candole, C. A., and McPhail, M. K., *Can. J. Biochem. Physiol.* **35**, 1071 (1957).
25. Eto, M., Casida, J. E., and Eto, T., *Biochem. Pharmacol.* **11**, 337 (1962).
26. Eto, M., Matsuo, S., and Oshima, Y., *Agr. Biol. Chem.* (*Tokyo*) **27**, 870 (1963).
27. Ford, I. M., Menn, J. J., and Meyding, G. D., *J. Agr. Food Chem.* **14**, 83 (1966).
28. Fukami, J., and Shishido, T., *Botyu-Kagaku* **28**, 77 (1963).
29. Fukuto, T. R., Metcalf, R. L., March, R. B., and Maxon, M. G., *J. Econ. Entomol.* **48**, 347 (1955).
30. Grob, D., *In* "Cholinesterases and Anticholinesterase Agents," Handbuch der Experimentellen Pharmakologie (G. B. Koelle, ed.), Vol. 15, Chapt. 22. Springer, Berlin, 1963.
31. Harris, L. W., Braswell, L. M., Fleisher, J. H., and Cliff, W. J., *Biochem. Pharmacol.* **13**, 1129 (1964).
32. Hobbiger, F., *In* "Cholinesterases and Anticholinesterase Agents," Handbuch der Experimentellen Pharmakologie (G. B. Koelle, ed.), Vol. 15, Chapt. 21. Springer, Berlin, 1963.
33. Hodgson, E., and Casida, J. E., *J. Agr. Food Chem.* **10**, 208 (1962).

34. Iuchi, I., *Bull. Yamaguchi Med. School* **6**, 1 (1958).
35. Kleinwachter, L., *Berlin Klin. Wachschr.* **1**, 369 (1864).
36. Knaak, J. B., and O'Brien, R. D., *J. Agr. Food Chem.* **8**, 198 (1960).
37. Kojima, K., "Studies on the Selective Toxicity and Detoxication of Organophosphorus Compounds with Reference to the Studies on Carboxyesterase as a Factor in the Selective Toxicity of Malathion." Inst. Agr. Chem., Toa Nayaku Co., Odawara, Japan, 1961.
38. Kojima, K., and O'Brien, R. D., Unpublished observations, 1966.
39. Kok, G. C., and Walop, J. N., *Biochim. Biophys. Acta* **13**, 510 (1954).
40. Krueger, H. R., and Casida, J. E., *J. Econ. Entomol.* **54**, 239 (1961).
41. Krueger, H. R., Casida, J. E., and Niedermeier, R. P., *J. Agr. Food Chem.* **7**, 182 (1959).
42. Krueger, H. R., and O'Brien, R. D., *J. Econ. Entomol.* **52**, 1063 (1959).
43. Krueger, H. R., O'Brien, R. D., and Dauterman, W. C., *J. Econ. Entomol.* **53**, 25 (1960).
44. Main, A. R., *Biochem. J.* **74**, 10 (1960).
45. March, R. B., Metcalf, R. L., Fukuto, T. R., and Maxon, M. G., *J. Econ. Entomol.* **48**, 355 (1955).
46. Marco, G. J., and Jaworski, E. G., *J. Agr. Food Chem.* **12**, 305 (1964).
47. McNamara, B. P., Koelle, G. B., and Gilman, A., *J. Pharmacol. Exptl. Therap.* **88**, 27 (1946).
48. Mengle, D. C., and Casida, J. E., *J. Econ. Entomol.* **51**, 750 (1958).
49. Mengle, D. C., and Casida, J. E., *J. Agr. Food Chem.* **8**, 431 (1960).
50. Mengle, D. C., and O'Brien, R. D., *Biochem. J.* **75**, 201 (1960).
51. Menn, J. J., and McBain, J. B., *J. Agr. Food Chem.* **12**, 162 (1964).
52. Menzer, R. E., and Casida, J. E., *J. Agr. Food Chem.* **13**, 102 (1965).
53. Metcalf, R. L., Fukuto, T. R., and March, R. B., *J. Econ. Entomol.* **50**, 338 (1957).
54. Metcalf, R. L., and March, R. B., *Ann. Entomol. Soc. Am.* **46**, 63 (1953).
55. Meunier, P., Vinet, A., and Jouanneteau, J., *Bull. Soc. Chim. Biol.* **29**, 507 (1947).
56. Mounter, L. A., *J. Biol. Chem.* **209**, 813 (1954).
57. Mounter, L. A., *In* "Cholinesterases and Anticholinesterase Agents," Handbuch der Experimentellen Pharmakologie (G. B. Koelle, ed.), Vol. 15, Chapt. 10. Springer, Berlin, 1963.
58. Murphy, S. D., and DuBois, K. P., *Proc. Soc. Exptl. Biol. Med.* **96**, 813 (1957).
59. Myers, D. K., and Mulder, H. E. W., *Nature* **172**, 773 (1953).
60. Nachmansohn, D., and Feld, E. A., *J. Biol. Chem.* **171**, 715 (1947).
61. Nakatsugawa, T., and Dahm, P. A., *J. Econ. Entomol.* **58**, 500 (1965).
62. Nakatsugawa, T., and Dahm, P. A., *Bull. Entomol. Soc. Am.* **11**, 157 (1965).
63. Niessen, H., Tietz, H., and Frehse, H., *Pflanzenschutz-Nachr.* **15**, 125 (1962).
64. O'Brien, R. D., *Can. J. Biochem. Physiol.* **34**, 1131 (1956).
65. O'Brien, R. D., *Can. J. Biochem. Physiol.* **35**, 45 (1957).
66. O'Brien, R. D., "Toxic Phosphorus Esters." Academic Press, New York, 1960.
67. O'Brien, R. D., *J. Econ. Entomol.* **54**, 1161 (1961).
68. O'Brien, R. D., *J. Agr. Food Chem.* **11**, 163 (1963).
69. O'Brien, R. D., Kimmel, E. C., and Sferra, P. R., *J. Agr. Food Chem.* **13**, 366 (1965).
70. O'Brien, R. D., Dauterman, W. C., and Neidermeier, R. P., *J. Agr. Food Chem.* **9**, 39 (1961).
71. O'Brien, R. D., and Spencer, E. Y., *J. Agr. Food Chem.* **1**, 946 (1953).
72. O'Brien, R. D., and Spencer, E. Y., *J. Agr. Food Chem.* **3**, 56 (1955).
73. O'Brien, R. D., Thorn, G. C., and Fisher, R. W., *J. Econ. Entomol.* **51**, 714 (1958).
74. Plapp, F. W., and Casida, J. E., *J. Agr. Food Chem.* **6**, 662 (1958).
75. Scaife, J. F., and Campbell, D. H., *Can. J. Biochem. Physiol.* **37**, 297 (1959).

76. Schonbrod, R. D., Philleo, W. W., and Terriere, L. C., *J. Econ. Entomol.* **58**, 74 (1965).
77. Seume, F. W., and O'Brien, R. D., *J. Agr. Food. Chem.* **8**, 36 (1960).
78. Shishido, T., and Fukami, J., *Botyu-Kagaku* **28**, 69 (1963).
79. Smallman, B. N., and Fisher, R. W., *Can. J. Biochem. Physiol.* **36**, 575 (1958).
80. Smith, H. V., and Spalding, J. M. K., *Lancet* **II**, 1019 (1959).
81. Smith, M. I., Elvove, E., and Frazier, W. H., *Public Health Repts.* (*U.S.*) **45**, 2509 (1930).
82. Stegwee, D., *Can. J. Biochem. Physiol.* **38**, 1417 (1960).
83. Uchida, T., Dauterman, W. C., and O'Brien, R. D., *J. Agr. Food Chem.* **12**, 48 (1964).
84. Uchida, T., and O'Brien, R. D., *Toxicol. Appl. Pharmacol.* (in press, 1967).
85. Uchida, T., Rahmati, H. S., and O'Brien, R. D., *J. Econ. Entomol.* **58**, 831 (1965).
86. Uchida, T., Zschintzsch, J., and O'Brien, R. D., *Toxicol. Appl. Pharmacol.* **8**, 259 (1966).
87. Winteringham, F. P. W., *Chem. Ind.* (*London*) p. 1195 (1957).

CHAPTER 5

Carbamates

"Trial by ordeal" is a basic form of justice among primitives. In West Africa, a favored variant was to force the suspect to consumes beans of a poisonous plant, *Physostigma venenosum*. If he survived, he was assumed to be innocent; if not, verdict and punishment were accomplished simultaneously. Those who dislike the notion of unfairness in primitive justice suggest that innocent suspects ate the beans rapidly and vomited them up because of gastric irritation. The nature of the poison aroused interest in Europe, and in 1864 the active principle, physostigmine or eserine, was isolated (29) and its pharmacological properties were much studied. Not until 1925 was its structure established by Stedman and Barger (51), when it was revealed to be an ester of a derivative of carbamic acid, $HOC(O)NH_2$. The basis for its pharmacological properties had to await the discovery of acetylcholine as a transmitter substance, and the role of cholinesterase in degrading acetylcholine. A few years later, in 1930, Engelhart and Loewi (18) showed that eserine acted by blocking cholinesterase. Before this discovery, Stedman had begun in 1926 his extensive and brilliant studies on synthetic analogs of eserine, of which the best known is prostigmine, also called neostigmine. This aspect of the subject has been very fully reviewed (35,52).

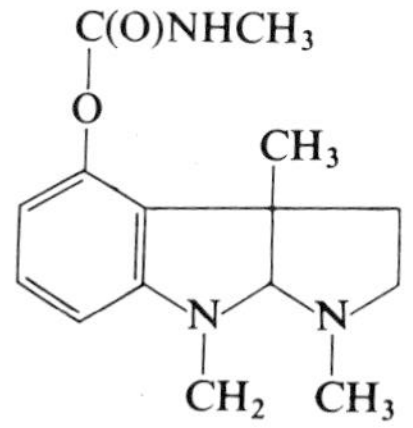

$C(O)NHCH_3$ — O — ; CH_3 ; N — CH_2 ; N — CH_3

Eserine (physostigmine)

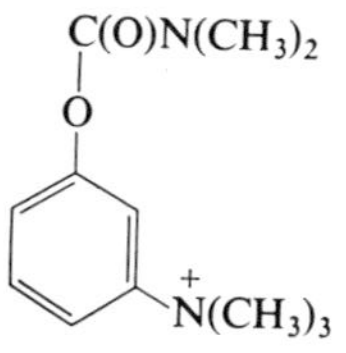

$C(O)N(CH_3)_2$ — O — ; $\overset{+}{N}(CH_3)_3$

Prostigmine (neostigmine)

All the above medicinal carbamates were ionized or ionizable and, presumably for this reason (see p. 282), were not toxic to insects. In 1947, the Geigy Company of Switzerland began work which led to the first insecticidal carbamates. The best known of these are shown in Table 5.1. These were all *N*-dimethylcarbamates, for the reason that the particular synthetic route employed did not permit preparation of the *N*-methyl compounds. It is now generally recognized that the *N*-methyl compounds are more potent insecticides, and this fact may contribute to the rather minor interest shown in the United States to these Geigy carbamates. Elsewhere they have been used on a relatively modest scale.

TABLE 5.1

SOME *N*-DIMETHYLCARBAMATES

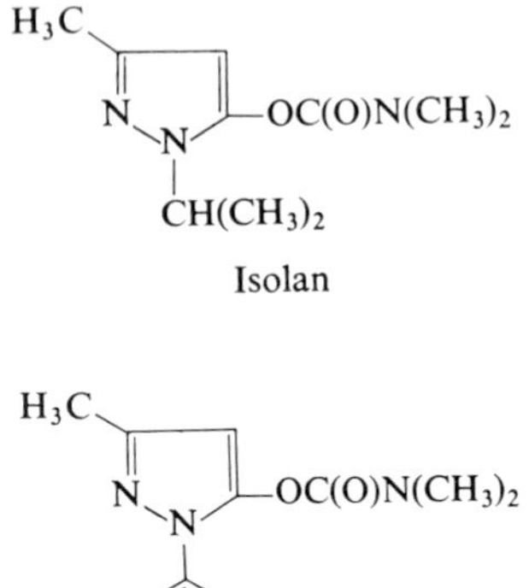

H_3C, N, N, $OC(O)N(CH_3)_2$, $CH(CH_3)_2$

Isolan

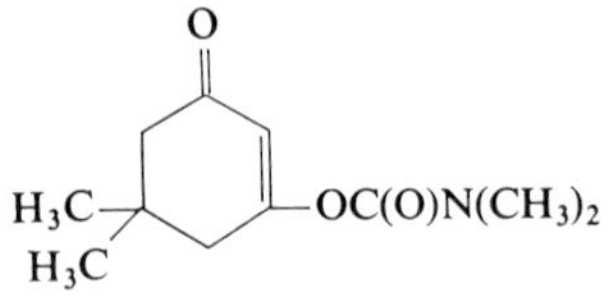

O, H_3C, H_3C, $OC(O)N(CH_3)_2$

Dimetan

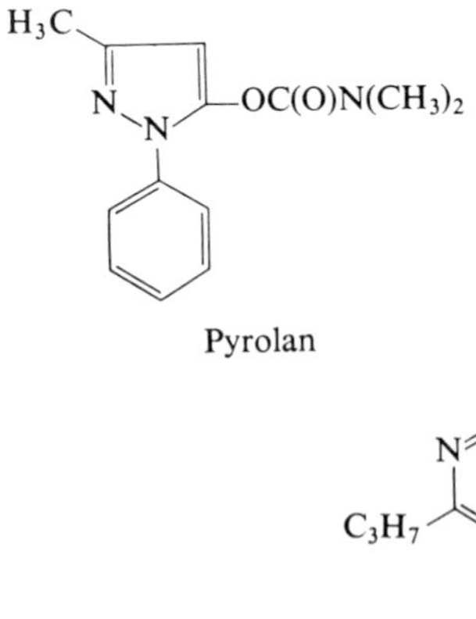

H_3C, N, N, $OC(O)N(CH_3)_2$

Pyrolan

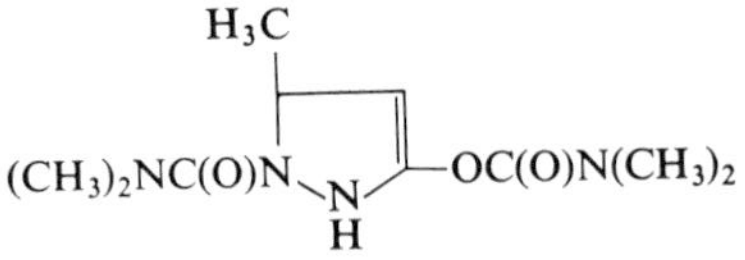

H_3C, $(CH_3)_2NC(O)N$, N, H, $OC(O)N(CH_3)_2$

Dimetilan[a]

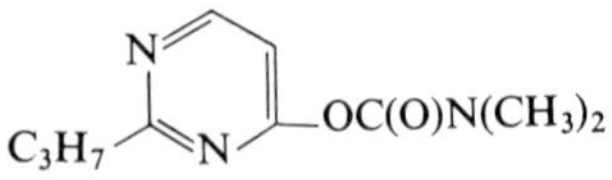

N, C_3H_7, N, $OC(O)N(CH_3)_2$

Pyramat

[a] Note: Early compositions of Dimetilan contained 25% of H_3C, N, N, H, $OC(O)N(CH_3)_2$

Almost 10 years later, the best known of the present carbamate insecticides, carbaryl (or Sevin), was described (4). This, like virtually all later carbamates, is an *N*-methyl compound. It is a naphthyl carbamate, whereas the early Geigy compounds were all heterocyclic. Most of the subsequent carbamates have been aromatic, but phenolic rather than naphtholic. A very new kind of compound, the oxime carbamate, was described in 1965 (54). Carbaryl and some more recent compounds are shown in Table 5.2.

Certain of the carbamates have been shown to be plant systemic, including Isolan, carbaryl, and the *m*-isopropyl- and *m*-*tert*-butylphenyl methylcarbamates. Others, such as the *m*-ethoxy and *m*-butoxy analogs were inactive systemically (10).

TABLE 5.2

SOME *N*-METHYLCARBAMATES

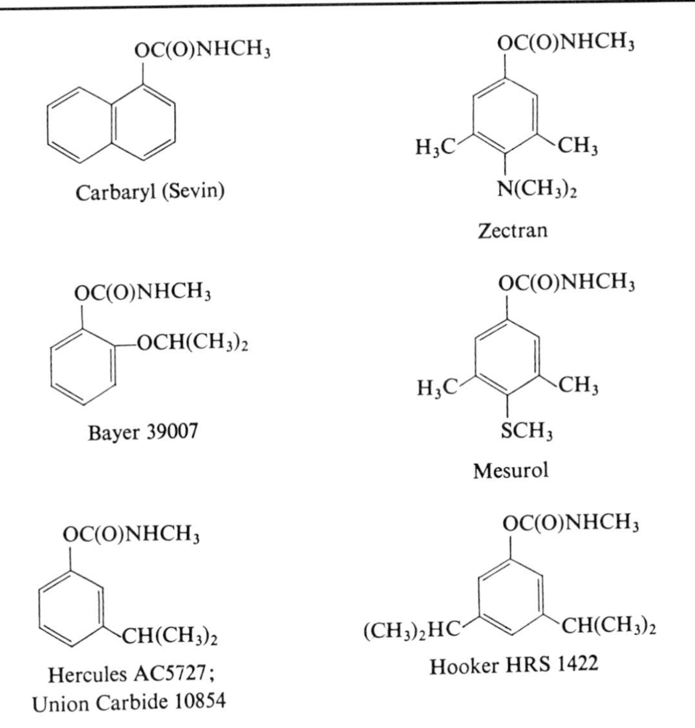

For reviews on insecticidal carbamates, see Casida (6), Metcalf (36), O'Brien and Matthysse (47), O'Brien (44), and Weiden and Moorefield (53).

Toxicity

The carbamates typically show erratic patterns of selective toxicity to insects. These are not "broad-spectrum insecticides." Table 5.3 gives one example of this specificity for Zectran with nine insects. However, Table 5.4 shows, with three insects and eight carbamates, that there is a certain pattern for phenyl methylcarbamates, for the housefly is rather insensitive, the bee rather sensitive, and the German cockroach almost immune.

TABLE 5.3

TOXICITY OF ZECTRAN SPRAY[a]

Insect	LD_{50} (ppm)
Two-spotted spider mite, adult	150
Mexican bean-beetle, larva	3
Plum curculio, adult	65
Southern armyworm larve	2.5
Bean aphid, adult and nymph	60
American cockroach, nymph	500
Housefly, adult	300
Confused flour beetle, adult	350
Water flea, adult and nymph	1

[a] From Kenaga *et al.* (30).

Table 5.4 also shows the oral toxicity of these compounds for rats. In most cases, hazard is relatively slight; only *m*-isopropylphenyl methylcarbamate and Isolan can be said to constitute any serious hazard, and this hazard is less than that of most organophosphates.

Mode of Action

The toxic carbamates are usually fairly potent inhibitors of cholinesterase, and the symptoms accompanying their action in intact animals are typically cholinergic, involving lachrymation, salivation, myosis, convulsions, and death. This statement is based primarily on the earlier findings with medicinal carbamates, and rather few studies exist on the detailed symptomology of

TABLE 5.4

TOXICITY OF CARBAMATES TO INSECTS AND RATS[a]

Carbamates	LD_{50}, topical ($\mu g/g$)			LD_{50}, oral ($\mu g/g$)
	Housefly	Bee	German cockroach	Rat
Methylcarbamates				
m-Isopropylphenyl	90	1.0	15	16
o-Isopropylphenyl	95	2.8	> 130	500
o-Isopropoxyphenyl	26	0.8	11	250
m-sec-Butylphenyl	100	0.6	52	30
Zectran	60	0.6	> 133	60
Mesurol	24	1.1	> 133	100
Carbaryl	> 500	2.3	> 133	540
Dimethylcarbamates				
Dimetan	3.2[b]	—	—	150
Isolan	25	13[b]	—	13
Pyrolan	3.2[b]	13[b]	—	90

[a] Data from Metcalf and Fukuto (37), O'Brien and Matthysse (47), Negherbon (48), and Gordon and Eldefrawi (26).
[b] Oral route.

poisoning of insects and mammals by insecticidal carbamates. Yet the insecticidal carbamates show antienzyme properties differing from eserine; perhaps the most important is that whereas eserine inhibits only cholinesterases (44), some and perhaps all of the insecticidal carbamates can inhibit insect aliesterase both *in vivo* and *in vitro* (49). Nevertheless, the arguments which were quite common in the 1950's, claiming the importance of properties other than cholinesterase inhibition in causing acute poisoning by organophosphates, have never arisen for carbamates.

Even with un-ionized compounds no general correlation has been found between anticholinesterase activity and insecticidal activity. For instance, Casida *et al.* (8) found compounds that were good anticholinesterases and were nontoxic to houseflies (such as *p*-nitrophenyl isopropylcarbamate) and others that had toxicity for houseflies and were very poor anticholinesterases (such as dimethylcarbamyl fluoride). Kolbezen *et al.* (32) did indeed find quite a good correlation between anticholinesterase activity and toxicity to thrips for 22 carbamates; but their toxicity data for houseflies shows no such correlation, a fact also observed by others (15). However, the nontoxicity of good anticholinesterases could well be due to rapid metabolic destruction in the insect, and the "poor anticholinesterases" of Casida might have turned out to be effective if tested against cholinesterase of houseflies rather than of electric eel. There is therefore no solid evidence against the belief that cholinesterase inhibition is the cause of death in carbamate poisoning. A single exception is Casida's suggestion (6) that differences in integumental darkening observed between Zectran and carbaryl in the course of their poisoning of lepidopterous larvae (50) might imply different modes of action. But such minor differences in symptomology are, in the author's view, the rule rather than the exception for virtually any pair of compounds.

The position is, therefore, that carbamates are considered to kill insects and mammals entirely by cholinesterase inhibition.

A query arises in considering the above view. Why is it that so many carbamates with excellent anticholinesterase activity, e.g., the medicinal carbamates, have no insecticidal action? The reason presumably is precisely that advanced in the analogous case of ionized organophosphates (p. 282): insects do not utilize cholinesterase in their neuromuscular junctions, and their vital cholinesterase is all central and protected by a barrier system which hinders penetration of ionized molecules. All the medicinal carbamates are ionized or ionizable, and therefore have little effect on insects.

Although broadly based evidence is lacking, there has been no suggestion that carbamates can cause demyelination (p. 58). For carbaryl, such a lack of effect has been documented (5).

Mechanism of Cholinesterase Inhibition

The literature in this area is rather confusing because various views have been advanced at different times. Individual experts have transferred their allegiance from one theory to another and have occasionally hung suspended between alternatives. This writer's opinion is that the most recent view explains the earlier uncertainties. Consequently, it will be presented first, and the alternative views will be shown as variants of it.

Carbamates react with cholinesterase in a way precisely analogous to the reactions of organophosphates (see p. 39) and acetylcholine. In all these cases, there is first complex formation; second, phosphorylation, acetylation, or carbamylation of the enzyme (presumably at the serine OH in the active site); and third, hydrolysis, i.e., dephosphorylation, deacetylation, or decarbamylation, to yield the original enzyme. In every case there is a leaving group which we may call X (e.g., choline in acetylcholine, *p*-nitrophenol in paraoxon, or 1-naphthol in carbaryl), which is released in the second step.

Using A as a symbol for either the acetyl group, or the dialkyl phosphoryl group, or the methylcarbamyl group, and EOH for cholinesterase, we have:

$$\mathrm{EOH+AX} \underset{k_{-1}}{\overset{k_1}{\rightleftharpoons}} \underset{\text{Reversible complex}}{\mathrm{EOH\cdot AX}} \xrightarrow[\searrow \mathrm{X^- + H^+}]{k_2} \mathrm{EOA} \xrightarrow[\mathrm{H_2O}]{k_3} \mathrm{EOH+A^-+H^+} \quad (1)$$

For all three groups of compounds, we now have values for k_{-1}/k_1 (which we can call K_a, an affinity constant) and for k_2 and k_3. Always K_a is quite small, so that formation of EOH•AX is favored. With acetylcholine, k_2 and k_3 are extremely fast, so that total reaction, from left to right in Eq. (1), occurs; acetylcholine is a typical substrate. With organophosphates, k_2 is moderately fast, e.g., 30 per minute, and k_3 is extremely slow. Consequently, EOA accumulates; the values of k_1, k_{-1}, and k_2 are such that under normal conditions practically no EOH•AX is ever present. With carbamates, k_2 is much slower, e.g., 1 per minute; k_3 is even slower, yet still significant, e.g., 0.05 per minute; but K_a is exceptionally low. These values lead to the existence of small levels of the complexed EOH•AX and large levels of carbamylated enzyme, EOA, under practical conditions. But also if one at any stage of the reaction removes inhibitor (for instance, by dialysis, by great dilution, or by passing the solution through Sephadex*), the enzyme recovers activity, in part by reversal of EOH•AX, and in part by the working of the k_3 or decarbamylation step. From the above typical value of $k_3 = 0.05\ \mathrm{min}^{-1}$, one can calculate a half time of decarbamylation of about 40 minutes, so that fully carbamylated enzyme (EOA) would be almost fully restored by several hours of dialysis.

The above description accounts for the following features of carbamate inhibition of cholinesterase.

(1) It is usual to find that some of the inhibited enzyme is in the reversible form (EOH•AX) and some of it in the carbamylated form (EOA). Because of the presence of the reversible form, the experimentally determined inhibition will depend upon the concentration of substrate used in the determination and the affinity of the substrate for the enzyme. If one uses a substrate of excellent affinity, such as acetylcholine, at high concentration, for instance, $10^{-2}M$, one will usually reverse all of EOH•AX, and therefore the inhibition one observes will be entirely due to EOA. If one uses extremely low concentrations, e.g., $10^{-6}M$, of high-affinity substrates, such as Winteringham and Disney (58) have used with C^{14}-acetylcholine, or else rather low concentrations, e.g., $10^{-4}M$, of low-affinity substrates, such as indophenyl acetate, then all the EOA and much of the EOH•AX forms will contribute to the observed inhibition.

* Sephadex is a modified dextran. It absorbs small molecules and not macromolecules. Consequently, Sephadex columns can be used to free enzymes from inhibitors.

Throughout this discussion it should be noted that although the carbamylated form EOA is distinguished from the reversible form EOH·AX, yet EOA does decarbamylate, by hydrolysis, to give rise to the original enzyme, and therefore the carbamylation reaction *appears* to be reversible from the point of view of the enzyme; however, it is not reversible from the point of view of the carbamate, which is cleaved in the process.

(2) Although carbamates share with true reversible inhibitors the sensitivity to dialysis and to the substrate concentration used for assay, they differ from them in that the reaction with carbamates is progressive with time. This progressive nature is rendered complex by two factors. First, it is only the formation of EOA which clearly shows time dependence. If one is employing a low-substrate assay such that the presence of EOH·AX is detected, this reversible complex is formed almost instantly; in other words, k_1 in Eq. (1) is too fast to measure by conventional means, whereas k_2 is readily measurable. Second, because of the measurable k_3 rate, total inhibition of enzyme is seldom encountered, because of two factors. One factor is an assay artifact: the moment one adds substrate, thereby substantially blocking fresh EOH·AX formation, the enzyme begins to recover by decarbamylation. In a case where the decarbamylation (k_3) step has a half-life of 40 minutes, then even with a 5-minute assay time 9% of an enzyme which was totally carbamylated would have decarbamylated. The second factor is that total carbamylation never occurs in practice. To illustrate this point, we may consider the case where the carbamate concentration is much greater (e.g., 100 times) than K_a. Then as soon as decarbamylation occurs, the EOH produced is promptly complexed, and we have a cyclic reaction:

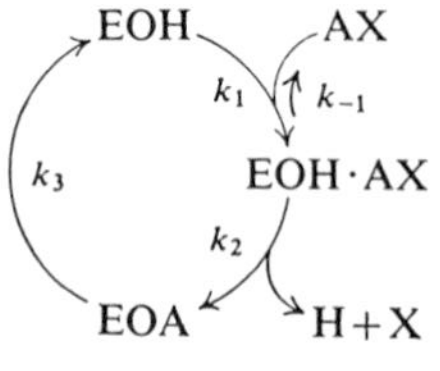

Under the conditions hypothesized, $k_1 - k_{-1}$ is so fast that we can neglect EOH and consider in essence:

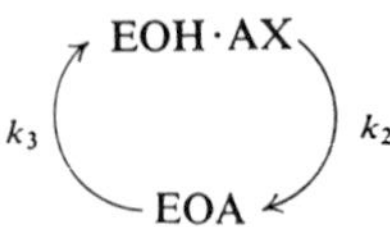

Now this system will clearly settle down to a steady state when the actual rates of the k_2 and k_3 steps are equal. Since the two rates are, respectively, given by

k_2[EOH·AX] and k_3[EOA], where square brackets indicate concentrations, the steady state is reached when:

$$k_3[\mathrm{EOA}] = k_2[\mathrm{EOH \cdot AX}]$$

Experimental values suggest that typically $k_2 = 20k_3$. Steady state will then be reached when [EOA]=20[EOH·AX], that is, when about 95% is in the carbamylated form and 5% in the reversible form. By the reverse argument, the position of the steady state can therefore be used to calculate the ratio k_3/k_2 if k_1 is assumed to be extremely large.

In summary: Although organophosphates can inhibit cholinesterase virtually completely, because the k_4 step is so slow, carbamate inhibition, as measured by an assay with high substrate concentration so that EOH·AX is reversed, does not go to completion. It is not correct to say that this situation represents an *equilibrium* between inhibitor and enzyme; it represents an *apparent steady state*; apparent because in fact carbamate is steadily destroyed, and if the reaction is allowed to proceed long enough, all the carbamate will be destroyed and the enzyme will recover totally.

This rather complex situation has given rise to a variety of earlier views which differ from the above theory, which we can now call Theory A. The properties of reversibility by dialysis (25), washing (3), dilution (24), and sensitivity to the substrate concentration employed for assay (24) led earlier workers to assume that inhibition was due entirely to formation of a reversible complex (Theory B). Using our notation:

$$\mathrm{EOH + AX} \rightleftharpoons \mathrm{EOH \cdot AX} \tag{2}$$

This formulation was proposed by Easson and Stedman in 1936 (13). As late as 1963, an important reference text (35) treated carbamates as reversible inhibitors. The most elaborate treatment of it was that of Goldstein (24) in 1944 for eserine. Ironically, several pages of his paper were concerned with the known fact (16) that cholinesterase "destroys" (hydrolyzes) eserine, with a rate constant $k = 0.0018\ \mathrm{min}^{-1}$ (pH 7.4, 38°C). Presumably this "destruction" rate is (in current terms) given by k_3, the decarbamylation step, which controls the overall reaction by virtue of being the slowest step. However, Goldstein treated this "destruction" as a phenomenon quite unrelated to inhibition.

Theory C originated with Myers in 1952 (40) and was espoused by Kolbezen *et al.* (32) in their important study of 49 new carbamates. Myers realized that the hydrolysis of the carbamate in the reaction could not be ignored and proposed, in essence, the following:

$$\mathrm{EOH + AX} \rightleftharpoons \mathrm{EOH \cdot AX} \rightarrow \mathrm{EOH + A^+ + X^-} \tag{3}$$

This theory is correct in stressing the analogy between carbamate and substrate, but of course ignores what is under many conditions the most vital step: carbamylation of the enzyme. Kolbezen *et al.* concluded from this formulation that the primary factors were excellence of fit (low K_a in our terms) and that "the carbamate should be reasonably stable to hydrolysis at the site." The forces which they considered important were therefore those of complex formation (K_a), and consideration of the carbamylation (k_2) step does not arise in this theory; hydrolysis of the carbamate was for them, as for Goldstein, a factor which diminished the excellence of a carbamate rather than an intrinsic aspect of the inhibitory process.

One more variant (Theory D) completes the roster of theories on mechanism. Before the theory of Main was published for organophosphates (p. 42), the reaction of organophosphates with cholinesterase was treated as a simple bimolecular reaction (2):

$$EOH + AX \rightarrow EOA + H^+ + X^- \qquad (4)$$

This formulation, which neglects complex formation, was sufficient to explain the outstanding factors influencing cholinesterase inhibition. Its special virtue was to show the precise analogy with the hydrolysis of organophosphates and carbamates in alkali:

$$OH^- + AX \rightarrow XOH + A^- \qquad (5)$$

Many variations in AX, such as the nature of X, had precisely the same effects on reactions (4) and (5), as clearly shown by Aldridge (2). Now reaction (5) is a nucleophilic substitution reaction, if one considers OH^- to be the reagent; or an electrophilic substitution reaction if one considers, as is more convenient for the present argument, AX to be the reagent. Consequently (see p. 11), the substitution of electrophilic substituents into X speeded up reaction (5), and had precisely the same effect, generally speaking, upon reaction 4, thus underlining the analogy. The most elegant culmination of this view was achieved by Ooms (see p. 42).

An analogy between carbamates and phosphates was at first drawn by various workers (41) who later dismissed the analogy (8,42) on the following grounds: electrophilic substituents upon X accelerated reaction (5) for both organophosphates and carbamates; but while they accelerated the inhibition reaction for organophosphates, they slowed it for carbamates (32,42). This was indeed fatal for an analogy based upon Theory D, which was the prevailing view. But Theory A offers a resolution of the dilemma. As Eq. (1) shows, the rate of formation of EOA is influenced by K_a as well as k_2. Whereas the k_2 step is undoubtedly electrophilic, the k_1 step is very probably nucleophilic. Consequently, an electrophilic substituent can in principle either accelerate or retard the overall reaction, depending upon its relative influence on the k_1 and k_2 steps, and on the relative contributions of K_a and k_2.

The crucial study which returned a carbamylation theory to favor was that of Wilson *et al.* in 1960 (57). Their demonstration was precisely that which had been used years earlier in the case of the organophosphates; they showed that the nature of the carbamate-inhibited enzyme, judged by its capacity to recover from inhibition, was dependent only upon the nature of A, and was entirely independent of X. Thus AX_1 and AX_2 would give the same inhibited enzyme, whereas A_1X and A_2X would give different inhibited enzymes; in more concrete terms, all *N*-methylcarbamates give the same inhibited enzyme. Very probably, then, the X group must depart in the course of the reaction. It follows that one of the carbamylation theories, Theory A or Theory D, must be true. This argument was reinforced by the later demonstration (46) that when carbamates reacted with cholinesterase, the X group was released at the same rate that EOA was formed. At the same time it was shown by an extension of Main's argument that the kinetics of inhibition demanded that Theory A be accepted (45,46). Table 5.5 shows the kinetic constants for a variety of carbamates. In inspecting it, it should be recalled that k_i (see p. 43) measures the overall potency against cholinesterase, and is made up of k_2/K_a; thus K_a measures (inversely) the affinity contribution, and k_2 the carbamylation contribution. Clearly, the enormous variation in potency is virtually all due

TABLE 5.5

Constants for Some Methyl- and Dimethylcarbamates as Inhibitors of Bovine Erythrocyte Cholinesterase at 38° C[a]

O-Substituent	k_i (min^{-1} moles^{-1} l)	K_a (*M*)	k_2 (min^{-1})
Methylcarbamates			
Phenyl	5.4×10^2	2.9×10^{-3}	1.6
3,5-Diisopropylphenyl	4.1×10^5	3.4×10^{-6}	1.4
o-Isopropoxyphenyl	1.1×10^5	1.0×10^{-5}	1.05
4-Methylthio-3,5-dimethylphenyl	1.9×10^5	6.7×10^{-6}	1.2
1-Naphthyl (carbaryl)	1.3×10^5	1.1×10^{-5}	1.3
Dimethylcarbamates			
Phenyl	1.5×10^2	1.5×10^{-3}	0.22
3.5-Diisopropylphenyl	1.3×10^4	5.8×10^{-5}	0.75
1-Naphthyl	2.6×10^4	9.3×10^{-5}	2.4
1-Isopropyl-3-methyl-5-pyrazolyl (Isolan)	1.6×10^5	8.0×10^{-6}	1.3

[a] Data from O'Brien *et al.* (46).

to variations in affinity, for the k_2 values are amazingly similar. This observation accounts for the fact that although these are carbamylating agents, the effect of varying substituents only influences affinity (K_a) and not carbamylating ability (k_2); it explains why the substituent data seemed to support the view that complex formation was *the* mechanism of inhibition (Theory B).

But in spite of the fact that variations in complexing ability account for the variations in potency, yet, under normal assay conditions, the only inhibited form one detects is carbamylated enzyme, because the complexed form is reversed by the huge excess of substrate normally exployed. By deliberately using low substrate concentrations, such as $10^{-5} M$ (e.g., with highly chromogenic or radioactive substrates), one can then detect complexed form as well. The complexed form can be a large percent of the total inhibited, i.e., complexed plus carbamylated enzyme, under suitable conditions; thus if one uses an inhibitor concentration that equals the K_a, for instance, $1.1 \times 10^{-5} M$ carbaryl (see Table 5.5), then for a few seconds 50% of the enzyme is complexed and little is carbamylated. But using normal assay conditions, one would see almost zero inhibition in these few seconds.

One might argue that if complex formation is not normally detectable, and under many conditions (such as the use of inhibitor concentrations well below K_a) exists only to a small extent, why not ignore it and accept Theory D? The answer would be that under such conditions one could ignore it, but that Theory D makes progressively more inaccurate predictions as one increases the inhibitor concentration. It predicts that every time one doubles the inhibitor concentration [AX], one doubles the rate of formation of carbamylated enzyme EOA, because this rate is given by k[EOH][AX]. By contrast, Theory A predicts that once the inhibitor concentration gets to be very much larger than K_a, then virtually all EOH disappears and is tied up as the complexed form EOH·AX, so that the rate of EOA formation can never exceed k_2[EOH·AX], and doubling the inhibitor concentration thereafter has virtually no effect on the rate of inhibition.

Let us now briefly consider the relation of carbamate structure to anticholinesterase activity. In essence, this involves review of the splendid work of the Metcalf and Fukuto group. In the more recent of these studies, they have listed the "affinities" of the various compounds. It should be clear that these are simply reciprocals of relative values of k_i, the reaction rate constant. Because (as described above) affinity, while it is only one component of k_i, is the primary variable in variations of k_i, their usage is fairly appropriate, although in fact the inhibited enzyme which they observed was the carbamylated form, and not the EOH·AX complex, as suggested by the "affinity" terminology.

The principal findings of this group are summarized in a 1965 review (37). The overall conclusions are that close fit ("complementariness") of carbamate to enzyme is the predominant requirement for antienzyme action, so that rather than electronic factors, which are so important for organophosphates, the steric factors predominate. The optimal configuration appears to be close to that of acetylcholine, which one would anticipate since presumably cholinesterase is "designed" especially for acetylcholine. However, because ionic anticholinesterases are not insecticidal (see pp. 282), the closest analogs of acetylcholine, such as (I), are good anticholinesterases but inactive as insecticides. Compounds such as (II) are not quite so potent as anticholinesterases, although (II) is 500 times as potent as the unsubstituted compound, but do have modest insecticidal activity.

$(CH_2)_3\overset{+}{N}—CH_2—CH_2—OC(O)CH_3$

Acetylcholine

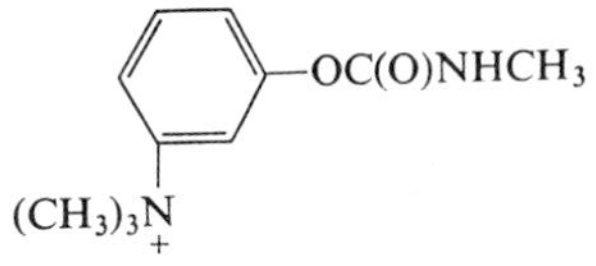

$(CH_3)_3\overset{+}{N}$ — C_6H_4 — $OC(O)NHCH_3$

(I)

$(CH_3)_3C$ — C_6H_4 — $OC(O)NHCH_3$

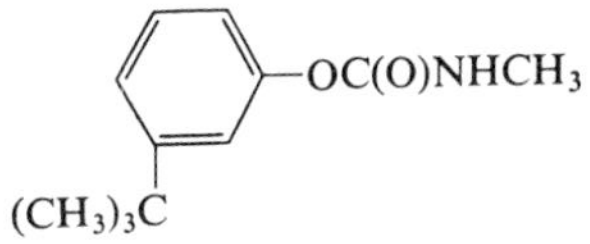

(II)

It appears that in spite of the absence of coulombic binding possibilities with (II), the steric similarity with acetylcholine is helpful in producing a good anticholinesterase, presumably because hydrophobic forces are important in binding groups such as $^+N(CH_3)_3$ and $C(CH_3)_3$ to the anionic site. A consequence of the importance of these forces is that, for phenyl methylcarbamates alkylated at any one position, the order of excellence is *tert*-butyl = isopropyl > ethyl > methyl > unsubstituted. In such compounds, *m*-substitution is optimal; the place of substitution, especially for potent compounds, is sometimes dramatically shown, for instance, for isopropyl derivatives, in which the ratio of anticholinesterase action, *ortho*:*meta*:*para* is 10:200:1. By contrast, when the phenyl substituent is alkoxy instead of alkyl, the *ortho* position is optimal, and for isopropoxy derivatives the above ratio is 145:10:1. This is expected if the locus of binding of the alkyl part of the alkoxy is in a zone roughly *meta* to the carbamyl substituent.

R   O—R

If steric features were far more important than electronic, then isosteric ring substituents should be equivalent in spite of any differences in electronic effect. An interesting case is the dichlorophenyl compared with the dimethylphenyl series. The relative anticholinesterase activities (taking the unsubstituted phenyl methylcarbamate = 1) for the 2,3:2,4:2,5:3,5 compounds are, for the dimethyl series, 25:2:22:33 and, for the dichloro series, 4:14:4:17. Clearly the groups are not truly equivalent, for in the 2,3 compounds the chloro group is six times poorer and in the 2,4 it is seven times better than the dimethyl. However, the 3,5 type is best in both series, and differs only 2-fold.

There is some doubt about the precise role of electronic features; a *negative* correlation between substituent constants (Hammett's constants, which measure electron-withdrawing ability) and anticholinesterase activity was claimed for methylcarbamates by Kolbezen *et al.* (32); but O'Brien *et al.* (46) found no correlation for methylcarbamates, and a *positive* correlation for dimethylcarbamates.

An additional factor to consider in relating structure to anticholinesterase activity (and toxicity) is optical activity. Fukuto *et al.* (21) have shown that in compound (III) (which has optical isomers because of the asymmetry around the C in the side chain), the *l*-form is six times more potent against cholinesterase and three times more toxic to houseflies than the *d*-form. Presumably the *l*-form fits more effectively onto the enzyme surface. Strangely enough, the thiolo analog (IV) shows no difference between *l*- and *d*-forms.

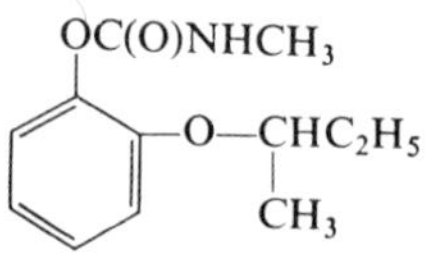

$C_6H_4(OC(O)NHCH_3)$–O–$CH(CH_3)C_2H_5$

(III)

$C_6H_4(OC(O)NHCH_3)$–S–$CH(CH_3)C_2H_5$

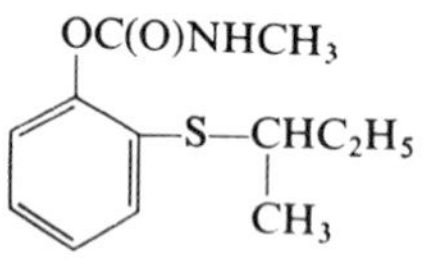

(IV)

In general, methylcarbamates are better inhibitors and insecticides than the equivalent dimethylcarbamates. The typical difference is about 5-fold with respect to inhibition (37,46). In spite of this, some of the most inhibitory and insecticidal compounds are dimethylcarbamates such as Isolan, for which no *N*-methyl analog exists, primarily because of synthesis problems.

What is the relation between anticholinesterase activity and insecticidal activity? In an early study from Metcalf's group (32) it was concluded that although there was a correlation between these factors for thrips, there was not for houseflies; the latter was confirmed by Casida *et al.* (8). If one studies instead the *synergized* toxicity for houseflies, using piperonyl butoxide as the synergist, a more respectable correlation is found, as shown in Fig. 5.1. Like all log-log plots, this figure may give a better impression than its data warrant. Thus, compounds all having a negative log of I_{50} equal to about 5 show a

100-fold spread in toxicity; and compounds with a log LD_{50} of 1.0 also vary almost 100-fold in I_{50}. Nevertheless, it remains true that the very bad inhibitors have very low toxicity, and vice versa. One may conclude that cholinesterase inhibition is a major factor in determining toxicity, if one eliminates, by synergists, other factors such as metabolism.

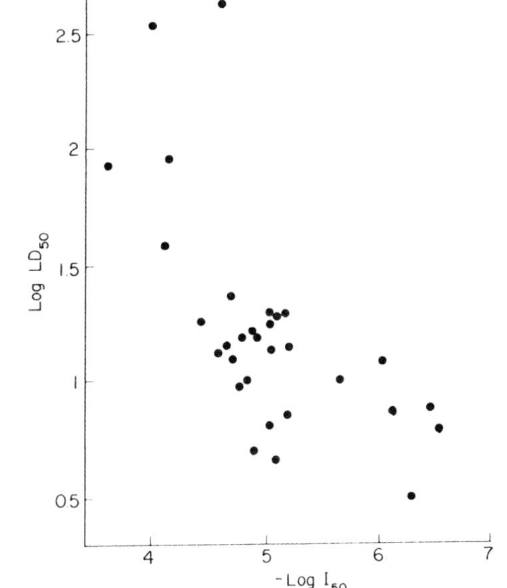

FIG. 5.1. Correlation of toxicity of methylcarbamates for houseflies with ability to inhibit fly head cholinesterase *in vitro*. The I_{50} is the molar concentration for 50% inhibition. Redrawn from Metcalf and Fukuto (37).

Metabolism

In considering the metabolism of carbamates, due caution must be maintained in view of the report that electrophoretically purified human serum albumin had "carbamatase" activity, at any rate towards *p*-nitrophenyl carbamates and carbaryl. Such activity was lacking in hydrolytic enzymes, such as serum cholinesterase, aliesterase, arylesterase, and chymotrypsin (7,8). It is therefore possible that degradation of carbamates can be catalyzed by nonspecific proteins, which are not enzymes in the usual sense of the word. This must be taken into account before reporting that some tissue contains a carbamate-hydrolyzing enzyme.

The first metabolic study, using ring-labeled C^{14}-carbaryl, was made in 1961 with insects (14). Variation with species was considerable; for instance, 1-naphthol was found only in German cockroach tissues, in which there were five other metabolites. By contrast, milkweed bug formed one metabolite, and houseflies three. No identifications, other than 1-naphthol, were made.

The most important advances in our understanding of carbamate metabolism have come from Casida's laboratory. In 1963 (12) a brief paper signaled that numerous other reactions than cleavage of the C—O—N bonds were important. The full account (11) described extensive studies, mainly with carbaryl labeled with C^{14} in the ring or the C=O or the N—CH_3 positions. Using liver microsomes with added $NADPH_2$,* thin-layer chromatography showed seven metabolites. Four of these were later identified (34). The three major organo-soluble metabolites were all hydroxylated derivatives. The parenthetic figures are the percent of radioactivity represented by each in a microsome preparation with $NADPH_2$:

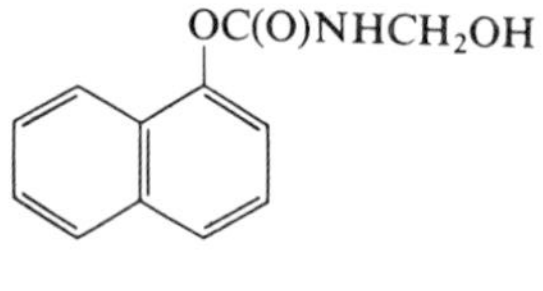

$OC(O)NHCH_2OH$

(V; 7.1%)

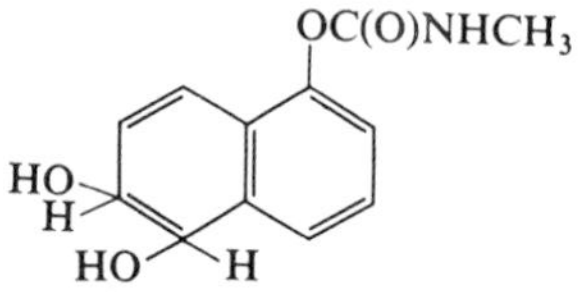

$OC(O)NHCH_3$

HO H HO H

(VI; 4.0%)

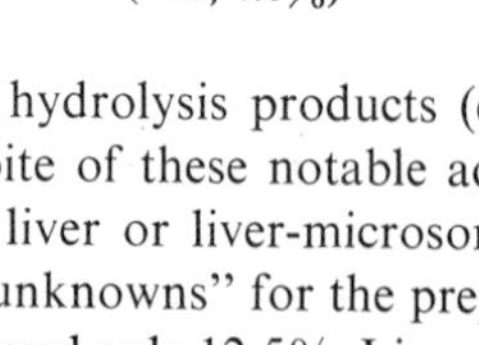

$OC(O)NHCH_3$

OH

(VII; 4.8%)

The other products were hydrolysis products (especially naphthol, 9%) or conjugates of these. In spite of these notable advances, the majority of the metabolic products from liver or liver-microsome preparations remain unidentified; the value for "unknowns" for the preparation referred to above is 64%, and the residual carbaryl only 12.5%. Liver metabolism of *o*-isopropoxyphenyl methylcarbamate was equally complex.

The species variation in carbaryl metabolism is not great, judged by work with liver microsomes from mice, rabbits, and rats. The same metabolites were found in all, and the extent of breakdown and of production of each metabolite was roughly the same.

Agents which (as discussed on p. 218 and p. 221) are inhibitors of microsomal metabolism were fairly effective inhibitors of carbaryl metabolism by liver microsomes. Table 5.6 shows that piperonyl butoxide at $10^{-4}M$ reduces total carbaryl degradation, which is normally 91% complete in this preparation,

* The standard microsomal system that accomplishes many reactions (p. 210).

to 69%. One would have anticipated a more spectacular effect. Nor is there any discrimination between the various hydroxylative products, each of whose relative contribution is almost unaffected. In fact the data are compatible with the unlikely hypothesis that conversion to known products only is insensitive to the inhibitors, while carbaryl degradation to some unknown product is fairly sensitive.

TABLE 5.6

EFFECT OF INHIBITORS ON CARBARYL METABOLISM BY FORTIFIED RAT LIVER MICROSOMES[a]

Inhibitor (all $10^{-4} M$)	Residual carbaryl	N-CH_2OH derivative	p-OH derivative	diH, diOH derivative	Naphthol
None	9.2	3.0	5.7	0.8	8.6
Piperonyl butoxide	30.8	5.5	8.0	0.9	9.9
SKF 525A[b]	35.1	7.2	5.9	0.5	15.4
MGK 264[c]	25.2	4.6	6.7	0.6	7.4
Lilly 18947[d]	20.7	4.0	7.6	0.8	10.7
2-(2,4-Dichloro-1-naphthoxy)ethyldiethylamine	16.8	5.4	5.6	0.8	8.5

[a] Data are percent of radioactivity (originally 100% carbaryl). From Leeling and Casida (34).
[b] SKF 525A is 2-diethylaminoethyl 2,2-diphenylvalerate.
[c] MGK 264 is *N*-(2-ethylhexyl)-5-norbornene-2,3-dicarboximide.
[d] Lilly 18947 is 2-(3,5-dichloro-2-biphenyloxy)ethyldiethylamine.

Metabolism in intact animals is even more complex. Urine from carbaryl-treated rabbits contained all the components (many of them unidentified) found in liver preparations, and four more as well, giving a grand total of thirteen products (34). The first detailed study on carbaryl metabolism was reported by Knaak *et al.* (31) in 1965, working with a variety of C^{14}-labeled positions, and studying the rat, the guinea pig, and man. In the rat, 94% of orally given carbaryl was recovered in urine, feces, and (in the case of $C^{14}ONHCH_3$ or $CONHC^{14}H_3$ labels) in expired CO_2, in the course of three days. Urinary metabolites were at least seven in rat, nine in guinea pig, including six which had an unhydrolyzed carbamyl group, and represented 57% of the output. In man, there were at least six metabolites, judged by fluorescent analysis in this case, but each peak was (disturbingly) at the same position as a weaker peak found in control urines, so the results must be accepted with due caution. In the rat and guinea pig, the peaks (which, being of radioactive material, are not subject to these doubts) were identified in some cases;

important metabolites were the glucuronide of 4-hydroxycarbaryl (10–15% of metabolites) and a rather tentatively identified *o*-glucuronide of the enol form of carbaryl (12–26%). Other tentative structural assignments that were

OC(O)NHCH$_3$ / O-glucuronide   O-glucuronide / OC=NCH$_3$

made included the *N*-glucuronide and *N*-acetyl derivatives of carbaryl. The residual 43% of metabolites which had suffered decarbamylation were the glucuronide and sulfate of 1-naphthol.

A study of several carbamates in rats (33) showed that decarbamylation, i.e., hydrolytic removal of the OC(O)NHCH$_3$ group, was a major feature of metabolism because in ten carbamates (including *N*-methyl and *N*-dimethyl) labeled as OC^{14}(O)N, much of the C^{14} (typically 60–80%) appeared as C^{14}O$_2$. Extensive data were gathered on radioactivity in twelve tissues and in urine,

TABLE 5.7

FATE OF C^{14}-CARBAMATES 49 HOURS AFTER INTRAPERITONEAL INJECTION INTO MALE RATS[a]

Compound	C^{14}O$_2$	Urine	Feces	Body	Total
Methylcarbamates					
1-Naphthyl	25	65	2	10	101
2-Isopropoxyphenyl	31	61	1	2	95
3-Isopropylphenyl	53	45	6	4	107
3,5-Diisopropylphenyl	49	37	3	9	97
2-Chloro-4,5-xylphenyl	58	16	2	9	85
4-Methylthio-3,5-xylenyl	66	22	3	9	100
4-Dimethylamino-3,5-xylenyl	77	12	3	12	103
4-Dimethylamino-3-cresyl	67	25	4	9	104
Dimethylcarbamates					
1-Isopropyl-3-methyl-5-pyrazolonyl (Isolan)	74	25	2	12	112
2-Dimethylcarbamyl-3-methyl-5-pyrazolonyl (Dimetilan)	49	50	1	9	108

[a] Figures are percent of administered C^{14} from carbonyl-labeled carbamates. Data rounded off from Krishna and Casida (33).

but the radioactive compounds were not identified. However, it was clear that, in the course of 2 days, over 90% of administered carbamate had been voided by one route or another in virtually every case (Table 5.7), a finding that is reassuring from the point of view of potential hazard from persistence of ingested material.

Zectran metabolism has been studied in dogs (56) using a C^{14}-ring-methyl label, so that all ring-containing metabolites could be followed; a distinct improvement over carbonyl labeling. Balance studies were not performed in this case, for the feeding was "chronic" (i.e., for 7 days). One-fourth of excreted radioactivity was fecal, the rest was urinary, and 86% of it was of conjugated forms (glucuronide or sulfate) of the simple phenol:

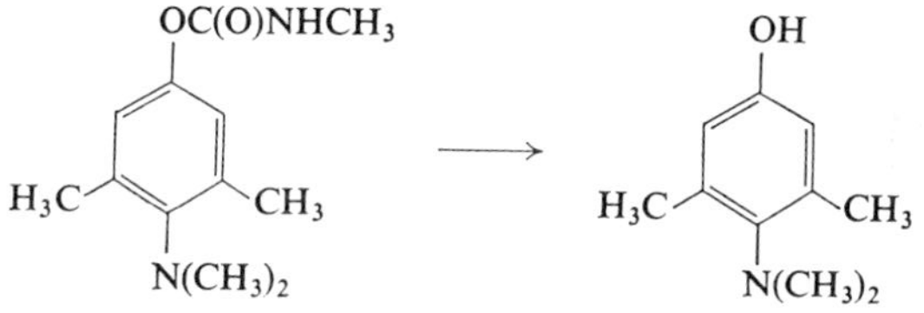

OC(O)NHCH₃ / H₃C, CH₃ / N(CH₃)₂ → OH / H₃C, CH₃ / N(CH₃)₂

Zectran

However, significant amounts (5%) of conjugated forms of the hydroquinone (see below) were also found.

Cockroaches also metabolized carbaryl to the same galaxy of metabolites; in this case, (V) and the conjugate of (VI) with glutathione were the most prominent metabolites identified.

It should be emphasized that several of the hydroxylated metabolites have pronounced anticholinesterase activity (11) giving inhibition at less than $10^{-6}M$, so that hydroxylation, although it always reduced inhibitory potency, by no means destroyed it. Also, compounds (V)–(VII) had toxicity to insects roughly comparable with carbaryl. These facts hardly support Leeling and Casida's view (34) that "the metabolites are of little toxicological importance in consideration of residue levels or hazards." On the contrary, it would seem that disappearance of carbaryl itself by no means implies loss of toxic material.

For *N*-dimethylcarbamates an important metabolic route appears to be (27, 28) hydroxylation of one methyl group, first shown with the *p*-nitrophenyl dimethylcarbamate:

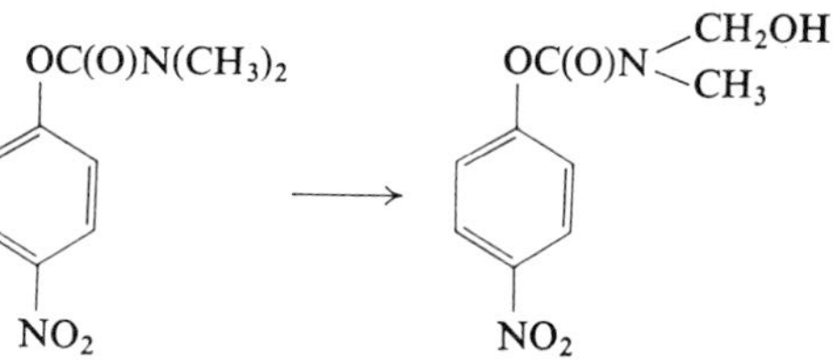

$OC(O)N(CH_3)_2$ / NO_2 → $OC(O)N(CH_2OH)(CH_3)$ / NO_2

The reaction can be followed by digesting the product with strong acid, whereupon formaldehyde is produced, presumably when NCH_2OH goes to NH and CH_2O. The enzyme system involved is found in liver microsomes, requires $NADPH_2$ and oxygen, and is almost certainly the same as the general drug-metabolizing system of liver which converts P=S to P=O and performs numerous other functions (p. 210). The system hydroxylates all the *N*-dimethylcarbamates tested, such as Dimetan, Isolan, and Pyrolan. It is blocked by $10^{-4}M$ concentrations of SKF 525A (the general blocking agent for microsomal metabolism, p. 221), piperonyl butoxide, and sesamex. Perhaps the last two agents owe some of their synergizing ability to this blockade.

The metabolism of carbamates in plants has received a good deal of attention. Casida's group has reported that in beans and cotton carbaryl underwent far less complex degradation than in the animal systems described above. Probably the only hydroxylation product was a conjugated form of (VI) (11). Other relatively simple substituted phenyl methylcarbamates (the 2-isopropoxy, the 3-isopropyl, the 3,5-diisopropyl, and the 2-chloro-4,5-dimethyl) all underwent rapid metabolism (1); the residual parent compound after treatment of bean leaves was 71% at one day for carbaryl, and for the compounds in parentheses above was, respectively, 26, 10, 39, and 44%. Only trivial amounts were converted to carbonyl-containing metabolites, so the major routes were presumably evaporative loss or metabolism which split off the $OC(O)NHCH_3$ group.

The evaporative aspect was explored by performing studies with glass plates, and the losses from such a surface were rather rapid; the half times of loss were, for carbaryl, 14 hours and for the compounds in parentheses above were, respectively, 1.8, 0.3, 5.2, and 0.7 hours. In view of this rapid evaporation, the loss from leaves was very probably entirely evaporative. Lest the reader should be surprised that one should even raise the question of non-evaporative loss from leaves, the remarkable "metabolic" (?) conversions of dimethoate applied to plant leaves should be recalled (p. 65).

When injected into plants in order to measure true metabolic effects, the rates of disappearance were somewhat different; the residual parent material after one day was 58% for carbaryl and for the above parenthetic compounds, 49, 22, 81, and 10%, respectively. Consequently, the rate of loss internally (compared to external loss) was somewhat greater for carbaryl, twice as great for the 2-chloro-4,5-dimethyl compound, but half as great for the other compounds. Once again, only trivial amounts of unconjugated hydroxylation products were recovered. Most of the metabolites were either water-soluble or unextractable, so that one cannot say whether they were conjugated hydroxylation products, or whether $C^{14}O_2$ was in fact released by decarbamylation, and then utilized metabolically.

In addition to these reactions of general importance for carbamates, other metabolic routes in plants involve specific substituents. Thus Mesurol is converted to its sulfoxide and sulfone in various unspecified plants (43):

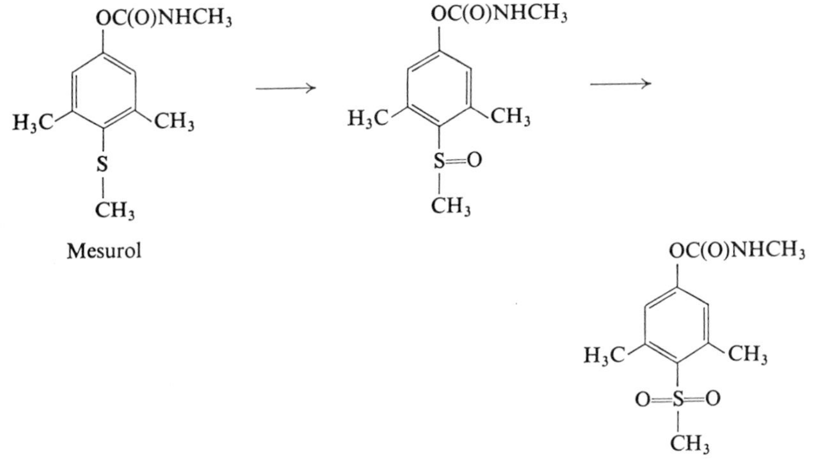

$OC(O)NHCH_3$ H_3C CH_3 S CH_3 → $OC(O)NHCH_3$ H_3C CH_3 S=O CH_3 → $OC(O)NHCH_3$ H_3C CH_3 O=S=O CH_3

Mesurol

Zectran is said (55) to be degraded in broccoli flowers to the metabolites shown, as well as to the phenol (shown on p. 101) and various conjugates; but the extraction procedure was rather vigorous, involving boiling methanol, so there is the possibility that some of the derivatives below were artifacts rather than metabolites:

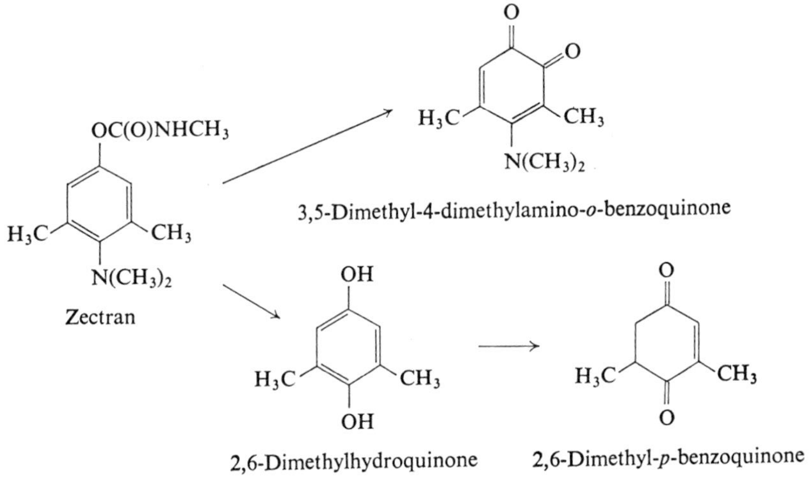

$OC(O)NHCH_3$ H_3C CH_3 $N(CH_3)_2$

Zectran

→ O O H_3C CH_3 $N(CH_3)_2$

3,5-Dimethyl-4-dimethylamino-*o*-benzoquinone

→ OH H_3C CH_3 OH → O H_3C CH_3 O

2,6-Dimethylhydroquinone 2,6-Dimethyl-*p*-benzoquinone

In another study involving C^{14}-carbonyl-labeled Zectran, in which only derivatives with an intact carbonyl could be detected, the following were stated to be the principal breakdown products from bean plants (1):

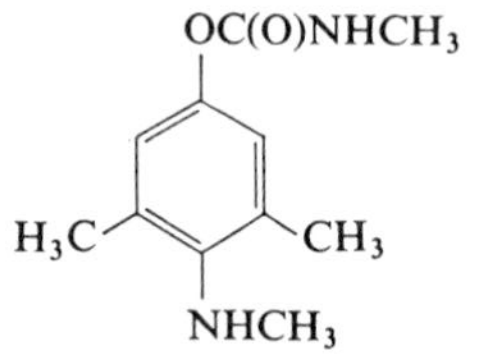

$OC(O)NHCH_3$, H_3C, CH_3, $NHCH_3$

4-Methylamino-3,5-xylyl methylcarbamate

$OC(O)NHCH_3$, H_3C, CH_3, NH_2

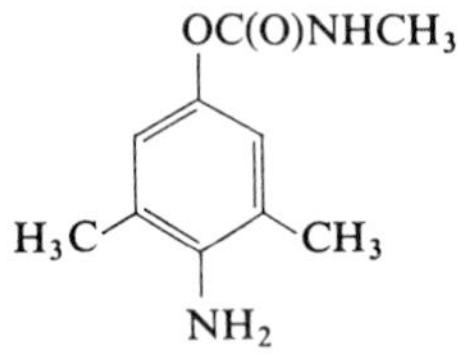

4-Amino-3,5-xylyl methylcarbamate

$OC(O)NHCH_3$, H_3C, CH_3, $CH_3—N—CH{=}O$

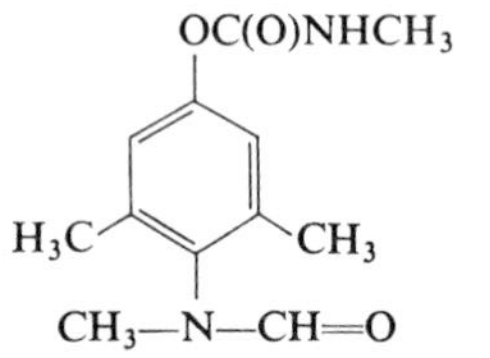

4-Methylformamido-3,5-xylyl methylcarbamate

$OC(O)NHCH_3$, H_3C, CH_3, $NH—CH{=}O$

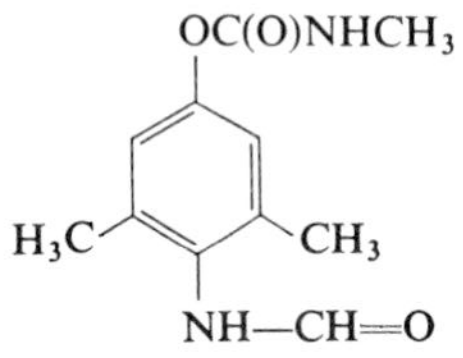

4-Formamido-3,5-xylyl methylcarbamate

Of the above, only the amino and methylamino compounds were major products, comprising together 15% of the applied radioactivity at 1 day. The others each constituted about 1%. Similar formamido and methylformamido compounds were formed when Matacil was metabolized by beans.

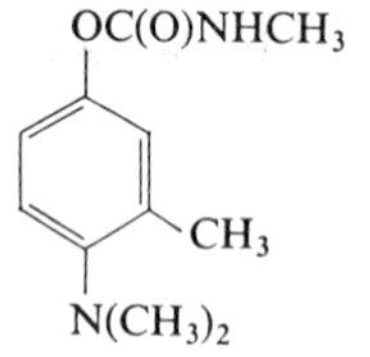

$OC(O)NHCH_3$, CH_3, $N(CH_3)_2$

Matacil

In both the above cases, metabolism was quite rapid; only 25% of parent Zectran or 36% of parent Matacil remained after 1 day. The major pathway(s) involved removal of the carbamyl group, for about 24% of the radioactivity disappeared in a day in both cases, presumably as CO_2 following decarbamylation.

Quite apart from metabolic conversion, carbamates can undergo light-catalyzed breakdown (9). Six methylcarbamates were irradiated by sun or ultraviolet light, and all gave numerous products, many of them with anticholinesterase activity, although simple phenols were also present. Apart from this, the products were unidentified. An earlier study on Zectran (30) also showed photodecomposition; intense ultraviolet light reduced the toxicity 3-fold in 70 hours.

Synergism

The term "synergism" will be used for cases where two compounds together show a toxicity greater than that predicted from the sum of their individual effects. Moorefield (39) in 1958 first showed the synergism of several carbamates against houseflies, using compounds well known as pyrethrin synergists: piperonyl butoxide, sesoxane, "sulfoxide," *n*-propyl isome, and sesamine oil extractives (see p. 167 for formulas). Such compounds were also effective synergists for *Drosophila* (20) but actually antagonized the toxicity of pyrolan and eserine for *Daphnia magna* (19). However, the synergists were used in about 10-fold excess over the carbamates, so the interest was academic rather than commercial. Later, other workers (15,22) found that compounds (VIII)–(X) were good synergists for Isolan, Pyrolan, and especially carbaryl against houseflies, when used at doses only a fraction of the carbamate.

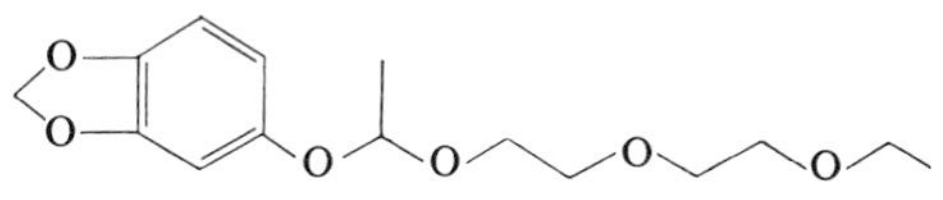

(VIII)
Sesamex

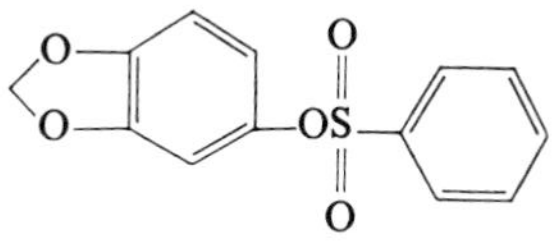

(IX)
3,4-Methylenedioxyphenyl benzenesulfonate

$$Cl_3C\text{—}CHCl\text{—}CH_2\overset{\displaystyle O}{\overset{\|}{C}}CH_2CHCl\text{—}Cl_2$$

(X)
Octachlorodipropyl ether

Synergism of a rather mild degree has also been shown to occur between certain pairs of carbamates, such as Pyrolan and carbaryl, with houseflies and German cockroaches; this phenomenon was termed "analog-synergism" by its discoverers (23). Certain organic thiocyanates are also carbamate synergists (17).

There is indirect evidence that synergists do not promote penetration, for their effects are not dependent upon application to the same place (22). But by contrast, Eldefrawi and Hoskins (14) showed (also with houseflies) that sesamex very greatly delayed penetration of C^{14}-carbaryl; yet the form of the penetration curve was rather unusual and the effect was not seen with resistant houseflies. There has also been considerable speculation that the synergists act by blocking carbamate degradation. With sesamex, most of the internal radioactivity after the application of radioactive carbaryl along with sesamex was the unchanged compound, whereas without sesamex there was far less (14). A moderate (20%) decrease in the breakdown of absorbed 3-isopropylphenyl methylcarbamate was demonstrated when a 5-fold excess of piperonyl butoxide was applied previously (23).

Metcalf *et al.* (38) noted that in a series of phenyl methylcarbamates with alkoxy ring substituents, the toxicities to houseflies varied enormously; but in the presence of piperonyl butoxide, the range of toxicities was much reduced. For five selected compounds, the unsynergized toxicities varied 16-fold, whereas the synergized toxicities varied 4-fold. This finding was held to be evidence that the inherent toxicity of these carbamates was similar, that the great differences in their toxicities were caused by variations in breakdown rate, and that piperonyl butoxide acted by blocking this breakdown. The argument is somewhat tenuous; the interesting findings, although *compatible* with the "breakdown" argument, are also compatible with other theories, e.g., that differences in excretion are crucial, and excretion is blocked by the synergists. Further evidence is discussed on p. 220.

REFERENCES

1. Abdel-Wahab, A. M., Kuhr, R. J., and Casida, J. E., *J. Agr. Food Chem.* **14**, 290 (1966).
2. Aldridge, W. N., *Biochem. J.* **46**, 451 (1950).
3. Aldridge, W. N., *Biochem. J.* **54**, 442 (1953).
4. Anonymous, *Sta. Sta. Res. News Union Carbide Chem. N.Y.* **2** (3), 1 (1956).
5. Carpenter, C. P., Weil, C. S., Palm, P. E., Woodside, M. W., Nair, T. H., and Smyth, H. F., *J. Agr. Food Chem.* **9**, 30 (1961).
6. Casida, J. E., *Ann. Rev. Entomol.* **8**, 39 (1963).
7. Casida, J. E., and Augustinsson, K. B., *Biochim. Biophys. Acta* **36**, 411 (1959).
8. Casida, J. E., Augustinsson, K. B., and Jonsson, G., *J. Econ. Entomol.* **53**, 205 (1960).
9. Crosby, D. G., Leitis, E., and Winterlin, W. L., *J. Agr. Food Chem.* **13**, 204 (1965).
10. David, W. A. L., Metcalf, R. L., and Winton, M. Y., *J. Econ. Entomol.* **53**, 1021 (1960).
11. Dorough, H. W., and Casida, J. E., *J. Agr. Food Chem.* **12**, 244 (1964).
12. Dorough, H. W., Leeling, N. C., and Casida, J. E., *Science* **140**, 170 (1963).
13. Easson, L. H., and Stedman, E., *Proc. Roy. Soc.* (*London*) **B121**, 142 (1936).
14. Eldefrawi, M. E., and Hoskins, W. M., *J. Econ. Entomol.* **54**, 401 (1961).
15. Eldefrawi, M. E., Miskus, R., and Sutcher, V., *J. Econ. Entomol.* **53**, 231 (1960).
16. Ellis, S., Plachte, F. L., and Straus, O. H., *J. Pharmacol. Exptl. Therap.* **79**, 295 (1943).
17. El-Sebae, A. H., Metcalf, R. L., and Fukuto, T. R., *J. Econ. Entomol.* **57**, 478 (1964).
18. Engelhart, E., and Loewi, O., *Arch. Exptl. Pathol. Pharmakol. Naunyn-Schmiedeberg's* **150**, 1 (1930).
19. Fuchs, W. H., and Seume, F. W., *Naturwissenschaften* **44**, 334 (1957).
20. Fuchs, W. H., and Zschintzsh, J., *Naturwissenschaften* **46**, 273 (1959).
21. Fukuto, T. R., Metcalf, R. L., and Winton, M. Y., *J. Econ. Entomol.* **57**, 10 (1964).
22. Gheorghiou, G. P., and Metcalf, R. L., *J. Econ. Entomol.* **54**, 150 (1961).

23. Gheorghiou, G. P., and Metcalf, R. L., *J. Econ. Entomol.* **54**, 231 (1961).
24. Goldstein, A., *J. Gen. Physiol.* **27**, 529 (1944).
25. Goldstein, A., *Arch. Biochem.* **34**, 169 (1951).
26. Gordon, H. T., and Eldefrawi, M. E., *J. Econ. Entomol.* **53**, 1004 (1960).
27. Hodgson, E., and Casida, J. E., *Biochim. Biophys. Acta* **42**, 184 (1960).
28. Hodgson, E., and Casida, J. E., *Biochem. Pharmacol.* **8**, 179 (1961).
29. Jobst, J., and Hease, O., *Ann. Chem.* **129**, 115 (1964).
30. Kenaga, E. E., Doty, A. E., and Hardy, J. L., *J. Econ. Entomol.* **55**, 466 (1962).
31. Knaak, J. B., Tallant, M. J., Partly, W. J., and Sullivan, L. T., *J. Agr. Food Chem.* **13**, 537 (1965).
32. Kolbezen, M. J., Metcalf, R. L., and Fukuto, T. R., *J. Agr. Food Chem.* **2**, 864 (1954).
33. Krishna, J. G., and Casida, J. E., *J. Agr. Food Chem.* **14**, 98 (1966).
34. Leeling, N. C., and Casida, J. E., *J. Agr. Food Chem.* **14**, 281 (1966).
35. Long, J. P., *In* "Cholinesterase and Anticholinesterase Agents," Handbuch der Experimentellen Pharmakologie (G. B. Koelle, ed.), Vol. 15, Chapt. 8. Springer, Berlin, 1963.
36. Metcalf, R. L., *Agr. Chem.* **16** (6), 20, 104, 106 (1961).
37. Metcalf, R. L., and Fukuto, T. R., *J. Agr. Food Chem.* **13**, 220 (1965).
38. Metcalf, R. L., Fukuto, T. R., and Winton, M. Y., *J. Econ. Entomol.* **53**, 828 (1960).
39. Moorefield, H. H., *Contrib. Boyce Thompson Inst.* **19**, 50 (1958).
40. Myers, D. K., *Biochem. J.* **52**, 46 (1952).
41. Myers, D. K., *Biochem. J.* **62**, 556 (1956).
42. Myers, D. K., Kemp, A., Tol, J. W., and DeJonge, M. H. T., *Biochem. J.* **65**, 232 (1957).
43. Niessen, H., and Frehse, H., *Pflanzenschutz-Nachr.* **16**, 205 (1963).
44. O'Brien, R. D., *In* "Metabolic Inhibitors" (R. M. Hochster and J. H. Quastel, eds.), Chapt. 25. Academic Press, New York, 1963.
45. O'Brien, R. D., *Exptl. Med. Surg.*, Dec. Suppl., p. 117 (1965).
46. O'Brien, R. D., Hilton, B. D., and Gilmour, L., *Mol. Pharmacol.* **2**, 593 (1966).
47. O'Brien, R. D., and Matthysse, J. G., *Agr. Chem.* **16** (10), 16, 83 (11), 27, 95 (1961).
48. Negherbon, W. O., "Handbook of Toxicology, Insecticides," Vol. 3. Saunders, Philadelphia, Pennsylvania, 1959.
49. Plapp, F. W., and Bigley, W. S., *J. Econ. Entomol.* **54**, 793 (1961).
50. Shorey, H. H., *J. Econ. Entomol.* **54**, 1243 (1961).
51. Stedman, E., and Barger, G., *J. Chem. Soc.* **127**, 247 (1925).
52. Stempel, A., and Aeschlimann, J. A., *In* "Medicinal Chemistry" (F. F. Blicke and R. H. Cox, eds.), Vol. 3, p. 238. Wiley, New York, 1956.
53. Weiden, M. H. J., and Moorefield, H. H., *World Rev. Pest Control* **3**, 102 (1964).
54. Weiden, M. H. J., Moorefield, H. H., and Payne, L. K., *J. Econ. Entomol.* **58**, 154 (1965).
55. Williams, E., Meikle, R. W., and Redemann, C. T., *J. Agr. Food Chem.* **12**, 453 (1964).
56. Williams, E., Meikle, R. W., and Redemann, C. T., *J. Agr. Food Chem.* **12**, 457 (1964).
57. Wilson, I. B., Hatch, M. A., and Ginsburg, S., *J. Biol. Chem.* **235**, 2312 (1960).
58. Winteringham, F. P. W., and Disney, R. W., *Biochem. J.* **91**, 506 (1964).

CHAPTER 6

DDT and Related Compounds

DDT is the best-known, the cheapest, and the most astonishingly effective of the synthetic insecticides. Although it was made in 1874, its insecticidal effectiveness was not discovered until 1939, by Paul Muller of the Geigy Company in Switzerland; it was patented in 1942. It soon became the "miracle insecticide" of the time, and even today it is in many ways the foremost insecticide. Apart from being cheap and easy to make, stable, and potent, it is of extreme persistence when applied to plant or other surfaces, and of extremely low hazard under most circumstances. Although it remains the most important insecticide on the international scene, its popularity has waned somewhat on account of the steady increase in insect resistance; on account of its extreme persistence in plants and animals, which has led to its widespread contamination of the environment, including the fat of man; on account of the ignorance of its mode of action, which makes it difficult to evaluate the significance of such persistent residues; and on account of a suspicion of the effects of low residues upon the fertility of animals. Thus the amount used in the United States dropped from 67 million pounds in 1962 to 51 million in 1964 (79).

Structure and Chemistry

DDT derives its name from its earlier chemical designation: *p,p'*-dichlorodiphenyltrichloroethane. The correct designation is 2,2-bis(*p*-chlorophenyl)-1,1,1-trichloroethane.

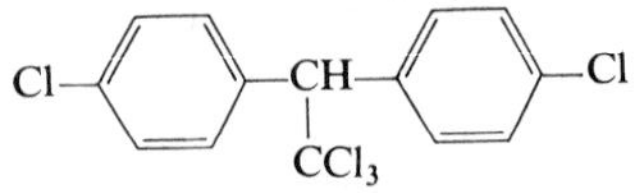

$$Cl-C_6H_4-CH(CCl_3)-C_6H_4-Cl$$

DDT

Its most interesting properties will now be discussed. It has an excessively low vapor pressure, 1.5×10^{-7} mm at 20°C (5); presumably this property is the cause of its remarkable persistence on surfaces, giving insect kills for 18 months on nonporous surfaces (10). A chemical stability, including relative insensitivity to sunlight, assists this residual efficacy. Under alkaline conditions, breakdown to the important nontoxic derivative, DDE, occurs by the elimination of HCl. DDT is also extraordinarily apolar, having a large oil–water partition coefficient [923 for olive oil:water (66)] and an excessively

Cl—C₆H₄—C(=CCl₂)—C₆H₄—Cl

DDE

small water solubility. The latter value has been variously reported, with one value as low as 0.2 ppb (parts per billion) (10), but the best estimate appears to be 1.2 ppb ($3.4 \times 10^{-10} M$) at 25°C, judged by ultracentrifugation of solutions of C^{14}-DDT (9). Higher apparent values are obtained if various colloidal formulations are (knowingly or otherwise) examined. One of the best ways to achieve high effective concentration in water, for biological studies, is to formulate in a special lipoprotein made from egg yolk; in this way, concentrations (presumably colloidal) of $10^{-2} M$ may be obtained (49).

The extreme apolarity of DDT, when considered along with the evident greasiness or waxiness of most insect integuments, has tempted several authorities into statements such as "the lipoid solubility of DDT and the presence of lipoids in the epicuticle are generally supposed to be responsible for this rapid penetration" (96); "... its specific contact action in arthropods results from its physical properties in connection with the properties of their skin" (22); "... the mammal interposes an effective barrier of protective tissue, the cuticle of the insect is an ineffective shield ..." (10). However, as shown in Chapter 16, direct measurements have shown that DDT penetrates rather poorly in insects, and no faster than in mammals. The above statements are based upon the observation that DDT is often about equally toxic to insects whether applied topically or by injection; the potential fallacy in this argument is reviewed on p. 256.

DDT Analogs

The effectiveness of DDT has led to numerous attempts to synthesize effective analogs, none of which have usurped the overall value of DDT. However, several have useful properties which make them desirable for particular uses. A few insecticidal active analogs will be described, but extensive tabulations of the insecticidal potency of numerous analogs should be sought elsewhere (10,58).

Methoxychlor is said to be more effective than DDT against a few insects (10) and has a distinctly lower toxicity to vertebrates; thus its oral LD_{50} for rats is 6000 mg/kg compared with 250 for DDT (58).

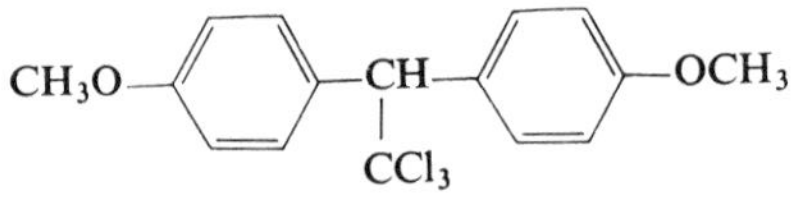

CH_3O—C_6H_4—CH(CCl_3)—C_6H_4—OCH_3

Methoxychlor

DDD is also less toxic than DDT to vertebrates, with a rat oral LD_{50} of 3400 mg/kg (58). It is used as an insecticide, but has an unfortunate effect upon the adrenal cortex of vertebrates, as discussed on p. 297.

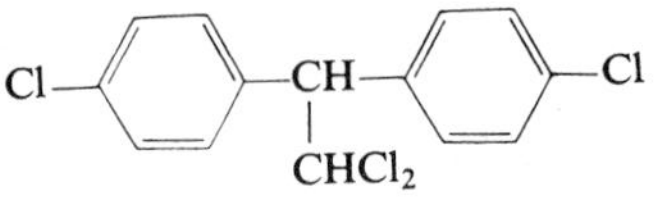

Cl—C_6H_4—CH($CHCl_2$)—C_6H_4—Cl

DDD (also TDE)

Prolan and Bulan, the principal constituents of the mixture known as Dilan, are better than DDT against some insects and have less toxicity than DDT to vertebrates; insect and rat oral LD_{50}'s are 4000 and 330 mg/kg, respectively (58).

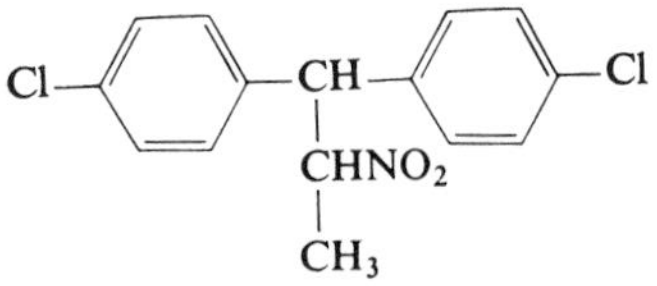

Cl—C_6H_4—CH($CHNO_2$—CH_3)—C_6H_4—Cl

Prolan

Cl—C_6H_4—CH($CHNO_2$—C_2H_5)—C_6H_4—Cl

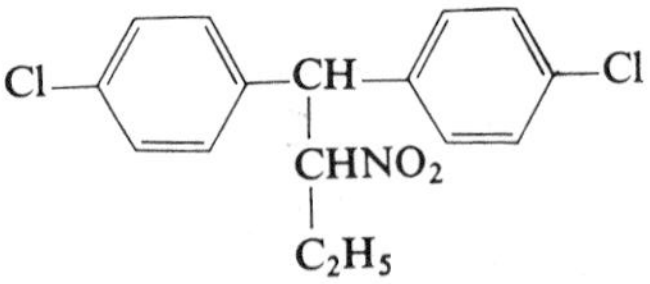

Bulan

Toxicity

The toxicity of DDT applied externally is low to all mammals tested; toward insects it shows a great variation of effectiveness with species, as shown in Table 6.1. The table also shows the great dependence of toxicity upon route: in mammals, intravenous DDT is fairly toxic (e.g., 50 mg/kg); and some insects, such as the bee, which are insensitive to external DDT, are very sensitive to injected DDT. These differences with route are commonly attributed to "barrier effects" of the skin or cuticle, but that interpretation is open to much doubt, as discussed on p. 256. As the table shows, such differences are not seen in all insects; the American cockroach and Japanese beetle are two such examples.

TABLE 6.1

TOXICITY OF DDT (LD_{50} IN MG/KG) TO INSECTS AND MAMMALS[a]

Animal	Cutaneous (topical)	Oral	Intraperitoneal (intra-abdominal)	Intravenous
Rat	3000	400	150	50
Rabbit	300–2820	300	2100	50
Milkweed bug	409	301	31	—
Bee	114	17	0.2	—
Japanese beetle	93	205	162	—
American cockroach	10	—	7	—
Housefly	8–21	—	—	—
Differential grasshopper	9380	2579	—	—
Greater wax moth (larva)	105	238	277	—

[a] Data from Metcalf (58) and O'Brien (64).

Mechanism of Action

It is painful to have to admit that, after decades of intensive research, we are far from understanding the mechanism of action of DDT. It is generally agreed now that its primary effects are virtually all upon the nervous system, both in vertebrates and invertebrates. The evidence for this view is as follows.

(1) The symptoms of poisoning suggest nervous impairment. In the American cockroach, for example (86), there is tremor throughout the body and appendages (DDT jitters) along with hyperexcitability, followed very slowly by ataxia (loss of motion) and apparent paralysis which may be total at 24 hours. In more sensitive insects, such as houseflies, fruit flies, and bees, the symptoms are similar but appear more rapidly, with paralysis in a few hours (10). Similarly, in mammals there is hyperexcitability and tremor, which is particularly evident in the face, and later there are convulsions, which may be both tonic (i.e., the animal is rigid) with opisthotonus (the head arched back) and clonic (frenzied uncoordinated movements). Finally there is weakness and prostration.

(2) When DDT is applied to isolated tissues and enzymes, only nervous tissue is sensitive to very low concentrations. This statement is true only if one excludes those effects given equally by DDT and nontoxic analogs, such as DDE. Details are given below.

(3) In the DDT-treated rat, an excellent correlation has been found between the level of DDT achieved in the central nervous system and the intensity of symptoms (19).

On the above evidence it seems safe to conclude that DDT is a neurotoxicant. Two questions follow naturally: Where does the disruption of the nervous system occur, and what is the explanation for the disruption?

The literature on the site of nervous disruption must be read with care: "the neuromuscular system" (58) and synaptic blockade (22) have been claimed, but in fact both ancient and modern experiments clearly show that these junctions are not involved, and that the effects of moderate concentration are almost exclusively on the axon.

Yeager and Munson in 1945 first showed the now familiar physiological symptoms of DDT poisoning of nerve: a multiplication effect, so that single nerve impulses arriving at a DDT-treated region give rise to prolonged volleys of impulses (61,98). This they demonstrated in crayfish, crabs, lobsters, and American cockroaches. Cockroach nerve was at least ten times less sensitive than crustacean, a fact that paralleled the 40-fold lower toxicity of DDT to whole cockroaches than to whole crayfish. The multiplication could be demonstrated on isolated nerve trunks; consequently DDT acts on axonic rather than on synaptic transmission (see p. 16), a property shared by very few drugs, the best known of which is veratrine.

The question of the relative sensitivity of various nerves to DDT has provoked different answers. In some early literature (22,98) it was claimed that motor nerves were more sensitive than sensory, but more recent work has shown the opposite to be true. In 1946, Roeder and Weiant (74) showed definitely in the American cockroach that although 1000 ppm of DDT in solution could affect motor nerves and even muscle fibres, low concentrations (0.01 ppm) have no effect on these, or on the central nervous system, but only upon sensory nerves. Welsh and Gordon (94) confirmed these findings a year later.

It therefore seems extremely likely that DDT is lethal because of its effects on sensory nerves. What physiological mechanism gives rise to this effect? An early speculation, by Welsh and Gordon in 1947 (94), was that Ca^{++} permeability of the nerve was reduced, because their work in crayfish showed that lowering the Ca^{++} level in the medium mimicked the effects of DDT, and raising the Ca^{++} level antagonized the DDT effect. However these Ca^{++} effects are not seen in insect nerve (63), and therefore probably have no connection with the poisoning of insects.

The most revealing studies on the mechanism of DDT excitation were begun in 1957 by Yamasaki and Narahashi (97), working with the crural nerve of the American cockroach, and using intracellular electrodes, which show the response of a single neuron rather than responses of bundles of nerves. They found that DDT affected the action potential in a specific way: it increased the negative after-potential (NAP). Because the NAP is associated with potassium efflux (see discussion on p. 17) in cockroaches as well as vertebrates

(63), they suggested that DDT specifically inhibits this efflux. They then showed that high potassium reduced the effects of DDT on cockroach nerve, and low potassium enormously enhanced them, so that the NAP in a potassium-free system appeared as a plateau rather than as a shoulder (Fig. 6.1) (62). Finally, Matsumura and O'Brien (56) have shown with radioactive K^+ that DDT greatly increases the K^+ permeability of cockroach nervous tissue.

One anomaly remains in the Yamasaki-Narahashi work. In one experiment, they selected a DDT dose such that cockroaches convulsed at 16.5°C, but were free of symptoms at 29°C (see discussion below). But the effect on the NAP was the same at both temperatures! This finding suggests the effect on the NAP is not the immediate cause of symptoms.

Let us now discuss the molecular basis for the physiological disruption in nerve caused by DDT. Several theories, which overlap a good deal, are based

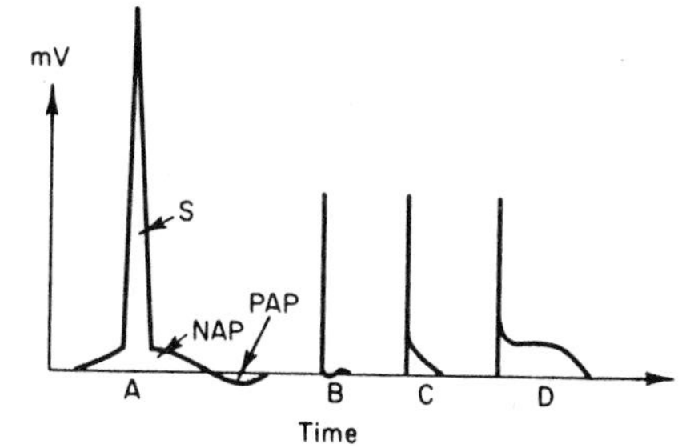

FIG. 6.1. Action potentials recorded intracellularly. A, a schematic diagram (S=spike, NAP=negative after-potential, PAP=positive after-potential); B, drawing based on normal Cockroach giant axon data; C, 100 minutes after 10^{-4} *M* DDT; D, same in potassium-free solution. Based on Narahashi and Yamasaki (62).

upon formation of some sort of complex between DDT and "the nerve membrane," by which is usually meant the axonic membrane whose change in ion permeability is involved in the action potential.

Lauger *et al.* (45) in 1945 demonstrated the strong affinity of DDT for cholesterol, which is common in nerve tissue, and speculated that combination with some important nerve-cell lipoids might cause "a state of excitability." Two attempts have been made to put this concept on a more specific footing. Mullins (60) suggested in 1955 that the target for lindane and DDT was a hypothetical lattice, whose dimensions he calculated by assuming that inactive compounds were of the wrong size or the wrong shape to fit snugly into (see fuller discussion on p. 185). This purely steric conception may be contrasted with the almost purely electronic picture of Gunther *et al.* (28) in 1954, who examined the role of bonding energies, which they speculated were entirely of the van der Waals type. They examined 30 DDT analogs, and treated the data by considering the substituted phenyls together as a "head" and the substituted alkane portion as the "tail."

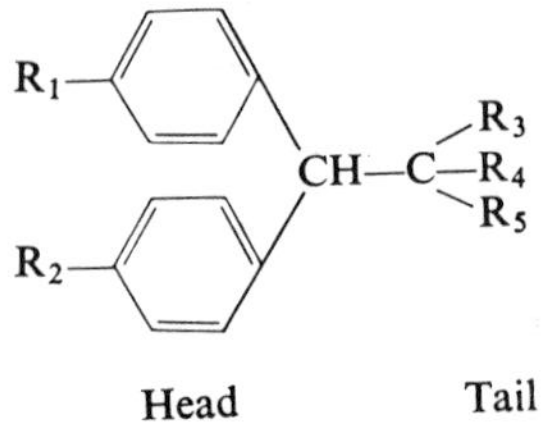

R_1, R_2 (phenyl rings) — CH—C—R_3, R_4, R_5

Head **Tail**

The various R's could be Cl, H, or CH_3, so that for any tail, for instance, one could have six heads: Cl,Cl, or H,H or CH_3,CH_3 or Cl,H or Cl,CH_3 or H,CH_3. Of the many tails that could be made, they chose five: H,H,H or H,H,CH_3 or H,Cl,Cl or H,H,Cl or Cl,Cl,Cl. They reported that if one end (a head or a tail) were held constant, then the toxicity for mosquitoes, *Culex quinquefasciatus*, increased linearly with each logarithmic increment of the total van der Waals forces of the chlorines plus the methyls plus the hydrogens. The slopes of the eleven graphs prepared in this way (one graph for each head and one for each tail) were remarkably constant in eight cases, varying only between 0.5 and 0.7. Unfortunately, neither correlation coefficients nor the graphs themselves were reported; if we assume that the fit was good, the implication is that by increasing nonspecific bonding forces one can improve affinity for a hypothetical target whose shape is complementary to DDT, and hence increase potency. Just why it is the *logarithms* of the van der Waals forces, rather than the force values themselves, is not clear; it implies that it becomes progressively more difficult to improve the affinity, so that logarithmic force addition achieves only linear toxicity increases. The underlying assumption is that the fit to the target is comparable in all the compounds, and indeed chlorine and methyl groups have fairly similar van der Waals radii, 1.80 and 2.27 Å, respectively (93). Now hydrogen has a very different radius, 0.3 Å, so one might imagine the H-substituted analogs to fit badly, and it is perhaps this that causes the slopes for an all-hydrogen head or all-hydrogen tail to be abnormal (1.6 and 0.1, respectively). Yet in four out of the eight cases in which the slopes *were* "normal," there was at least one hydrogen in the head or tail of the whole group, and one would have thought that in these cases a different relationship would hold. This interesting study was capped with a conclusion that goes far beyond the facts: "These data are consistent and therefore in agreement with our postulate that these particular insecticides are reacting with a protein-like substance, presumably an enzyme." In fact, the extreme nonspecificity observed rather suggests that an enzyme is not involved, and there is certainly no indication at all whether the target is proteinaceous or not. This sort of approach, however, which was originally inspired by Pauling and Pressman's great work on antigen–antibody interaction (69) deserves far more attention. In particular, it would be desirable to use substituents with widely differing van der Waals bonding energies; the relative energies of $H:Cl:CH_3$ are 1:0.5:0.65.

In other work from Gunther's laboratory, 16 DDT analogs with hydroxylated alkane groups were examined against mites and no relation between van der Waals forces and toxicity was found (30), and 44 diphenylmethane derivatives were tested against confused flour beetles with no evident relation ship emerging (29).

Matsumura and O'Brien (55,56,65) suggested that the complex involved was of the charge-transfer type,* since DDT is known to have a very high electron affinity, judged by its ready detection by electron-capture devices in gas chromatography. They isolated two complexes of C^{14}-DDT with unknown components of cockroach nerve, using gel filtration techniques followed by column chromatography, and demonstrated a shift in the ultraviolet spectrum of the DDT, as well as new fluorescent spectral bands in the complex. These findings were compatible with formation of a charge-transfer complex, but did not prove it.

At this point of the narrative it may be appropriate to mention some of the very extensive structure–activity studies on DDT analogs, for they relate to the "structural" view of DDT action which is particularly appropriate to hypotheses that demand a close fit into a lattice or onto a membrane component. Rogers *et al.* (75) suggested in 1953 that the important property of the CCl_3 group was its bulk. If one considers the diphenylmethylene nucleus:

$$C_6H_5{-}CH_2{-}C_6H_5$$

then, if substituents on the methylene group are small, the phenyl groups rotate freely around their bond to the methylene. But if a bulky substituent is inserted on the methylene, such a rotation is inhibited, especially if one imagines the bulky substituent "demanding" room to rotate freely, and the phenyls then take up the well-known "butterfly" configuration seen in DDT, in which the phenyls are as coplanar as they ever can be. Rogers *et al.* suggested that this coplanarity is (for unknown reasons) necessary, and went on to show that

* Charge-transfer complexes may be formed when one kind of molecule (the donor) has a low ionization potential, so that it loses an electron easily, and another (the acceptor) has a high electron affinity, so that it picks up an electron easily. The two molecules also must fit together closely. One may then get a complex formed, with an electron belonging partially to one molecule, partially to another, forming a new bond and therefore producing new spectral bands. The wavelength of the band is related to the affinity of donor and acceptor.

bulky substituents other than CCl_3 were as effective, e.g., $C(CH_3)_3$. Thus the unchlorinated compound dianisyl neopentane had good insecticidal activity.

$CH_3O-C_6H_4-CH(C(CH_3)_3)-C_6H_4-OCH_3$

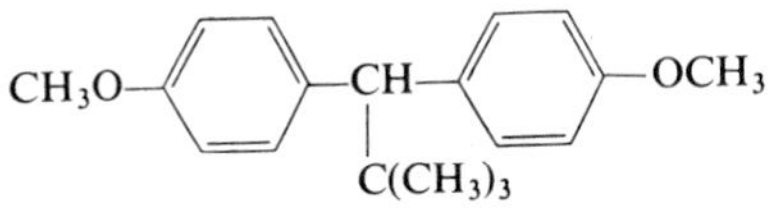

Dianisyl neopentane

The theory also helps explain the activity of Prolan and Bulan, but unfortunately it turns out that if one replaces the CCl_3 group of DDT by $CH(NO_2)Cl$ or $C(CH_3)_2Cl$ or $C(NO_2)Cl_2$, the compounds are inactive (54).

Another celebrated hypothesis seems at first almost the opposite of the above. Riemschneider and Otto (73) argued that some ability of the phenyls to rotate was a *requirement* for activity. However, in harmony with Rogers view, Riemschneider considered that free rotation was required to permit the taking up of the "almost planar" configuration described above. For this reason, they felt, *o,o′*-DDT, is inactive, for the two *o*-chlorines restrict rotation. Similarly, one could account for the properties of analogs with two methyl substituents per ring; when these were in the 2 and 4 positions, or the 2 and 5, rotation was impossible and insecticidal activity lacking, but when they were in the 3 and 4 positions, rotation was possible and activity was found. But unfortunately for the theory, *o,p′*-DDT does not have such rotatability, yet is a perfectly good insecticide (54).

The very extensive studies on structure–activity relationships in DDT analogs, mostly carried out before 1950, have been admirably reviewed by Brown (10) who concludes that "any attempt to obtain any complete quantitative correlation with any single property ends in failure," and that symmetry is the only hallmark of all good DDT analogs.

There is another theory of DDT action, the "toxin" theory, introduced by Sternburg and Kearns in 1952 (82). These workers observed that cockroaches which had been poisoned with DDT contained in their blood a factor which could kill flies and cause DDT-like effects when applied to untreated cockroach nerve cords. This factor was not DDT itself, for (unlike DDT) it was not extractable by ether. Since this observation, others have shown that a variety of stressful treatments cause cockroaches to produce such factors in their blood. For instance, pinning cockroaches down so that they struggle for days (7) or putting them on a kind of treadmill that forces them to walk continuously for many hours (47), alters their blood composition so that transfer of it into untreated cockroaches causes paralysis or death. Other chemicals than DDT, specifically tetraethyl pyrophosphate and dieldrin, have also induced a blood-borne paralysis factor in cockroaches (17).

These observations suggest a refined version of an early view that death from DDT was "due to exhaustion," caused perhaps by excessive activity induced in sensory nerves. The refinement would consist in having a chemical factor, induced by DDT or other stressful treatments, as the immediate cause of death. It seemed that the story was complete when it was shown in 1958 and 1959 (37,67) that the corpora cardiaca of cockroaches have a "neuroactive principle" which reduces the spontaneous activity of an isolated nerve cord, and that this principle was depleted from the corpora cardiaca by stimulating the cockroaches electrically. And also about this time, it was shown that both DDT and mechanical stress caused a transient but profound increase in respiration rates (36) and acetylcholine levels (47) of cockroach nerve, and that cockroach strains tolerant of DDT were also tolerant of mechanical stress (36).

Alas, from then on the attractive stress theory becomes more complex. It turns out (21,84) that there are three quite separate blood factors: (a) a heart accelerating factor released by mechanical stress, in corpus cardiacum, nerve cord, brain, blood, etc., which has no effect on nervous action; (b) a neuroactive factor present only in corpus cardiacum—the factor whose depletion by electrical stimulation is described above; and (c) the neuroactive factor which appears in the blood of DDT-poisoned cockroaches. Factors (b) and (c) have no effects on heart rate; they are readily separable chromatographically. But factor (c) chromatographs in the same way as the neuroactive factors found in the blood of mechanically stressed cockroaches, which contained no factor (b) (84). In summary, it does seem that DDT and mechanical stress produce in blood a neuroactive principle which could play an important role in causing death.

Extensive studies have given moderate information about the DDT-induced factor, but have not led to elucidation of its structure. It is dialyzable and it loses activity on standing in the presence of cockroach blood (78). It can be chromatographed on paper, and its R_f in several systems has been established. With this procedure, it was shown that the same factor can be produced by poisoning crayfish with DDT. The crayfish-DDT factor has been collected in relatively large quantity by collecting a liter of blood from poisoned crayfish, and some clues to its identity were obtained by spot color tests on the chromatograms. These tests suggested that the factor was an aromatic amine containing an ester group (32).

The "toxin" theory could, in principle, be compatible with the theories on interference with the nerve membrane; one might argue that DDT causes toxin production, which then causes membrane disruption. However, the toxin is detectable only after fairly prolonged DDT treatment; and furthermore, the underlying notion is that hyperexcitability in the sensory nervous system is the equivalent of mechanical or electrical excitation, and gives rise to toxin production. Therefore the "toxin" theory does not suggest an explanation for the primary lesion, which is presumably membrane destabilization.

A number of earlier theories on DDT action were somewhat speculative. One held that HCl, released by dehydrochlorination of the $CHCCl_3$ at the active site, was the active principle (53). Perhaps the clearest disproof of this idea is the existence of chlorineless analogs of DDT, such as dianisyl neopentane (see above), which are excellent insecticides. Another theory (44) held the opposite, that the role of the CCl_3 group was only that of a "conductophore" to bear the lethal chlorophenyl groups to the site; but this theory has no evidence in favor of it. Many effects upon enzymes or enzyme systems have been reported, but usually these effects have required extremely high concentrations of DDT, or else have been duplicated by nontoxic analogs of DDT, and so discredited. An inhibition of oxidative phosphorylation at fairly low concentrations ($5 \times 10^{-5} M$) was reported for rat liver mitochondria in 1955 (76) and 1960 (68), but in 1959 was shown to be produced also by seven nontoxic analogs, including DDE, DDA, and chloro-DDT (27). Inhibitions of glycolysis and of nine glycolytic enzymes have been reported for the bug *Triatoma infestans*. The effects were typically 30% inhibition by DDT, and only 10–20% by DDE, but gigantic doses were required, of the order of 3000 μg/g (3). Inhibitions of succinic dehydrogenase, cytochrome oxidase, carbonic anhydrase (58), and stimulation of glucose catabolism (80) have been reported, but shown on one or other of the above criteria to be irrelevant to the poisoning process. Numerous reports exist showing the absence of effect of DDT upon a variety of miscellaneous enzymes, such as aminoxidase, nitroreductase, aldolase, pyruvic oxidase, and others (34). Nor have histological procedures proved enlightening; a variety of degenerative changes have been described after poisoning, including breakdown of the golgi bodies of central neurons (13) and vacuolation of midgut epithelial cells (77), but these effects are almost certainly the result rather than the cause of poisoning, for degeneration must be extreme before it becomes visible (96). A different suggestion (75) was that DDT might have a specifically "antisteroid" effect as a result of its ability to complex with steroids. The suggestion has not been followed up.

A theory that runs like an undercurrent through the literature on DDT is that the compound has an effect upon cholinesterase. There were early reports that DDT was a cholinesterase inhibitor *in vitro* (e.g., in ref. 81), but these have been either unconfirmed or specifically denied (88–90). Tobias *et al.* (85) reported in 1946 that poisoning of the American cockroach or housefly by DDT led to a 2-fold elevation in the acetylcholine level in the nervous system at the late stages of poisoning; cholinesterase was unaffected. Fernando described in 1952 increases of 2- to 3-fold in cockroach nerve-cord acetylcholine caused by DDT, lindane, and aldrin (24), but it was later stated (42) that much of the so-called acetylcholine was in fact trichloracetic acid remaining from the extraction procedure. A thorough investigation by Colhoun (16) in 1959 confirmed the delayed 27-fold rise in acetylcholine in the nerve cord of DDT-poisoned cockroaches, but showed that it occurred when the cord was almost silent electrically; in very late poisoning, when the cord was necrotic, the level fell below normal (Fig. 6.2). Colhoun suggested that acetylcholine synthesis occurred at an elevated rate, but in a form unavailable to cholinesterase (nowadays one would suspect that the increases were in the synaptic vesicles; see p. 18). His evidence was that free acetylcholine was found in the nerve cord along with cholinesterase which, judged by subsequent homogenization and assay, was not inhibited. Colhoun concluded (17) that the acetylcholine effect was only a secondary effect of DDT poisoning.

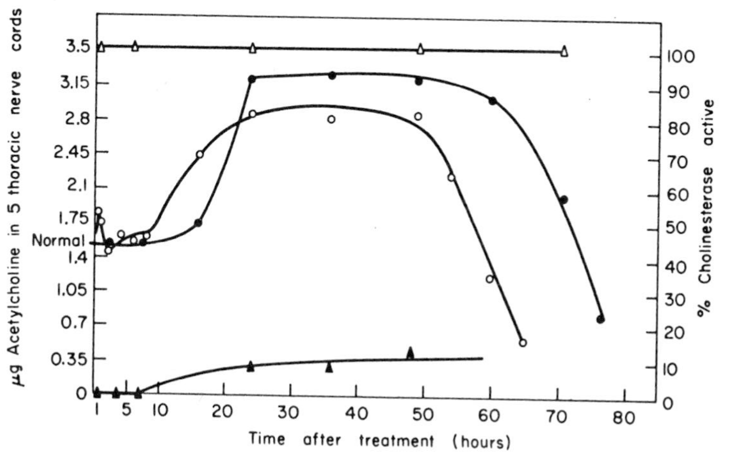

FIG. 6.2. Levels of cholinesterase and acetylcholine in the thoracic nerve cords of American cockroaches treated with tepp (5 μg/g) or DDT (50 μg/g): acetylcholine: ○ after tepp, ● after DDT; cholinesterase: ▲ after tepp, △ after DDT. From Colhoun (16).

A report by Lewis (46) is sometimes quoted as proving that DDT affects acetylcholine synthesis. That report states that acetylcholine synthesis in *Calliphora erythrocephala* fly homogenates prepared 1 hour after treating the flies with DDT (by confining them "in a glass cylinder coated with DDT") showed reduced acetylcholine synthesis (26 μg/g compared with 41 μg/g in controls), whereas at 4.5 hours after treatment there was increased synthesis (80 μg/g). The variance of the findings was not given, and since the results were obtained by a frog rectus muscle bioassay, variation is a very crucial problem. It seems inherently implausible that an enzyme is first inhibited and then activated. No data were given to assure one that varying acetylcholine levels present at the death of differently treated flies were taken into account. In short, this report leaves the matter in considerable doubt.

In 1962, Sternburg and Hewitt (83) pointed out that cholinesterases assays made subsequent to homogenization could give erroneous results, if the cholinesterase was inhibited reversibly *in vivo*; upon homogenization, such an inhibitor would be diluted away and inhibition would disappear. They therefore made ingenious use of an organophosphate TMPP, which was selected as an "irreversible" anticholinesterase which rapidly hydrolyses spontaneously, so that it eliminates itself within a few hours.

$$(CH_3O)_2P(O)OP(O)(OCH_3)_2$$
TMPP

When control and DDT-prostrate cockroaches were treated with TMPP, the resultant cholinesterase inhibition was far less in DDT-treated insects (e.g., 28% at 5 minutes after TMPP) than in controls (91% at the same time). It seemed that the cholinesterase of the DDT-treated insects was protected from inhibition; the alternative possibilities, that poor circulation existed in the DDT-treated insects, or that for other reasons TMPP did not penetrate the nerve cord, were experimentally disproved. Such protection was not found for lindane treatments. The protection increased as DDT poisoning developed, as Fig. 6.3 shows. Reversal of DDT-poisoning symptoms by manipulating temperature (see p. 121) removes the protective effect.

At least two mechanisms for the protective effect can be imagined, although Sternburg and Hewitt avoided any such speculation. DDT, or a derivative of it, or a compound whose production or release is stimulated by it, might be a reversible inhibitor of cholinesterase, thus protecting it from phosphorylation. It is unlikely that DDT itself is such an inhibitor, or an effect would be found at high concentrations *in vitro*. Alternatively, the well-established increased levels of acetylcholine might be protective; a case of protection by substrate rather than protection by a reversible inhibitor. There is evidence against acetylcholine protection, for Waller and Lewis (92) have shown that lindane (and also aldrin and pyrethrin) causes similar increases in acetylcholine of cockroach nerve cord but, as mentioned above, lindane does not protect against TMPP. A determination of which of these alternatives is correct is of major importance: if DDT provokes reversible inhibition of cholinesterase, the increases in acetylcholine might be a result, and the mechanism could be important in explaining central effects of DDT. But if it is the excess acetylcholine that is protective, then the TMPP findings tell us nothing more than that acetylcholine is elevated—a fact well established by more direct evidence.

We shall terminate this record of speculation about DDT with a postulate that denies any unique structural requirements, whether operating through membrane distortion or a biochemically specific mechanism. In 1947 Gavandan and Poussel claimed (26) that DDT is an indifferent narcotic, for its relative thermodynamic activity (see p. 24) at lethal concentrations was calculated to be between 0.1 and 1.0 for five different insects. This calculation requires a knowledge of the solubility of DDT in water, which they measured and found to be 0.1 ppm at 18°C. There are many problems in determining the true solubility of DDT, which tends to form colloidal solutions, and the best figure (measured with C^{14}-DDT) is 0.0012 ppm at 25°C (9), and therefore something less at 18°C. Insertion of this value in the above calculations gives values for

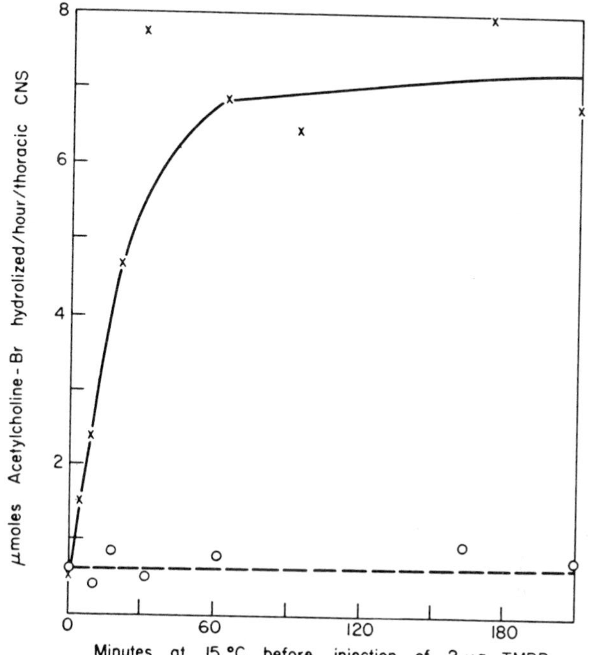

FIG. 6.3. Recovery of American cockroach cholinesterase from inhibition by tetramethyl pyrophosphate: top line, DDT-treated insects; bottom line, not DDT treated. After 60 minutes the DDT-treated insects were prostrate. Redrawn from Sternburg and Hewitt (83).

relative thermodynamic activities of between 10 and 100, which are of course impossible. Apart from this objection, it seems excessively unlikely that the isomers of DDT, such as *o,o′*-DDT, have solubilities much different from DDT; yet they are inactive.

So far, relatively coherent theories of the mode of DDT's action have been given. Many other scraps of information exist. A well-documented fact (58) is that DDT shows a negative temperature coefficient of activity, i.e., it is more active at low than at high temperatures. Insects treated with the appropriate dose can be cooled to 15°C and thrown into violent symptoms, then warmed to 35°C and appear entirely normal; this process can be repeated many times. The effect has been seen in numerous insect species, and is the opposite of the temperature dependence of organophosphates, pryethrins, and several chlorinated hydrocarbons. It suggests to the author that complex formation is the basis of the toxicity, for complex formations (of virtually any type) show just such temperature dependence, presumably because thermal agitation is disadvantageous for complexes. By contrast, chemical reactions usually show a positive temperature coefficient.

Recently, Eaton and Sternburg described an interesting analysis of the temperature effects (23). The destabilization of sensory nerves by DDT showed a positive temperature coefficient, but that in central nervous system showed a negative one. Since the overall toxicity shows a negative coefficient, these findings suggest that central phenomena are the more crucial in the poisoning process; this position conflicts with the widely accepted view that sensory nerves are of primary importance.

DDT causes a sharp and substantial increase in oxygen consumption of all the insects so far studied (11,31,50,51). In the German cockroach, for instance, 0.1 mg per insect (which is a high dose rate, perhaps about 500 mg/kg) caused a rapidly progressive increase in oxygen uptake, with a peak at 1-hour of four times the normal value; thereafter it declined, reaching normal levels at 10 hours (Fig. 6.4). The peak was associated with maximal tremor of the insects, and it therefore seems likely that the increased uptake was a consequence of excessive muscular activity, which in turn was caused by excessive nervous activity resulting from DDT. Alternative explanations, for instance, that oxidative phosphorylation is uncoupled and thereby more oxidation is required to produce the required phosphorylation product (adenosine triphosphate), suffer from the difficulty of explaining the peak of activity; one would expect, on such a basis, a continued and prolonged excess uptake.

There have been several reports of disturbances in amino acid metabolism caused by DDT. Corrigan and Kearns (18) showed that treatment of American cockroaches with DDT sufficient to give symptoms at 15°C led to alteration in blood amino acid levels: tyrosine fell 71%, proline fell 61%, and phenylalanine rose 131%, with only small changes in eleven other amino acids. α-Keto-glutarate levels also fell 50%. The proline effect was further explored. When the temperature was raised to 34°C, the symptoms disappeared, and proline returned to normal. Similar effects were found with DDT in houseflies, and with DDD in cockroaches and tobacco hornworms. When C^{14}-proline was injected into American cockroaches, DDT-poisoned insects respired two to three times more of it as $C^{14}O_2$ than did controls [others had previously shown (38) that after its injection into German cockroaches, C^{14}-proline disappears almost twice as fast from DDT-poisoned as from control insects]. The C^{14}-proline was not only respired more, but three times more of it was converted

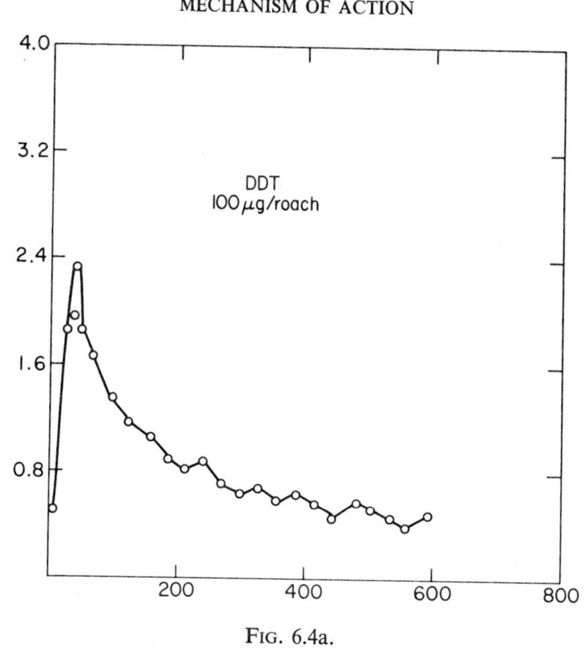

FIG. 6.4a.

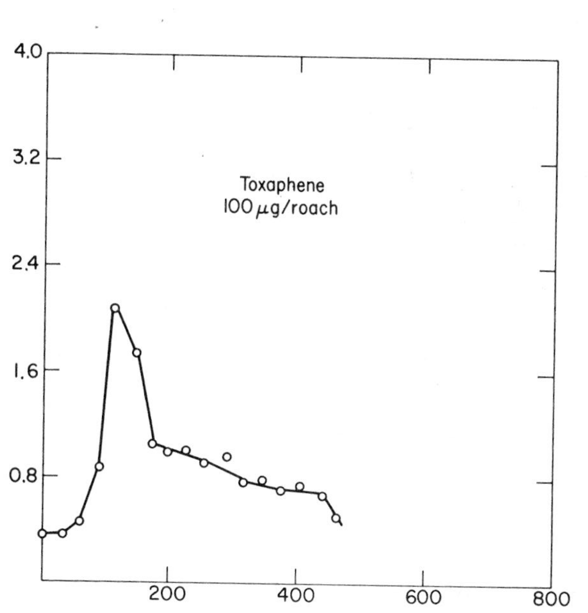

FIG. 6.4b.

FIG. 6.4. Oxygen consumption of treated German cockroaches: ordinate, mm^2/minute/insect; abscissa, time in minutes. Redrawn from Harvey and Brown (31).

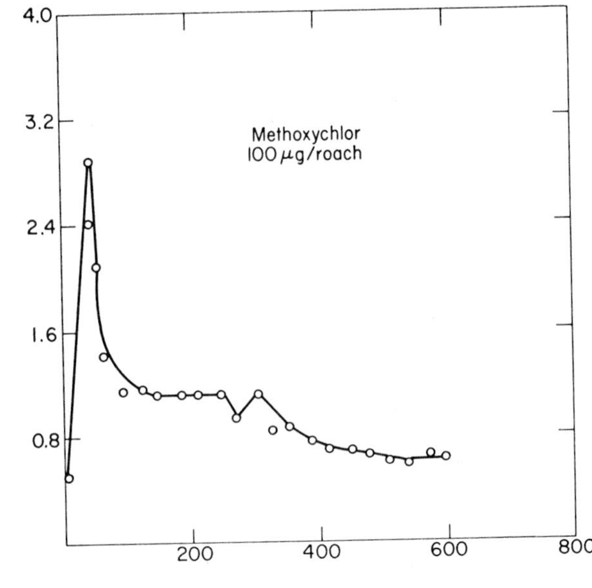

FIG. 6.4c.

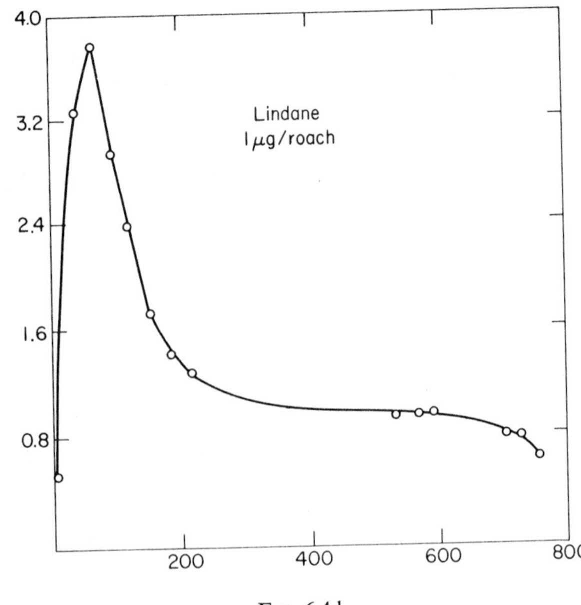

FIG. 6.4d.

FIG. 6.4 (*continued*)

to glutamine than was converted in controls. The authors suggested that this extra proline utilization was simply a reflection of a "demand for oxidizable carbon." However, there is no apparent reason why proline should be drawn upon in preference to other amino acids, some of which (such as glutamine) are particularly readily utilized for oxidation, yet suffered negligible change in the course of DDT poisoning in spite of the proline–glutamine conversion just described. As for the fall in tyrosine, it is tempting to suggest that it is accounted for by the equally mysterious rise in phenylalanine; the reverse reaction is very well known.

These amino acid interconversions may represent only a selection of other substantial changes. It has been shown (15) that DDT, unlike organophosphates, carbamates, or pyrethrin, causes poisoned houseflies to convert C^{14}-formate to uric acid and allantoin about four times more extensively, and to proline and serine about half as extensively, as untreated flies. This finding, taken together with the knowledge (52) that, in American cockroaches, formate is converted to various compounds, including proline, glutamate, and uric acid, suggests the possibility of more complex explanations for the Corrigan-Kearns findings. Because glutamate and glutamine are interconvertible, as are allantoin and uric acid, then proline, glutamate, uric acid, and allantoin are all in equilibrium, along with numerous other intermediates, with the formate pool. Consequently, the synthesis of excessive allantoin and uric acid, perhaps in a desperate attempt by the poisoned organism to elevate its ability to excrete a variety of compounds including toxicants, would lead to a depression of the formate pool and an attempt to replenish it at the expense of proline and, to a lesser extent, glutamine. One would have to add that proline acts as the ultimate carbon source, and is used not only for synthesis of the excessive uric acid and allantoin, but to replenish the glutamine level; hence, one explains the elevated proline-to-glutamine conversion mentioned above.

The effects of DDT analogs upon the adrenal cortex are reviewed on p. 297.

Metabolism of DDT*

There are five principal routes of DDT metabolism in various organisms (Fig. 6.5): oxidation to DDA (route 1) or to Kelthane (route 2) or dichlorobenzophenone (route 3); dehydrochlorination to DDE (route 4); or reductive dechlorination to DDD (route 5).

In vertebrates, it has been known for almost 20 years that DDA is a major metabolite in feces (40) and urine (95). Early reports claimed substantial amounts of unchanged DDT in urine and feces, but more recent findings have cast doubt on these reports (35), although there is no doubt that modest

* A recent review (1965) with emphasis on mammals has been prepared by Hayes (35).

amounts of DDT occur in feces (39). Furthermore, the best study (39) has shown that fecal DDA occurs as some derivatives whose nature is unknown; because DDA is produced from the derivative on acid, but not on alkaline, hydrolysis, it was suggested that the derivative might be an amide but was certainly not the usual glycoside. The pathway for DDA production in rats

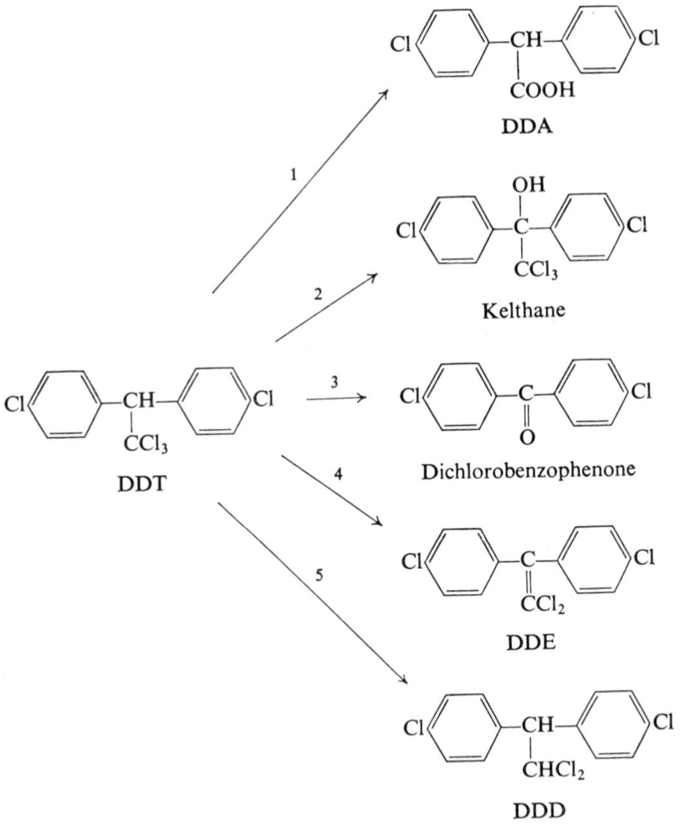

DDT → (1) DDA; (2) Kelthane; (3) Dichlorobenzophenone; (4) DDE; (5) DDD

FIG. 6.5 Routes of DDT metabolism.

has recently been reported (71) to involve alternate reduction and dehydrochlorination, followed by hydration and oxidation, as shown in Fig. 6.6. The evidence for this sequence is that the feeding of each compound to rats gave the subsequent intermediate as the major metabolite in liver. An exception is the last step, which is presumptive, for the metabolism of "DDOH" was not examined.

The simplifying view that DDA is *the* product of DDT metabolism in vertebrates is complicated by species variation. In man, DDE is the principal storage form of ingested DDT (33), and since DDE is not on the above route to DDA, that route is probably inoperative in man. By contrast, rats convert only small amounts of DDT to DDE, and monkeys none at all (35).

Only recently has it been realized that even in mammals another route of DDT metabolism is common: reductive dechlorination to DDD. The reason for the delayed realization is that the standard Schechter-Haller method does not distinguish DDT from DDD; consequently, chromatographic techniques are required to separate them. Because DDD is insecticidal, this metabolism is not a detoxification. In 1963, Finley and Pillmore (25) reported that DDD was widely found in samples of water, soil, plants, and animal tissues obtained

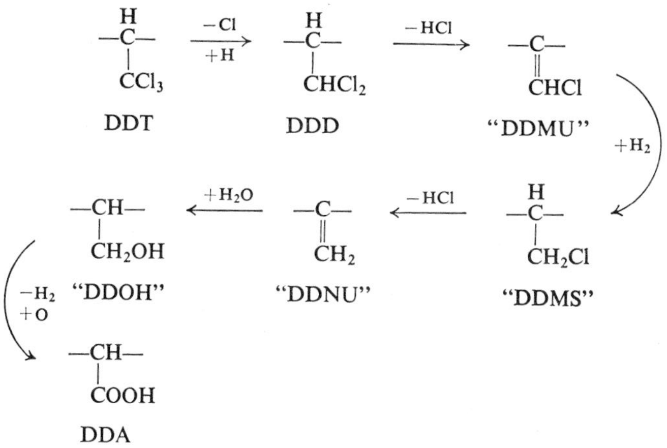

$$\underset{\text{DDT}}{\overset{H}{-C-}\atop CCl_3} \xrightarrow[+H]{-Cl} \underset{\text{DDD}}{\overset{H}{-C-}\atop CHCl_2} \xrightarrow{-HCl} \underset{\text{“DDMU”}}{-C-\atop \| \atop CHCl} \xrightarrow{+H_2} \underset{\text{“DDMS”}}{\overset{H}{-C-}\atop CH_2Cl} \xrightarrow{-HCl} \underset{\text{“DDNU”}}{-C-\atop \| \atop CH_2} \xrightarrow{+H_2O} \underset{\text{“DDOH”}}{-CH-\atop CH_2OH} \xrightarrow[+O]{-H_2} \underset{\text{DDA}}{-CH-\atop COOH}$$

FIG. 6.6. A possible route for DDA synthesis in the rat. The *p*-chlorophenyl groups have been omitted for clarity. Based on Peterson and Robinson (71).

from areas where DDT, but not DDD, has been sprayed. In the same year, the reaction was demonstrated in yeast (41) and in 1965 in rats (20,43,71), mice (6), and stagnant rumen fluid (59). In the case of rats, it was found that DDD was present in the liver, but none was in body fat (43). In 1965, it was found (59) that even lake water can convert DDT to DDD, and so can the two porphyrins, hematin and hemoglobin, in the reduced form. Since porphyrins are astonishingly stable [with a half-life of billions of years in many milieus (2)] it may be that the conversion in lake water utilizes porphyrins and is non-enzymic.

Isomerization *in vivo* is an unusual reaction for exotic compounds, but it has recently been shown that feeding *o,p'*-DDT leads to substantial residues of *p,p'*-DDT in the liver of rats (43). Although there were other metabolites, the isomer was a major one: The ppm of DDD, *p,p'*-DDT, *o,p'*-DDT, and

DDE were, respectively, 0.64, 0.47, 0.12, and 0.10 after feeding 50 ppm of *o,p′*-DDT. The reverse isomerization of *p,p′*-DDT to *o,p′*-DDT is of very small, perhaps zero, importance: In seven experiments in which *p,p′*-DDT was fed at 50 ppm, the *o,p′*-DDT was found only in two cases and at low levels: 0.09 and 0.03 ppm.

In insects, the best known metabolite of DDT is DDE, primarily because of the splendid work from Illinois which has shown that the ability to dehydrochlorinate DDT to DDE is the major cause of the resistance of DDT-resistant houseflies (82). The enzyme responsible for this reaction is DDT-dehydrochlorinase, and it has been greatly purified and its properties studied. It exists, in small titers, in susceptible as well as in resistant houseflies (48). It is an enzyme of moderate specificity, in that it also dehydrochlorinates DDD, but it is ineffective against *o,p′*-DDT. The Mexican bean beetle, which is normally tolerant to DDT and related compounds such as DDD and methoxychlor, has a relatively high titer of DDT-dehydrochlorinase. The level of this enzyme, measured by DDD dehydrochlorination, fluctuates during the development of the beetle, and this fluctuation is mirrored by parallel fluctuations in DDD tolerance (87) (see Fig. 16.6).

Work with homogenates of houseflies (rather than with purified enzyme) has suggested that there may be more than one dehydrohalogenase enzyme, for susceptible flies with little ability to dehydrochlorinate DDT can dehydrobrominate the CBr_3 analog excellently (8). Studies on homogenates of resistant houseflies show (8) that the CBr_3 analog is dehydrochlorinated four times faster than DDT, the $CHBr_2$ or CHClBr 15 times faster, and the $CHCl_2$ analog at one-thirtieth the rate. In view of the above suggestion of the existence of more than one dehydrohalogenase, these findings may not describe the specificity of a single enzyme, but rather suggest that, in resistant insects too, more than one such enzyme exists.

Degradation to DDE is also a major pathway in some insects other than houseflies, including Mexican bean beetle (14), pink bollworm (12) and *aedes aegypti* mosquito (1).

It seems that in resistant pink bollworms and *Aedes* (as in the housefly), the resistance is primarily due to a far greater titer in resistant than in susceptible strains. However, the DDT dehydrochlorinases may differ in different species. In the resistant housefly, the enzyme is specific enough that *o,p*-DDT is not dehydrochlorinated, so that resistant insects can be killed by this compound; whereas 2-deuterated DDT (DDT with deuterium in place of hydrogen in the 2-position of one ring) is easily dehydrochlorinated and is nontoxic. But in resistant *Aedes*, the opposites are true: *o,p*-DDT is dehydrochlorinated and is therefore nontoxic, but 2-deuterated DDT cannot be easily dehydrochlorinated and is toxic. This and related topics are dealt with at greater length in Chapter 15.

An inhibitor for DDT-dehydrochlorinase has been developed: "WARF antiresistant" (WARF are the initials of the Wisconsin Alumni Research Foundation). Its formula is:

$$Cl-C_6H_4-SO_2N(C_4H_9)_2$$

This compound has the ability to synergize the toxicity of DDT to resistant houseflies (see p. 227) and *Aedes* (72), and is therefore considered to operate by blocking DDT-dehydrochlorinase.

In 1963 (70) it was found that DDA, originally thought to be primarily a metabolite in vertebrates, is also important in a least one insect; in homogenates of the body louse, DDT is degraded to DDA, dichlorobenzophenone, and DDE in the ratio 2:2:1. The enzyme(s) involved showed astonishing heat stability, for it could be boiled for an hour without loss of activity! Fractionation suggested that at least two enzymes were involved.

In the domestic fruit fly *Drosophila melanogaster*, quite different metabolic routes exist. Tsukamoto in 1959 first (91) showed that there was quite extensive metabolism to Kelthane, the well-known miticide. Later studies made with C^{14}-DDT (57) showed that dichlorobenzophenone is the other major metabolite in the larvae: but in adults, two other principal metabolites were demonstrated without being identified. In this study, a remarkable strain variation was found: Kelthane was the major metabolite in strain Oregon Rc, but was not a metabolite in strain Oregon R. An enzyme system for converting DDT to Kelthane (or a Kelthane-like material) has been shown in microsomes from German cockroaches (4). Like related microsomal systems (p. 210), it requires oxygen, magnesium, nicotinamide, and $NADPH_2$. The same metabolite (i.e., Kelthane or something like it) was found in intact German cockroaches and in houseflies.

REFERENCES

1. Abedi, Z. H., Duffy, J. R., and Brown, A. W. A., *J. Econ. Entomol.* **56**, 511 (1963).
2. Abelson, P. H., *Ann. N. Y. Acad. Sci.* **69**, 276 (1957).
3. Agosin, S., Scaramelli, N., and Neghme, A., *Comp. Biochem. Physiol.* **2**, 143 (1961).
4. Agosin, M., Michaeli, D., Miskus, R., Nagasawa, S., and Hoskins, W. M., *J. Econ. Entomol.* **54**, 340 (1961).
5. Balsom, E. W., *Trans. Faraday Soc.* **43**, 54 (1947).
6. Barker, P. S., and Morrison, F. O., *Can. J. Zool.* **43**, 324 (1964).
7. Beament, J. W. L., *J. Insect Physiol.* **2**, 199 (1958).
8. Berger, R. S., and Young, R. G., *J. Econ. Entomol.* **55**, 533 (1962).

9. Bowman, M. C., Acree, F., and Corbett, M. K., *J. Agr. Food Chem.* **8**, 406 (1960).
10. Brown, A. W. A., "Insect Control by Chemicals," 817 pp. Wiley, New York, 1951.
11. Buck, J. B., and Keister, M. L., *Biol. Bull.* **97**, 64 (1949).
12. Bull, D. L., and Adkisson, P. L., *J. Econ. Entomol.* **56**, 641 (1963).
13. Chang, P.-I., *Ann. Entomol. Soc. Am.* **44**, 311 (1951).
14. Chattoraj, A. N., and Kearns, C. W., *Bull. Entomol. Soc. Am.* **4**, 95 (1958).
15. Cline, R. E., and Pearce, G. W., *Biochemistry* **2**, 657 (1963).
16. Colhoun, E. H., *Can. J. Biochem. Physiol.* **37**, 259 (1959).
17. Colhoun, E. H., *J. Agr. Food Chem.* **8**, 252 (1960).
18. Corrigan, J. J., and Kearns, C. W., *J. Insect Physiol.* **9**, 1 (1963).
19. Dale, W. E., Gaines, T. B., Hayes, W. J., and Pearce, G. W., *Science* **142**, 1474 (1963).
20. Datta, P. R., Lang, E. P., and Klein, A. K., *Science* **145**, 1052 (1964).
21. Davey, K. G., *J. Insect Physiol.* **9**, 375 (1963).
22. Dresden, D., Physiological investigation into the action of DDT. Ph.D. Thesis, Univ. of Utrecht, Netherlands, 1949.
23. Eaton, J. L., and Sternburg, J., *J. Insect Physiol.* **10**, 471 (1964).
24. Fernando, H. E., Ph.D. Thesis, Univ. of Illinois, Urbana, Illinois, 1952.
25. Finley, R. B., and Pillmore, R. E., *Am. Inst. Biol. Sci. Publ.* **13**, 41 (1963).
26. Gavadan, P., and Poussel, H., *Compt. Rend.* **224**, 683 (1947).
27. Gonda, O., Kaluszymer, A., and Avi-Dor, Y., *Biochem. J.* **73**, 583 (1959).
28. Gunther, F. A., Blinn, R. C., Carman, G. E., and Metcalf, R. L., *Arch. Biochem.* **50**, 504 (1954).
29. Gunther, F. A., Blinn, R. C., Carman, G. E., and Pappas, J. L., *J. Econ. Entomol.* **51**, 385 (1958).
30. Gunther, F. A., Blinn, R. C., and Metcalf, R. L., *J. Agr. Food Chem.* **4**, 338 (1956).
31. Harvey, G. T., and Brown, A. W. A., *Can. J. Zool.* **29**, 42 (1951).
32. Hawkins, W. B., and Sternburg, J., *J. Econ. Entomol.* **57**, 241 (1964).
33. Hayes, W. J., Quinby, G. E., Walker, K. C., Elliott, J. W., and Upholt, W. M., *A.M.A. Arch. Ind. Health* **18**, 398 (1958).
34. Hayes, W. J., *In* "DDT: Human and Veterinary Medicine" (S. W. Simmons, ed.), p. 11. Birkhäuser, Basel, 1959.
35. Hayes, W. J., *Ann. Rev. Pharmacol.* **5**, 27 (1965).
36. Heslop, J. P., and Ray, J. W., *J. Insect Physiol.* **3**, 395 (1959).
37. Hodgson, E. S., and Geldiay, S., *Biol. Bull.* **117**, 275 (1959).
38. Hoy, W., and Gordon, H. T., *J. Econ. Entomol.* **54**, 198 (1961).
39. Jensen, J. A., Cueto, C., Dale, W. E., Rotts, C. F., Pearce, G. W., and Mattson, A. M., *J. Agr. Food Chem.* **5**, 919 (1957).
40. Judah, J. D., *Brit. J. Pharmacol.* **4**, 120 (1949).
41. Kallman, B. J., and Andrews, A. K., *Science* **141**, 1050 (1963).
42. Kearns, C. W., Quoted in Spencer, E. Y., and O'Brien, R. D., *Ann. Rev. Entomol.* **2**, 261 (1957).
43. Klein, A. K., Lang, E. P., Datta, P. R., Watts, J. O., and Chen, J. T., *J. Assoc. Offic. Agr. Chemists* **47**, 1129 (1964).
44. Lauger, P., Martin, H., and Muller, P., *Helv. Chim. Acta* **27**, 892 (1944).
45. Lauger, P., Pulver, R., Montigel, C., Wiesmann, R., and Wild, H., *Joint Meeting Army Comm. Insect Rodent Control OSRD Insect Control Comm., Washington, D.C.,* 1945. Geigy Co., Basel, 1946.
46. Lewis, S. E., *Nature* **172**, 1004 (1953).
47. Lewis, S. E., Waller, J. B., and Fowler, K. S., *J. Insect Physiol.* **4**, 128 (1960).

48. Lipke, H., and Kearns, C. W., *Bull. Entomol. Soc. Am.* **4**, 95 (1958).
49. Lipke, H., and Kearns, C. W., *J. Econ. Entomol.* **53**, 31 (1960).
50. Lord, K. A., *Ann. Appl. Biol.* **36**, 113 (1949).
51. Ludwig, D., *Ann. Entomol. Soc. Am.* **39**, 496 (1946).
52. McEnroe, W. D., and Forgash, A. J., *Ann. Entomol. Soc. Am.* **51**, 126 (1958).
53. Martin, H., and Wain, R. L., *Nature* **154**, 512 (1944).
54. Martin, H., "The Scientific Principles of Crop Protection," 5th Ed. Arnold, London, 1964.
55. Matsumura, F., and O'Brien, R. D., *J. Agr. Food Chem.* **14**, 36 (1966).
56. Matsumura, F., and O'Brien, R. D., *J. Agr. Food Chem.* **14**, 39 (1966).
57. Menzel, D. B., Smith, S. M., Miskus, R., and Hoskins, W. M., *J. Econ. Entomol.* **54**, 9 (1961).
58. Metcalf, R. L., "Organic Insecticides," 392 pp. Wiley (Interscience), New York, 1955.
59. Miskus, R. P., Blair, D. P., and Casida, J. E., *J. Agr. Food Chem.* **13**, 481 (1965).
60. Mullins, L. J., *Science* **122**, 118 (1955).
61. Munson, S. C., and Yeager, J. F., *J. Econ. Entomol.* **38**, 618 (1945).
62. Narahashi, T., and Yamasaki, T., *J. Physiol.* (*London*) **151**, 75 (1960).
63. Narahashi, T., and Yamasaki, T., *J. Physiol.* (*London*) **152**, 122 (1960).
64. O'Brien, R. D., *Advn. Pest Control Res.* **4**, 75 (1961).
65. O'Brien, R. D., and Matsumura, F., *Science* **146**, 657 (1964).
66. O'Brien, R. D., and Dannelley, C. E., *J. Agr. Food Chem.* **13**, 245 (1965).
67. Ozbas, S., and Hodgson, E. S., *Proc. Natl. Acad. Sci. U.S.* **8**, 825 (1958).
68. Parker, V. H., *Biochem. J.* **77**, 74 (1960).
69. Pauling, L., and Pressman, D., *J. Am. Chem. Soc.* **67**, 1003 (1945).
70. Perry, A. S., Miller, S., and Buckner, A. J., *J. Agr. Food Chem.* **11**, 457 (1963).
71. Peterson, J. E., and Robison, W. H., *Toxicol. Appl. Pharmacol.* **6**, 321 (1964).
72. Pillai, M. K. K., Abedi, Z. H., and Brown, A. W. A., *Mosquito News* **23**, 112 (1963).
73. Riemschneider, R., and Otto, H. D., *Z. Naturforsch.* **9b**, 95 (1954).
74. Roeder, K. D., and Weiant, E. A., *Science* **103**, 304 (1946).
75. Rogers, E. F., Brown, H. D., Rasmussen, I. M., and Neal, R. E., *J. Am. Chem. Soc.* **75**, 2991 (1953).
76. Sacklin, J. A., Terriere, L. C., and Remmert, L. F., *Science* **122**, 378 (1955).
77. Salkeld, E. H., *Nature* **166**, 608 (1950).
78. Shankland, D. W., and Kearns, C. W., *Ann. Entomol. Soc. Am.* **52**, 386 (1959).
79. Shepard, H. H., and Mahan, J. N., *Chem. Eng. News* **43**, 108 (1965).
80. Silva, G. M., Doyle, W. P., and Wang, C. H., *Arquiv. Port. Bioquim.* **3**, 298 (1959).
81. Stegwee, D., *Biochem. Biophys. Acta* **8**, 187 (1952).
82. Sternburg, J., and Kearns, C. W., *Science* **116**, 144 (1952).
83. Sternburg, J., and Hewitt, P., *J. Insect Physiol.* **8**, 643 (1962).
84. Sternburg, J., *Ann. Rev. Entomol.* **8**, 19 (1963).
85. Tobias, J. M., Kollross, J. J., and Savit, J., *J. Cellular Comp. Physiol.* **28**, 159 (1946).
86. Tobias, J. M., and Kollross, J. J., *Biol. Bull.* **91**, 247 (1946).
87. Tombes, A. S., and Forgash, A. J., *J. Insect Physiol.* **7**, 216 (1961).
88. Truhaut, R., and Vincent, D., *Ann. Pharm. Franc.* **5**, 159 (1947).
89. Truhaut, R., and Vincent, D., *Compt. Rend.* **227**, 738 (1948).
90. Truhaut, R., and Vincent, D., *Bull. Soc. Chim. Biol.* **30**, 694 (1948).
91. Tsukamoto, M., *Botyu-Kagaku* **24**, 141 (1959).
92. Waller, J. B., and Lewis, S. E., *J. Insect Physiol.* **7**, 315 (1961).
93. Webb, J. L., "Enzyme and Metabolic Inhibitors," Vol. 1. Academic Press, New York, 1963.

94. Welsh, J. H., and Gordon, H. T., *J. Cellular Comp. Physiol.* **30**, 147 (1947).
95. White, W. C., and Sweeney, T. R., *Public Health Rept.* (*U.S.*) **60**, 66 (1945).
96. Wigglesworth, V. B., *In* "DDT. The Insecticide Dichlorodiphenyltrichloroethane and its Significance" (P. Muller, ed.), Vol. 1, p. 93. Birkhäuser, Basel, 1955.
97. Yamasaki, T., and Narahashi, T., *Botyu-Kagaku* **22**, 296 (1957).
98. Yeager, J., and Munson, S., *Science* **102**, 305 (1945).

CHAPTER 7

Cyclodienes

The Diels-Alder reaction is a well-known condensation reaction in which compounds containing the diene group —CH=CH—CH=CH— can add to a double-bonded compound to form an addition compound (adduct):

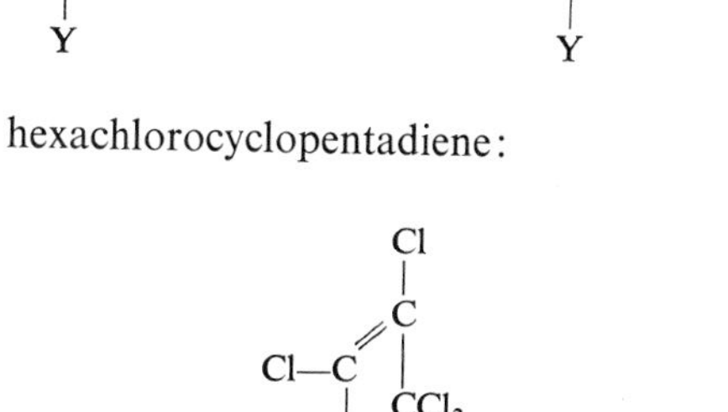

$$X{-}CH{=}CH{-}CH{=}CH{-}Y \;+\; A{-}CH{=}CH{-}B \longrightarrow \text{cyclohexene adduct (ring: }HC{=}CH\text{, }CH(X)\text{, }CH(A)\text{, }CH(B)\text{, }CH(Y))$$

When the diene is hexachlorocyclopentadiene:

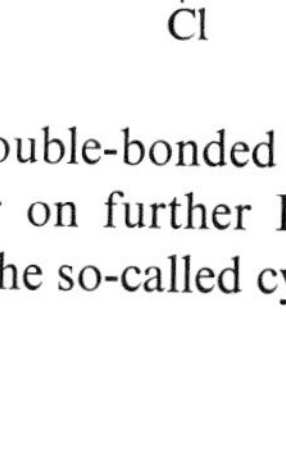

$$C_5Cl_6 \;(\text{ring: } ClC{=}CCl{-}CCl{=}CCl{-}CCl_2)$$

one can add it to a variety of double-bonded compounds and obtain derivatives which, on chlorination or on further Diels-Alder reaction, may give highly insecticidal compounds, the so-called cyclodiene insecticides (Fig. 7.1).

These compounds are all cyclic, but in spite of their generic name, only a few of them are dienes, i.e., have two double bonds. They all share the ring system shown on the left in each case, which is fully chlorinated and shows the chlorinated "endomethylene bridge" bridging the ends of the ring. Some of the compounds have (shown on their right) another such ring, except that it is

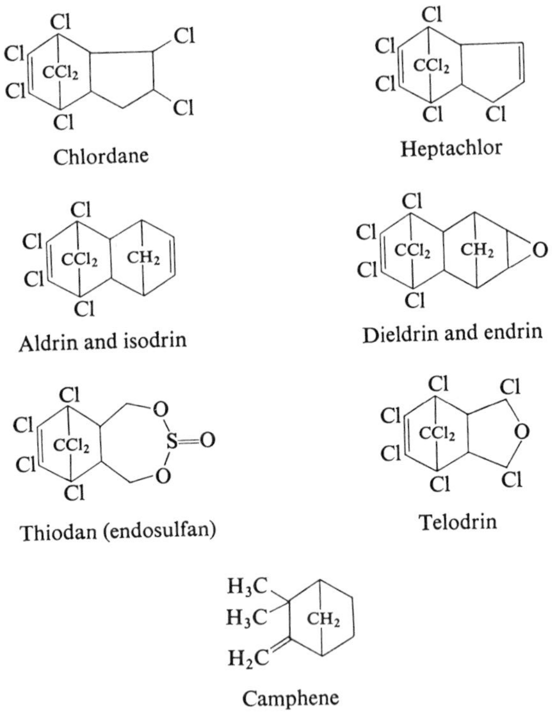

Chlordane

Heptachlor

Aldrin and isodrin

Dieldrin and endrin

Thiodan (endosulfan)

Telodrin

Camphene

Toxaphene is not truly a cyclodiene, but a chlorinated terpene; it is a mixture made by chlorinating camphene till it has 69% chlorine. Strobane is similarly prepared and may be identical.

FIG. 7.1. "Flat formulas" of common cyclodienes.

unchlorinated (aldrin, isodrin); these compounds have insecticidal analogs in which the C═C of the unchlorinated ring is oxidized or, to be more specific, epoxidized to

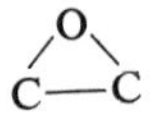

The epoxide of aldrin is dieldrin, and that of isodrin is endrin.

These compounds were first developed in and after 1945, by Julius Hyman in the United States and, in the case of chlordane, by Riemschneider in Germany. Thiodan and Telodrin are relative newcomers, and were introduced in 1956 and 1957, respectively, in Germany.

Figure 7.1 makes it clear that the "flat formulas" shown are inadequate representations; for instance the flat formulas of aldrin and isodrin are identical, but they are very different compounds. One must consider two kinds of isomerism: one kind is ring isomerism. If one were to make the models of chlordane-like compounds, he would find several choices in his disposition of the rings. If one ignores the disposition of the endomethylene bridge and looks at the 6-member ring end-on, it has a flattened V-shape. If the 5-membered ring is in position (*a*) with respect to the V, the ring isomerism is said to be *endo*; if in position (*b*), it is called *exo*:

(*a*) *endo* (*b*) *exo*

When one makes aldrin-like models, the unchlorinated ring offers additional possibilities, and by extension of the above terminology the naming is evident.

endo, endo *endo, exo* *exo, endo* *exo, exo*

The evidence (33) suggests that chlordane is *endo*, that aldrin (and consequently its epoxide, dieldrin) is *endo,exo*, and that isodrin (and its epoxide, endrin) is *endo,endo*.

The flat formulas also fail to show the true relation of the endomethylene bridge. A more accurate picture of the skeleton of aldrin, for instance is:

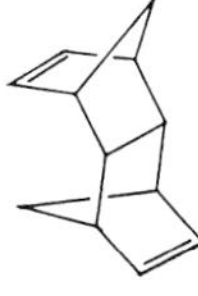

In the case of chlordane, additional isomerism exists. The chlorines on the 5-membered ring could be on the same side of the ring (*cis* isomer) or on opposite sides (*trans* isomer). Technical chlordane does indeed contain two such isomers, which differ by about a degree in melting point. The *cis* isomer is called β-chlordane, the *trans* is α-chlordane.

Toxicity

The cyclodienes vary a great deal in mammalian toxicity (Table 7.1); endrin and isodrin are very toxic, while α-chlordane has little hazard. Examination of insect toxicity (Table 7.1) suggests that these are rather wide-spectrum insecticides, and that the marked variation between compounds observed for mammalian toxicity is not quite so prominent in insects. For instance, the rat oral LD_{50} values for the seven compounds listed vary 64-fold, while the housefly LD_{50}'s vary 24-fold.

TABLE 7.1

TOXICITY OF CYCLODIENES[a]

	LD_{50} (mg/kg)				
	Rat, oral				
Insecticide	Metcalf	Treon and Cleveland	Housefly, topical	American cockroach, topical	Milkweed bug, topical
α-Chlordane	700	—	7	—	459
Heptachlor	90	—	1.7	1.0	31
Aldrin	67	46	1.7	1.0	10.3
Dieldrin	87	38	1.3	1.5	15
Isodrin	15	16	2.1	—	5.6
Endrin	11	17	1.6	—	47
Toxaphene	69	—	31	—	—

[a] From Metcalf (36) and Treon and Cleveland (46).

It is claimed (47) that complete recovery is the rule even after severe poisoning of humans by dieldrin, although this recovery may take 4 weeks.

Mode of Action

In summary of what is to follow, the cyclodienes appear, on the basis of symptomology and their effects on isolated nerve preparations, to be neurotoxicants. It will be apparent that their precise loci of action within the nervous system vary from compound to compound. The molecular or biochemical basis of the neurotoxic action has not been demonstrated.

VERTEBRATES

A series of reports (20–22) by Gowdey and co-workers in 1952–1955 have described symptoms of aldrin and dieldrin poisoning (in cats) associated with the autonomic nervous system. Whereas aldrin caused peripheral parasympathetic symptoms (very like those in organophosphate poisoning, p. 56) such as slowing of the heart and salivation by the submaxillary gland, dieldrin did not. Furthermore, these effects of aldrin were still seen when the connections of the heart and submaxillary gland to the central nervous system were severed, showing that the effects were truly produced peripherally, and were not merely a consequence of central stimulation. It was claimed that blood from the aldrin-poisoned cats had a lowered cholinesterase level, whereas that from dieldrin-poisoned cats did not; but Smallman (quoted in ref. 22) found aldrin was not an anticholinesterase *in vitro*. Quite apart from these peripheral effects, both aldrin and dieldrin produced effects by a central mechanism; for example, dieldrin slowed the heart, but this effect disappeared if the nerve supply to the heart, i.e., the vagus nerve, was severed. Other central effects produced by both compounds included lowering of the blood pressure, excessive excitability, and convulsions.

Details of the effects of endrin on vertebrates were lacking until 1964, when it was shown (17) for dogs that 10 mg/kg iv gave effects very much like those described above for aldrin, including salivation, slowing of the heart (which could be antagonized by atropine), and increased blood pressure. Some indirect evidence suggested that these phenomena were caused by central actions. A drop in blood pH was noted, typically about 0.2 units, and it was suggested that this effect might decrease cholinesterase activity and contribute to the parasympathomimetic symptoms, e.g., on heart. Although such a contribution would be small it is very likely the cause of the puzzling apparent decline in cholinesterase activity of blood reported above for aldrin poisoning. Another study (43) from the same laboratory showed that in severe endrin poisoning, kidney function could be affected because of vasoconstriction, caused most probably by overactivity of the adrenal glands, for the effects were much reduced by removing the adrenals. Once again, a central stimulation was probably the cause of the overactivity.

Biochemical changes in brain following dieldrin poisoning have been described. In 1960 it was claimed (28) that in brains of poisoned rats the following three compounds were released from the mitochondria in the form of esters with coenzyme A:

$(CH_3)_3\overset{+}{N}CH_2CH_2CH_2COOH$
γ-Butyrobetaine

$(CH_3)_3\overset{+}{N}CH_2CH{=}CHCOOH$
Crotonbetaine

$(CH_3)_3\overset{+}{N}CH_2CH(OH)CH_2COOH$
Carnitine

These compounds are all betaines (i.e., straight-chain compounds with a quaternary nitrogen at one end and a carboxyl group at the other) and it was implied that they were pharmacologically potent, since "intracranial injection of less than 100 μg of the methyl, ethyl or choline esters ... caused violent and fatal convulsions in the unanesthetized rat." However, there was no evidence that the (presumably more labile) CoA esters had such potency, and it is probable that the unesterified betaines are inactive, for the methyl, ethyl, and choline esters had activity (of an unstated extent) against a muscle preparation (frog rectus), whereas the unesterified betaines did not. The evidence that these compounds were released from the mitochondria was that the same workers claimed (27) that in untreated animals they were present in mitochondria only, and that brain mitochondria were "damaged" in the course of poisoning, judged by an increase in their succinoxidase activity. The validity of this last piece of evidence is perhaps questionable.

This same study showed that three other, entirely unrelated, convulsant treatments led to a similar release of betaine–CoA esters. These treatments were by electroshock, ammonium chloride, and camphor. It was suggested that all acted initially by damaging mitochondria, and then releasing the esters, which caused convulsions and (in some cases) death. However, it is entirely possible that dieldrin and the other treatments cause convulsions, each by its own mechanism, and that a consequence of these convulsions is mitochondrial damage and release of the esters.

However, this whole question of the existence in brain of large amounts of betaine esters with acetylcholine-like activity is open to doubt. The 1959 papers of this group claimed that γ-butyrobetaine itself was acetylcholine-like in its effects upon nervous systems (26) and it did not inspire confidence when, following a report by Colhoun and Spencer (12) that the betaine was pharmacologically inert but that its methyl ester was active, the reader was told in 1960 that the early work was in fact done with the methyl ester of γ-butyrobetaine (27). Next, Hosein *et al.* reported in 1962 that 75% of the acetylcholine-like activity of rat brain was made up of CoA esters of betaine derivatives (29). But in 1963 McLennan *et al.* (35) showed that the chromatographic band which had been claimed as a betaine derivative was in fact the trichloroacetate of acetylcholine, formed when the tissue was treated with trichloroacetic acid.

Very substantial changes in intermediates of brain metabolism occur in rats poisoned by dieldrin or Telodrin (23). But since comparable changes also occur in poisoning by the entirely unrelated convulsant picrotoxin (Table 7.2), it seems more likely that these effects are a result rather than a cause of the convulsions. An independent study (48) confirmed the validity of the alanine elevation, and extended it to γ-aminobutyrate; DDT produced neither of these effects. Glutamine and glutamate (the precursor of γ-aminobutyrate) were unaffected. It is interesting to reflect that γ-aminobutyrate is the primary amine analog of γ-butyrobetaine. More interesting, its possible role as an inhibitory transmitter has been widely discussed, i.e., as a compound which

TABLE 7.2

INCREASES IN INTERMEDIATES OF RAT BRAIN CAUSED BY DIELDRIN, TELODRIN, AND PICROTOXIN[a]

Insecticide	Alanine	Lactate	Pyruvate	Ammonia
Dieldrin, 100 mg/kg	153	165	50	30
Telodrin, 7.5 mg/kg	85	39	—	—
Picrotoxin, 18.9 mg/kg	157	235	0	93

[a] Values are average percent increases at 15–20 minutes after intraperitoneal injection; calculated from Hathway *et al.* (23).

antagonizes the excitatory effects of transmitters such as acetylcholine. However, if convulsants acted via a γ-aminobutyrate mechanism, they should *lower* its level, thus lessening its "damping" effect. Such a lowering has been shown for agents, primarily hydrazines, which may inhibit the enzyme that converts glutamate to γ-aminobutyrate (34). Since dieldrin *elevates* γ-aminobutyrate, it is unlikely that this effect could exacerbate convulsive action; it is possible that it is a compensatory mechanism designed to antagonize the convulsive trend.

INSECTS

Some ingenious experiments on aldrin and dieldrin action in insects were performed by Gianotti *et al.* (19) with American cockroaches. By severing various nerves in poisoned insects, it was shown that tremor in the legs was caused primarily by central effects, for such severing stopped the tremors. Similarly, legs amputated from untreated insects could not be caused to tremor. These findings contrast with their observations for DDT which, by the same criteria, produced effects which were largely peripheral.

Nevertheless, direct effects of cyclodienes upon insect nerve were shown by Lalonde and Brown (31) in 1954, using a crural nerve of the American cockroach. Short trains of impulses (spikes), typically lasting 0.2 seconds, were produced just as in the case of DDT. However, the effects were somewhat more delayed, appearing 2 hours after treatment by dieldrin, 3 hours with toxaphene or heptachlor, and 5 hours with chlordane (cf., 1–2 hour delay with DDT). The spikes were of a low height for cyclodienes, typically 50–100 μV, in contrast to 250–700 μV for DDT. The repeat rate of the spikes was about the same for cyclodienes and DDT, i.e., about 250 per second. In comparing these findings to those of Gianotti, it should be noted that Lalonde and Brown had crushed the ganglion, so that they were observing true peripheral effects. It may be that these low-voltage spikes were insufficient to cause pronounced tremor in the leg. If so, one might anticipate that a similar preparation with an uncrushed ganglion might demonstrate large DDT-like spikes.

It has been shown by Colhoun (13) that γ-butyrobetaine or its esters do not appear in nerve cords of dieldrin-poisoned cockroaches. Acetylcholine levels increase in the nervous tissue of aldrin and dieldrin-poisoned insects as in the corresponding case of DDT (p. 119), the implications of this rise are obscure, but one may guess that it is a consequence of nervous hyperactivity.

Conclusion

In spite of fairly copious data, there is still not much to be said about the action of cyclodienes except that they probably interfere with nerves. It is the author's guess that these compounds are not antienzymes, but that they complex with a neural membrane in such a way as to modify its properties.* One might have hoped that the extensive survey by Soloway (44) of structure–activity relations in cyclodienes would lead to insight into the topography of the target, but it led only to the view that two spatially separated zones of electronegativity (e.g., the chlorinated ring and the oxygen atom of dieldrin) were often helpful, but not necessarily so. Direct experiments are needed on the ability of cyclodienes to react with components of real membranes and on the biophysical consequences of such interactions as tested with both real and model membranes.

Metabolism

The best-established pathway for cyclodiene metabolism is that of epoxidation, which occurs whenever the appropriate double bond exists. The epoxide is found, along with its parent, in the body fat, and to a lesser extent in other tissues, in both insects and vertebrates. For instance, dieldrin has been found (2) in fat of the following animals after treating them with aldrin: beef and dairy cattle, pigs, sheep, rats, and poultry. Dieldrin and heptachlor epoxide have also been found in the milk of cows which have been fed aldrin and heptachlor, respectively (18).

The first case of epoxidation in insects was reported in 1956, when Gianotti *et al.* (19) showed qualitatively that aldrin was converted to dieldrin by American cockroaches. In 1958 it was first shown that houseflies converted heptachlor to its epoxide (39). In the locust *Schistocerca gregaria*, Cl^{36}-aldrin was used (11) to show that epoxidation to dieldrin occurred, but very slowly: 50% conversion took 7 days; at that time, a little (4%) degradation—to the inevitable unidentified water-soluble metabolite—had occurred. Dieldrin

* For confirming evidence, see Matsumura, F., and Hayashi, M., *Science* **153,** 757 (1966).

itself was not metabolized, but was slowly excreted, unchanged. It was shown by Brooks in 1960 (3) that resistant and susceptible houseflies epoxidized aldrin to dieldrin and isodrin to endrin at a fairly fast rate, viz., about 20% of the dose within 4 hours. Dieldrin itself was not metabolized. The findings with respect to aldrin and dieldrin metabolism were later confirmed by Earle (16), who showed that dieldrin's stability was so great that dieldrin taken up by housefly larvae persisted through metamorphosis and into the adult, when it was slowly excreted (as unaltered dieldrin) throughout the 8-day observation period.

Chronic feeding of C^{14}-aldrin to rats, at 0.2 ppm in the diet for 3 months, produced massive excretion into feces, eventually reaching 94% of the intake, and much less in urine, reaching 10% of the intake. Thus eventually a steady state was achieved, with output balancing intake. The materials excreted were aldrin, dieldrin, and unidentified "hydrophilic metabolites," in ratios that varied; during the steady state, the ratios were about 1:1:5 in feces and 1:7:90 in urine (32). Similarly, intravenous aldrin was excreted primarily in the bile, in catheterized animals, to give similar products in roughly similar ratios (37).

Other routes of degradation exist as well as epoxidation, although epoxidation may well be a first step. These other routes have been shown particularly with the epoxides themselves, especially dieldrin. In 1960 it was shown (24) that in mice injected with 10 mg/kg of dieldrin, substantial quantities of water-soluble metabolites occurred in feces (2.7 mg/kg of feces) and to a lesser extent in tissues. In 1962 it was shown (14) that the urine of men who had been occupationally exposed to dieldrin contained at least two metabolites. Both were neutral, polar, and chlorinated. This study also revealed an artifact possible in less careful studies: unknown dieldrin derivatives broke down in the gas chromatograph column to give dieldrin. Consequently, data reported only on gas chromatographic evidence may be suspect. Indeed, five metabolites appeared in gas chromatograms in this 1962 study, but it was impossible to say whether the extra three were artifacts or not.

A later study (37) on C^{14}-dieldrin intravenously administered to rats at 0.42 mg/kg (calculated assuming 200-g rats) showed that it was excreted primarily in bile, and that 95% of the excreted material was an unknown polar product or products, while the remainder was dieldrin itself. The products were the same as those that are found after aldrin treatment, suggesting that epoxidation to dieldrin is the first step in aldrin metabolism. The relation to polar metabolites in urine, described above, is unknown. However, in more recent work (25) on the metabolite in bile, based on the use of Cl^{36}-dieldrin, only one major metabolite was found, representing 78% of the radioactivity; it was probably a glucuronide of a dieldrin derivative. The derivative itself was neutral and somewhat more polar than dieldrin, yet still extractable from water by organic solvents.

In 1955 it was shown by Davidow and Radomski (15,42) that the feeding of heptachlor to dogs and rats leads to deposition of heptachlor epoxide, but no heptachlor in the fat. Deposition was roughly five times greater in female than in male rats, and increased with increasing dose. At 5 ppm in the diet, about 5 ppm of epoxide was found in males and 25 ppm in females. It was also shown that the epoxide was not a detoxication product, for it was about twice as toxic to mice as heptachlor.

A short study (41) on C^{14}-chlordane metabolism in rats showed that excretion was primarily via the feces: 60 hours after an intravenous dose of 0.14 mg/kg (calculated from original data, assuming 200-g rats), 29% of the radioactivity was found in feces, of which three-quarters was "hydrophilic metabolites," and the remainder was stated (without evidence) to be chlordane. Similar ratios of "hydrophilic metabolites" to chlordane were found in many tissues of the treated animals, but in muscle the major material was unchanged chlordane. Only 1% of the dose was excreted in the urine over 60 hours.

A possible clue to the identity of the mysterious "polar metabolite" is provided by a 1964 study on C^{14}-dieldrin metabolism by adult *Culex pipiens* mosquitoes. Oonnithan and Miskus (38) found that moderate amounts of the dieldrin, e.g., 20% in 6 days, were converted to a more polar compound that chromatographed, in the one paper system used, like the following dieldrin glycol (which is identical with aldrin glycol):

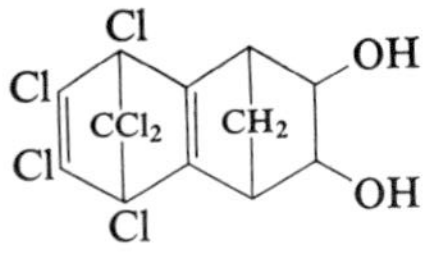

Cl, Cl, Cl, Cl, CCl_2, CH_2, OH, OH

This metabolite is simply dieldrin hydrated at the epoxide group. It should easily undergo formation of glycosides or other derivatives, such as ethereal sulfates. Such a derivative may well be the polar metabolite found in the insect and mammalian work described above.

In contrast to mammals, the ability of insects to degrade dieldrin is small, and in some species, nonexistent. The above paragraphs describe the moderate breakdown by *Culex* mosquitoes and housefly larvae. The locust (11) and the adult housefly (3,40) are unable to metabolize dieldrin. However, pathways of aldrin degradation may exist in addition to the familiar epoxidation route, for locusts given Cl^{36}-aldrin excrete a little water-soluble material in their feces (18); a similar situation was shown for certain microorganisms (30). In the housefly (16), 24 hours after aldrin treatment one-quarter of the dose was recovered as aldrin, one-quarter as dieldrin, and the remainder was unaccounted for. The stability of dieldrin (and, to a lesser extent, aldrin) in houseflies does not extend to all cyclodienes. Many related compounds are degraded rather readily by intact houseflies (5) and this degradation is blocked by the pyrethrin synergist sesamex (p. 105), as shown by the synergistic effect of sesamex on cyclodiene toxicity, and also, for the compounds of Table 7.3, by direct metabolic studies with C^{14} compounds. By contrast, the toxicity of aldrin or dieldrin is not affected by sesamex.

TABLE 7.3

CYCLODIENES WHOSE DEGRADATION IN HOUSEFLIES IS BLOCKED BY SESAMEX[a]

Compound	LD_{50} alone (mg/kg)	LD_{50} with sesamex
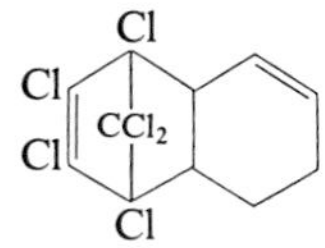 Cl, Cl, Cl, Cl, CCl_2	125	10
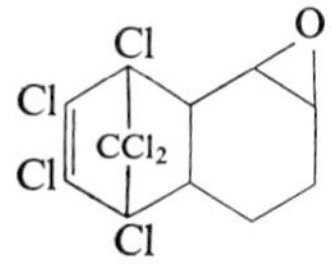 Cl, Cl, Cl, Cl, CCl_2, O	90	2
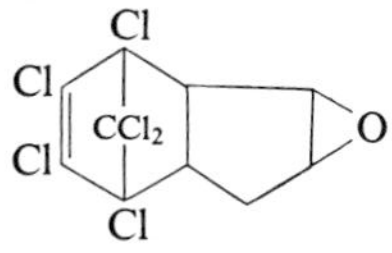 Cl, Cl, Cl, Cl, CCl_2, O	35	4
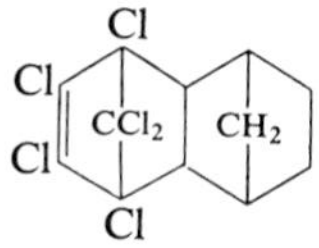 Cl, Cl, Cl, Cl, CCl_2, CH_2	40	3

[a] LD_{50}'s are computed on the assumption that the flies averaged 20 mg each. From Brooks and Harrison (8).

Does the well-established epoxidation of aldrin, heptachlor, and isodrin in insects constitute a toxification or a detoxification? Brooks *et al.* (4,5) suggest that it is a toxification, but that (unlike the corresponding case of phosphorothionate activation) the parent compound is also effective. An ingenious proof (4) consisted of treating houseflies with aldrin or isodrin, and holding some in air and others in nitrogen for 1 hour. The time before symptoms appeared was almost doubled by the nitrogen treatment, suggesting that oxidation was required to produce the actual toxicant.* The authors pointed out that probably the unoxidized parent compounds have some innate potency, because related compounds which cannot be epoxidized are somewhat insecticidal, e.g., the two ring isomers of:

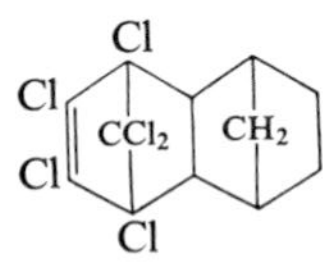

Further evidence (6) that epoxidation enhances potency was the finding that for the following compounds:

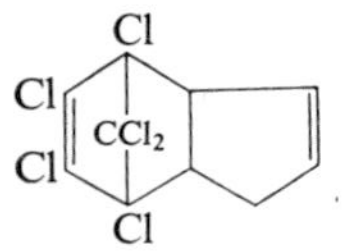

(I)
Chlordene

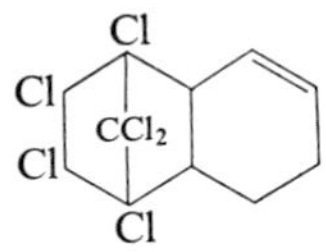

(II)

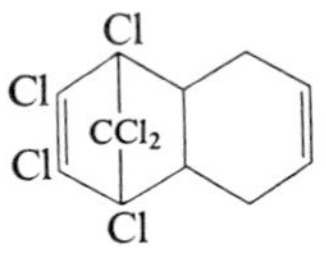

(III)

The abilities for form epoxides were paralleled by their toxicities to houseflies. Compound (I), the most toxic, most readily formed an epoxide; compound (III) was the least toxic and formed no epoxide. However, data provided by these authors elsewhere (7) show the LD_{50}'s of compounds (II) and (III) to be in the ratio 2.5:2.6, a small enough difference to suggest that epoxide formation is not of much significance in these compounds. Additional evidence in favor of epoxidation being a toxification is the delay in symptoms observed when heptachlor, aldrin, or isodrin are applied to houseflies (3,39). Because the epoxidation of aldrin is inhibited by sesamex (45), one would anticipate that sesamex would synergize aldrin's toxicity *if* the epoxidation were necessary for toxicity. In fact, sesamex delays the onset of symptoms caused by aldrin in the housefly, but has no effect on its ultimate toxicity (8) or (according to others workers) slightly reduces it (45). In summary, the author's opinion is that the above data show only that, in the case of aldrin, epoxidation produces a faster-acting toxicant, but that epoxidation is in fact not required for toxicity.

* However, there were weaknesses in the experiment: the time-to-death was increased less dramatically (34%) for isodrin; and endrin and dieldrin, which should have showed no nitrogen effect, showed, respectively, a 13 and 22% increase in time-to-death in nitrogen. Data for time-to-symptoms were not reported for dieldrin or endrin.

In contrast to those cyclodienes which are good insecticides, the compound chlordene was rapidly degraded by houseflies following its epoxidation (9). The degradation product was probably the hydroxylated derivative:

Chlordene

The hydroxylation step was blocked by sesamex, and the LD_{50} of the epoxide was increased almost 10-fold by sesamex, suggesting that the hydroxylation was a detoxification (the LD_{50} of the hydroxylation product would have proved the point, but it was not available). The LD_{50} of the epoxide was 35 $\mu g/g$ in comparison with a value of 50 for chlordene, suggesting that the epoxidation is, to a mild degree, a toxification in this case. The authors made the intriguing speculation that perhaps the reason that certain chlordene analogs such as heptachlor are good insecticides is that their epoxides cannot be degraded by hydroxylation, for the hydroxylation site is blocked by a chlorine atom. In other studies (8) they have shown that the compound designated above as (II), which is a poor insecticide, is more than 10-fold synergized by sesamex, in spite of the very small amount of epoxidation that it undergoes. Also the epoxide of (II) is synergized 45-fold by sesamex. These findings suggest that these compounds also are degraded rapidly by a sesamex-blocked route; perhaps hydroxylation is involved.

A recent report (1) described the metabolism by houseflies of some rather different cyclodiene-like compounds, *viz.*, endosulfan (or Thiodan) and its alcohol and ether. Endosulfan was shown to be metabolized to its sulfate, and the other compounds to unknown derivatives (Fig. 7.2). The conversion is not

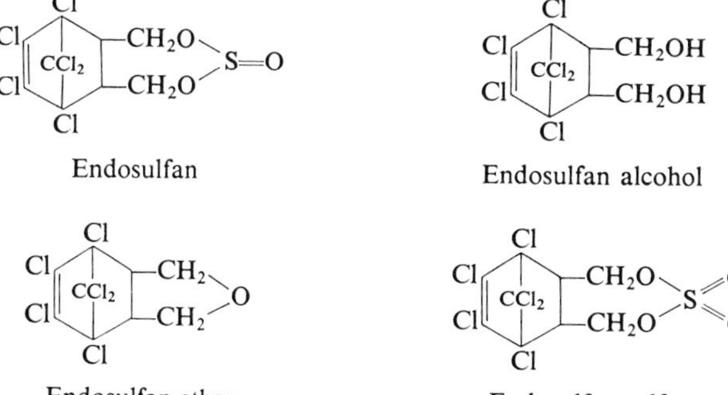

Fig. 7.2. Endosulfan analogs and metabolite.

a detoxification, for the sulfate has a toxicity to houseflies almost identical with endosulfan itself (the ether and alcohol are nontoxic). The extent of metabolism was not described. An identical oxidation product occurs as a plant metabolite on leaves of various trees and also vegetables, including spinach, celery, and alfalfa; it is not produced on non-living surfaces such as glass plates (10).

REFERENCES

1. Barnes, W. B., and Ware, G. W., *J. Econ. Entomol.* **58**, 286 (1965).
2. Bann, J. M., DeCino, T. J., Earle, N. W., and Sun, Y. P., *J. Agr. Food Chem.* **4**, 937 (1958).
3. Brooks, G. T., *Nature* **186**, 96 (1960).
4. Brooks, G. T., Harrison, A., and Cox, G. T., *Nature* **197**, 311 (1963).
5. Brooks, G. T., and Harrison, A., *Nature* **198**, 1169 (1963).
6. Brooks, G. T., and Harrison, A., *Biochem. J.* **87**, 5P (1963).
7. Brooks, G. T., and Harrison, A., *J. Insect Physiol.* **10**, 633 (1964).
8. Brooks, G. T., and Harrison, A., *Biochem. Pharmacol.* **13**, 827 (1964).
9. Brooks, G. T., and Harrison, A., *Nature* **205**, 1031 (1965).
10. Cassil, C. C., and Drummond, P. E., *J. Econ. Entomol.* **58**, 365 (1965).
11. Cohen, A. J., and Smith, J. N., *Nature* **189**, 600 (1961).
12. Colhoun, E. H., and Spencer, E. Y., *Science* **130**, 504 (1959).
13. Colhoun, E. H., *J. Agr. Food Chem.* **8**, 252 (1960).
14. Cueto, C., and Hayes, W. J., *J. Agr. Food Chem.* **10**, 366 (1962).
15. Davidow, B., and Radomski, J. L., *J. Pharmacol. Exptl. Therap.* **107**, 259 (1953).
16. Earle, N. W., *J. Agr. Food Chem.* **11**, 281 (1963).
17. Emerson, T. E., Brake, G. M., and Hinshaw, L. B., *Can. J. Physiol. Pharmacol.* **42**, 41 (1964).
18. Gannon, N., Link, R. P., and Decker, G. C., *J. Agr. Food Chem.* **7**, 826 (1959).
19. Gianotti, O., Metcalf, R. L., and March, R. B., *Ann. Entomol. Soc. Am.* **49**, 588 (1956).
20. Gowdey, C. W., Graham, A. R., Seguin, J. J., Stavraky, G. W., and Waud, R. A., *Can. J. Med. Sci.* **30**, 533 (1952).
21. Gowdey, C. W., Graham, A. R., Seguin, J. J., and Stavraky, G. W., *Can. J. Biochem. Physiol.* **32**, 498 (1954).
22. Gowdey, C. W., and Stavraky, G. W., *Can. J. Biochem. Physiol.* **33**, 272 (1955).
23. Hathaway, D. E., Mallinson, A., and Akintornva, D. A. A., *Biochem. J.* **94**, 976 (1965).
24. Heath, D. F., "Radioisotopes and Radiation in Entomology," Bombay, 1960, p. 83. Intern. At. Energy Agency, Vienna, 1962.
25. Heath, D. F., and Vandekar, M., *Brit. J. Ind. Med.* **21**, 269 (1964).
26. Hosein, E. A., and McLennan, H., *Nature* **183**, 328 (1959).
27. Hosein, E. A., and Proulx, P., *Nature* **187**, 321 (1960).
28. Hosein, E. A., and Proulx, P., *J. Agr. Food Chem.* **8**, 428 (1960).
29. Hosein, E. A., Proulx, P., and Ara, R., *Biochem. J.* **83**, 341 (1962).
30. Kortes, F., Ludwig, G., and Vogel, J., *Ann. Chem.* **656**, 135 (1962).
31. Lalonde, D. I. V., and Brown, A. W. A., *Can. J. Zool.* **32**, 7A (1954).
32. Ludwig, G., Weis, J., and Kortes, F., *Life Sci.* **3**, 123 (1964).
33. Martin, H., "The Scientific Principles of Crop Protection," 5th Ed. Arnold, London, 1964.

34. McCormick, D. B., Guirard, B. M., and Snell, E. E., *Proc. Soc. Exptl. Biol. Med.* **104**, 554 (1960).
35. McLennan, H., Curry, L., and Walker, R., *Biochem. J.* **89**, 163 (1963).
36. Metcalf, R. L., "Organic Insecticides." Wiley (Interscience), New York, 1955.
37. Morsdorf, K. Von, Ludwig, G., Vogel, J., and Kortes, F., *Med. Exptl.* **8**, 90 (1963).
38. Oonnithan, E. S., and Miskus, R., *J. Econ. Entomol.* **57**, 425 (1964).
39. Perry, A. S., Mattson, A. M., and Buckner, A. J., *J. Econ. Entomol.* **51**, 346 (1958).
40. Perry, A. S., Pearce, G. W., and Buckner, A. J., *J. Econ. Entomol.* **57**, 867 (1964).
41. Poonawalla, N. H., and Kortes, F., *Life Sci.* **3**, 1497 (1964).
42. Radomski, J. L., and Davidow, B., *J. Pharmacol. Exptl. Therap.* **107**, 266 (1953).
43. Reins, D. A., Holmes, D. D., and Hinshaw, L. B., *Can. J. Physiol. Pharmacol.* **42**, 599 (1964).
44. Soloway, S. B., *Advan. Pest Control Res.* **6**, 85 (1965).
45. Sun, Y. P., and Johnson, E. R., *J. Agr. Food Chem.* **8**, 261 (1960).
46. Treon, J. F., and Cleveland, F. P., *J. Agr. Food Chem.* **3**, 402 (1955).
47. Winthrop, G. J., and Felice, J. R., *Am. M. A. Arch. Ind. Health* **19**, 68 (1959).
48. Witter, R. F., and Farrior, W. L., *Proc. Soc. Exptl. Biol. Med.* **115**, 487 (1964).

CHAPTER 8

Nicotinoids

In 1746, Collinson, in England, recommended to Bertram, in America, the use of an infusion of tobacco leaves as an insecticide for plum curculio (21). Undoubtedly the effectiveness of this preparation was due to its content of the alkaloid nicotine, which is present in tobacco leaves in concentrations up to 14%, depending on species. Nowadays, nicotine is obtained from tobacco commercially by steam distillation or solvent extraction. It can also be synthesized, but the natural product is far cheaper and is therefore preferred.

Chemically, nicotine is *l*-3(1-methyl-2-pyrrolidyl)pyridine:

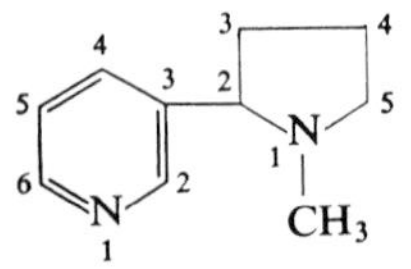

4 3 2 3 4
5 N 5
6 2 1
N CH$_3$
1

The six-membered pyridine ring has a nitrogen which, because of the aromatic character of the ring, is only very weakly basic (pK_a about 3). The nitrogen of the five-membered pyrrolidine ring, which is not aromatic, has moderate basicity (pK_a about 8). Consequently, at pH 7, 90% of the compound would be protonated at the pyrrolidine nitrogen. The formula also shows that the 2-carbon of the pyrrolidine ring is asymmetric, being attached to four different groups. Consequently, the compound has optical activity; the *l*-rotatory enantiomorph is the natural one.

Tobacco extracts contain other closely related insecticidal alkaloids, of which the most important are:

Nornicotine

Anabasine

Nicotine is most frequently used in its sulfate form, when it is known as Black Leaf 40. A splendid review of the structure and action of nicotinoids has recently appeared (23).

Toxicity

INSECTS

There is an enormous literature on nicotine toxicity, a summary of which occupies almost ten large pages in Negherbon (15). Unfortunately, there are drastic differences in reports, for instance the findings for nicotine injected into the silkworm *Bombyx mori* vary over a 200-fold range (6,11,13). Nevertheless, the reported LD_{50}'s are almost all extremely large, as Table 8.1 shows for some

TABLE 8.1

TOXICITY OF NICOTINE TO INSECTS[a]

Insect	LD_{50} (mg/kg)
American cockroach	650
Squash bug	350
Milkweed bug	190
Japanese beetle	650
Yellow mealworm	3200
Bombyx silkworm	4
Honey bee	315

[a] Values are for the free-base form applied topically. From Menusan (13) and Beard (1).

common insects, among which only the silkworm is very sensitive. Unfortunately, the insects against which nicotine is principally used, such as aphids, are not suitable subjects for true LD_{50} determinations, and although extensive data for median lethal concentrations (MLC) of vapors are available (15), these provide poor bases for accurate estimations of doses. However, they do suggest that there is an extremely large species variation in sensitivity to vapors, with MLC values (in mg/liter) in the 0.003–0.008 range for aphids, thrips, and silkworms, contrasting with values of 0.28 for the Japanese beetle and 0.145 for the Mexican bean beetle.

Nicotine toxicity varies a great deal with the mode and form of application. Hansberry *et al.* (6) found that they could feed 570 mg/kg of the free base form to Colorado potato beetles without effect, whereas the Reinekate salt* had an LD_{50} of 4 mg/kg. Other such examples abound, and no satisfactory explanation has been given. Although Hansberry found no great difference in toxicity if nicotine derivatives were fed or injected, Beard (1) found large differences between some results from topical and injected doses: the latter route was 6 times more effective for bees, 28 times for the wax moth, 3 times for the milkweed bug, but about equieffective for the Japanese beetle. But variations of such magnitude are not uncommon with many diverse insecticides.

Vertebrates

Nicotine has moderate to high toxicity for all vertebrates. Typical values (15) for the LD_{50} in mg/kg after intravenous injection are: mouse 0.8, rat 1, rabbit 9, dog and guinea pig 5. As is often the case, the corresponding oral values are (in the few examples available) much lower, e.g., mouse 24, rat 55.

Mechanism of Action

Vertebrates

Nicotine has long been of interest to pharmacologists because it mimics certain of the effects of acetylcholine, so that those effects of injected acetylcholine which are mimicked by nicotine are called "nicotinic effects." Figure 1.2 shows, diagrammatically, the places where neuronal junctions are cholinergic, i.e., mediated by acetylcholine. The cholinergic junctions, which (with the exception of the category IV type) are affected by injected acetylcholine, can be classified into four categories on the basis of their sensitivity to drugs.

Category I contains only the skeletal neuromuscular junctions, where nerve and voluntary muscle meet. These are affected by nicotine, and blocked by curare (a drug derived from a South American arrow poison), but not by atropine. When the neuromuscular junctions are blocked, the muscle is paralyzed. When the junctions are overstimulated, fasciculation occurs, i.e., an uncoordinated twitching of the muscles, often with no corresponding movement of the limb.

Category II contains the neuroeffector junctions of the parasympathetic system, i.e., the places where parasympathetic nerves meet the muscles and

* Derived from Reineke's salt, $NH_4[Cr(NH_3)_2(SCN)_4]$; this salt forms insoluble complexes with certain amines.

glands they innervate, including the iris of the eye, the bladder, the heart, tear glands, salivary glands, and so on. These sites are not affected by nicotine or curare, but they are blocked by atropine. The compound muscarine (p. 20), obtained from certain poisonous mushrooms, stimulates the junctions of category II; consequently, the effects of such stimulation are called "muscarinic effects," and include constriction of the pupil (myosis), urination, weeping, and salivation. Many of the early symptoms of organophosphate poisoning are muscarinic, and consequently can be removed by atropine.

Category III contains the autonomic ganglia. As Fig. 1.2 shows, both sympathetic and parasympathetic ganglia are cholinergic, and so acetylcholine can lead to stimulation of sympathetic and parasympathetic systems. These sites are affected by nicotine and not by muscarine, atropine, or curare, except at high concentrations. Sympathetic nerves innervate many smooth muscles and organs which also have parasympathetic innervation, for instance the iris of the eye, the bladder, the heart, and salivary glands. In several cases, the parasympathetic and sympathetic nerves operate antagonistically; thus the former slows the heart and constricts the pupil while the latter accelerates the heart and dilates the pupil. In such cases, the effects of ganglionic drugs are hard to predict, since they will depend on whether the sympathetic or parasympathetic ganglion is the more affected. In a few cases no such uncertainty arises; thus, only the parasympathetic ganglion controls muscular activity in the bladder, while only the sympathetic controls the blood supply.

Category IV contains all cholinergic junctions in the central nervous system. Because of the difficulties in establishing the chemical transmitter in such complex webs of neurons as are found in the central nervous system, only a few have been thus characterized. However, it is certain that the respiratory center of the brain (situated in the reticular formation, in the brain stem) is cholinergic. This center controls respiratory rate, and breathing stops if the center is blocked. Compounds which induce convulsions are assumed to operate on central neurons because a convulsion is a relatively coordinated affair (unlike fasciculation, mentioned above), and must therefore originate centrally. At least some Category IV junctions are affected by nicotine, and some others, particularly those of the respiratory center, by atropine. Because of the so-called "blood-brain barrier" which excludes large ions, ionic compounds have virtually no effects on Category IV junctions, and injected acetylcholine, muscarine, or curare have little effect. In spite of the fact that nicotine produces convulsions, the term nicotinic effect is not applied to such central effects; the terms muscarinic effects and nicotinic effects apply only to those symptoms of *injected* acetylcholine which can be mimicked by muscarine and nicotine.

Let us now concentrate on the effects of nicotine. Because under the right conditions nicotine mimics acetylcholine, nicotine must operate on the acetylcholine receptor (p. 18). In other words, the receptor fails to distinguish between acetylcholine and nicotine: It binds both, and it responds to both. A complicating factor, common in many analogous situations, is that while a small surplus of nicotine or acetylcholine produces excessive activity, a large surplus blocks activity. In actual poisoning, one frequently observes these two opposite effects in sequence, so that early twitching and convulsions are followed later by paralysis.

Species variations in toxicant action are the rule rather than the exception. Thus nicotine dilates the pupil in the cat and dog, but constricts it in the rabbit and in birds, while in man an early contraction is later followed by dilation (3). Presumably, different potencies with respect to sympathetic and parasympathetic ganglia are involved. Nicotine produces twitching and prolonged contraction of muscle. But in frogs, reptiles, and birds, these effects are blocked by curare and not by sectioning the nerves supplying the muscle; they are therefore effects directly on the junction. In mammals, moderate concentrations cause similar symptoms which are prevented by sectioning the nerve, and consequently central effects are responsible (10).

In poisoning of vertebrates by nicotine, the symptoms are as follows: salivation and vomiting (presumably both from ganglionic stimulation), muscular weakness and fibrillation (from the effect on the neuromuscular junction), and finally clonic convulsions* and cessation of respiration (due to effects on the central nervous system). Poisoning can be treated by drugs (the molecular bases for whose effects are not understood) which are anticonvulsants, particularly Panparnit (Caramiphen) and Diparcol.

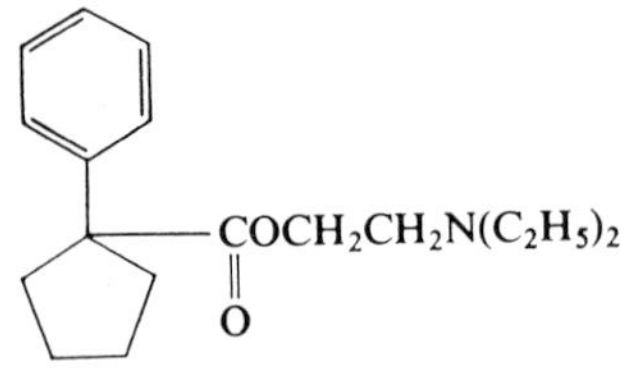

$COCH_2CH_2N(C_2H_5)_2$

Panparnit

S N $CH_2CH_2N(C_2H_5)_2$

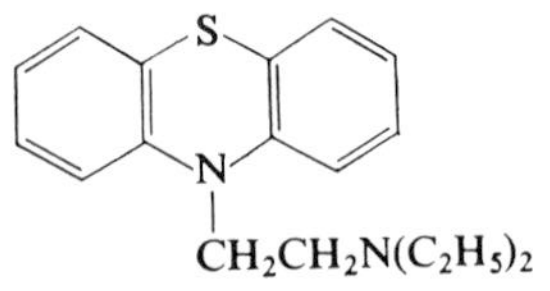

Diparcol

INSECTS

Nicotine kills insects rapidly, often within an hour. When applied externally, one usually sees tremors and convulsions, followed by paralysis. Such symptoms suggest an effect on nerve function, but leave open the question: Is it on the ganglia (i.e., the central nervous system in the case of an insect) or is it peripheral; and if peripheral, is it on the nerve axon or elsewhere? The site of action in the cockroach was studied with classic pharmacological techniques

* Convulsions are classified as clonic when they involve rapid and frenzied movements of the limbs; they are tonic when they involve a rigid and "frozen" extension of the limbs.

by Yeager and Munson in 1945 (25,26). Nicotine applied to the isolated leg had no effect; application into the body cavity produced leg tremors which vanished when the nerve was severed close to the ganglion. Consequently, the tremors were ganglionic in origin. Subsequent work by Welsh and Gordon (22) showed that axonic transmission in crayfish was only affected by high concentrations of nicotine, such as $6 \times 10^{-4} M$. But although it is frequently stated in reviews that nicotine affects only ganglia of insects, in fact experiments have shown that nicotine at $10^{-3} M$ can stimulate the neuromuscular junction, judged by nerve-muscle experiments in locusts (7) and American cockroaches (16). However, the work with the locust did indeed show the ganglion to be much more sensitive than the neuromuscular junction, so that it is probably true that the ganglion is the primary target of nicotine poisoning. This situation is in complete contrast to that in mammals, where the primary effects are at the neuromuscular junction rather than on the central nervous system; and this contrast parallels the view that neuromuscular transmission in mammals is cholinergic, but in arthropods it is not (p. 20).

The well-established findings with nicotine in mammals have shown that it acts by mimicking acetylcholine, the normal transmitter. Since it has long been held that transmission in the central nervous system of insects is cholinergic, there is every reason to suppose that nicotine affects ganglia by mimicking (on an excessive scale) acetylcholine there. This reasoning has until very recently not been appreciated, and consequently has not been utilized in the search for new, potent nicotine analogs.

Until recently, it was true that no excellent synthetic analogs of nicotine existed. The brilliant work of Yamamoto and co-workers from Tokyo has changed this picture. They prepared (9,24) 26 nicotine-like compounds, 11 of which were new. All active compounds had an intact pyridine ring connected in the 3-position to various more basic nitrogen-containing substituents. They found a remarkable connection of toxicity with the pK_a of the more basic nitrogen. If its pK_a was high (above 7), the compound was a good insecticide, if the pK_a was about 7, it was a moderate insecticide, and if low (below 6) the compounds were ineffective. Contrary to earlier belief, the more basic nitrogen did not have to be a ring nitrogen, and several excellent compounds had alkylamine chains instead of such a ring.

The detailed requirements suggested by these workers are as follows: (1) A pyridine ring is required; for instance, compounds (I) and (II) were relatively inactive.

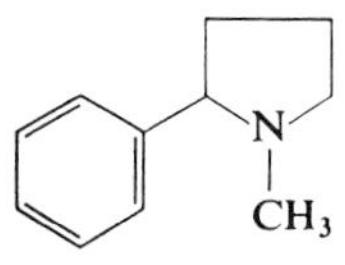

N
CH_3

(I)

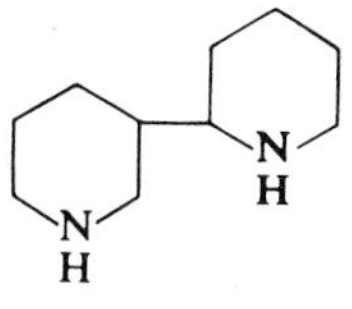

N
H
N
H

(II)

(2) The more basic nitrogen, i.e., that on the group attached to the pyridine, should have a moderately strong basicity, with a pK_a in the 8–9 region. Thus compound (III), with a pK_a of 5.5, is inactive.

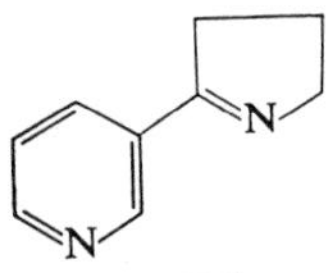

(III)

(3) The distance between the two nitrogens should be about 4.2 Å (the significance of this is discussed below); so anabasine (see formula above) is highly toxic whereas compound (IV) is not.

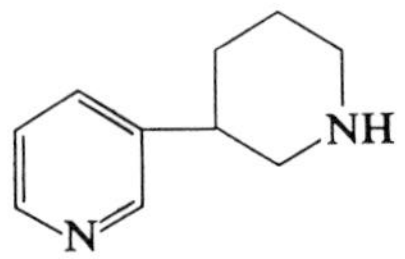

(IV)

(4) The pyridine ring must not be substituted in the 2-position; so compound (V), in spite of having the right distance between the nitrogens, is inactive.

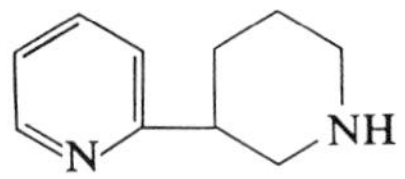

(V)

(5) There are restrictions and requirements for the substitutions permitted on the more basic nitrogen; for instance compound (VI) is as good as nicotine.

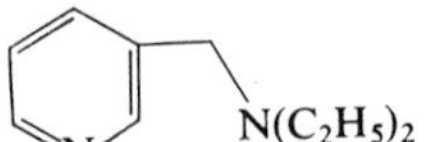

$N(C_2H_5)_2$

(VI)

But the corresponding NH_2, $NHCH_3$, and NHC_2H_5 compounds are poor. This is the more surprising in that the $NHCH_3$ compound bears the same relation to compound (VI) as nornicotine does to nicotine.

(6) Neither nitrogen should be quaternized, for this abolishes activity.

Yamamoto and his colleagues have thus demonstrated the two essential requirements for activity in nicotine analogs: They should resemble acetylcholine with respect to their conformation and electronic makeup, and they are required to be fairly strong bases but not quaternized. Quaternized compounds behave like supremely strong bases in being cations even at high pH, but differ from tertiary nitrogens in having no un-ionized form with which to be in equilibrium. Unquaternized strong bases have the dual properties that they can penetrate ion barriers (although slowly if the medium on the near side of the barrier is aqueous), but once penetrated, they will be virtually all in the protonated form. And it is clear that for nicotine analogs to mimic acetylcholine, they must have a protonated nitrogen *when at the receptor site*, so that their $—N^+HR_2$ group may mimic the $—N^+(CH_3)_3$ group in acetylcholine.

Metabolism

Mammals

Nicotine is metabolized primarily in the liver (14), and appears in urine of dogs (12) and humans (2) as cotinine and the acid of which cotinine is a lactam. Qualitative evidence was also reported of the presence in human urine of demethylcotinine and perhaps a derivative of cotinine with a hydroxylated pyrrolidine ring. Unfortunately no clue was given to the relative quantities involved.

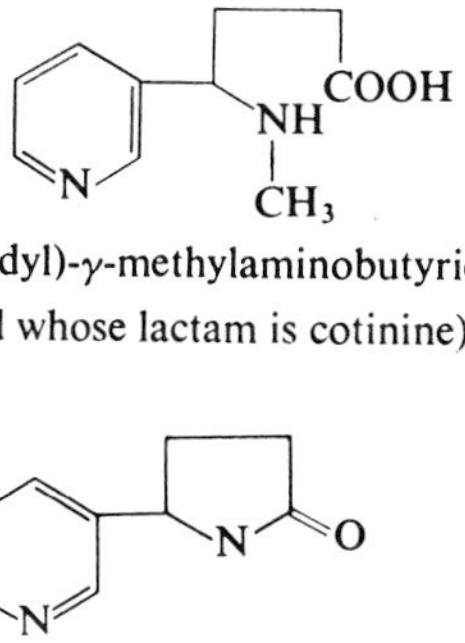

COOH
NH
N
CH_3

γ-(3-Pyridyl)-γ-methylaminobutyric acid
(acid whose lactam is cotinine)

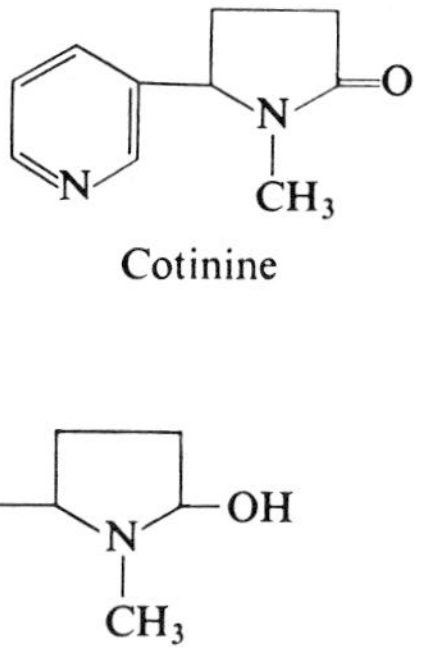

O
N
N
CH_3

Cotinine

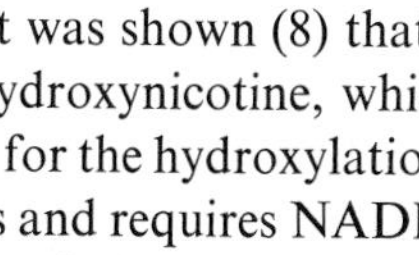

N
O
N

Demethylcotinine

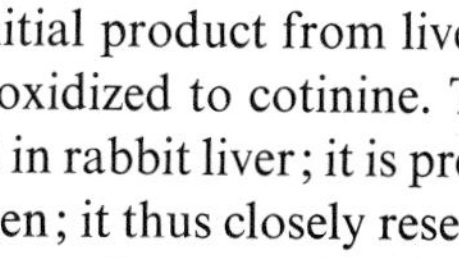

OH
N
N
CH_3

5-Hydroxynicotine

In 1960 it was shown (8) that the major initial product from liver preparations is 5-hydroxynicotine, which is rapidly oxidized to cotinine. The system responsible for the hydroxylation was studied in rabbit liver; it is present in the microsomes and requires $NADPH_2$ and oxygen; it thus closely resembles, and might be identical with, the microsomal oxidases discussed elsewhere (p. 210). Another enzyme, perhaps an aldehyde oxidase, then oxidizes the hydroxynicotine to cotinine; by using cyanide, an aldehyde oxidase inhibitor, one can prevent cotinine formation from microsomes and convert the nicotine only to 5-hydroxynicotine. Presumably the partial hydrolysis of the lactam, cotinine, gives rise to the urinary acid mentioned above.

The most recent work (17) has shown that rabbit liver microsomes can produce numerous other metabolites from nicotine, including demethylnicotine, demethylcotinine, pyridylacetic acid, and perhaps nicotine *N*-oxide.

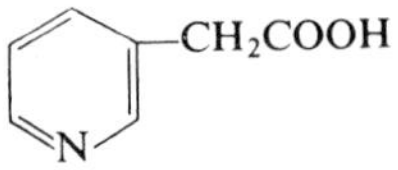

CH_2COOH

Pyridylacetic acid

CH_3

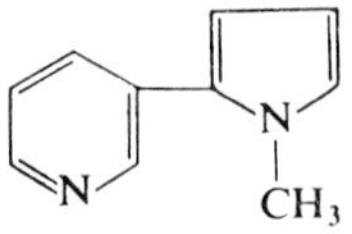

Nicotyrine

Another study (20) has shown that rabbit liver mitochondria can produce nicotyrine. The relevance of these findings to events *in vivo* may be small if the above work on urinary metabolites is correct. However, the work with liver has been done on rabbits, and that with urine has been done on dogs and man, so that it would be premature to conclude that cotinine and its acid are indeed the prime metabolites in all intact mammals. Demethylation products should now be searched for in a variety of urines. Since many nicotine metabolites are not separable in common one-directional chromatographic systems (17), stringent criteria for identification of metabolites are essential.

Insects

The first study on nicotine metabolism in insects was by Guthrie *et al.* in 1957 (5). In insects treated or fed with large quantities of nicotine, the major metabolites in the body of American and German cockroaches were cotinine and an unidentified compound. Cotinine was shown to be nontoxic to German cockroaches. In Southern armyworms, several metabolites were demonstrated but not identified.

Later work (19) showed that nicotine was extensively metabolized when it was fed to different grasshoppers, or applied topically to tobacco wireworms, cigarette beetles, or houseflies. At periods of 10 hours after feeding or 18 hours after topical application, about 75% of the dose was found in the body as cotinine. Other minor and unidentified metabolites were also noted for all these insects except the grasshopper. In interesting contrast, tobacco budworms or cabbage loopers did not metabolize nicotine at all after feeding, and were also insensitive to nicotine poisoning. The authors say that these two insensitive species "do not metabolize nicotine but have an efficient excretory metabolism." Their evidence for the second part of this statement is that when fed on tobacco, there two insects showed alkaloids in the feces which "correponded chromatographically and spectroscopically to the alkaloids in the tobacco." But in the absence of data on the amount of excretion in these species after feeding a known dose of nicotine, and on the quantitative analysis of alkaloids in food compared with feces when tobacco was fed, the efficiency of nicotine excretion cannot really be evaluated. In the case of the nicotine-sensitive housefly, it was indeed shown that no more than 10% of a dose of nicotine was excreted after 18 hours. However, since only 12% of the retained alkaloids was nicotine, whereas 79% was cotinine (and therefore probably not toxic), the sensitivity of the housefly is not explained by these findings. The data reviewed so far cannot therefore be taken as proving the attractive hypothesis that insensitivity to nicotine is caused by rapid metabolism in some species, and by ready excretion in others.

Guthrie's group has examined in depth the cause for insensitivity to nicotine of two other insects. In an elegant study (4), they showed that when the green peach aphid feeds on tobacco plants, it does not take up nicotine. This surprising fact might be caused, they suggest, by the feeding habit of the aphid: the insect feeds only on the phloem. When the insect has to penetrate xylem in order to reach the phloem, it finds an intercellular route through the xylem and consequently avoids the xylem contents. No evidence was provided that in fact nicotine was present in phloem and absent in xylem, but the authors did show that aphids were killed when fed artificially on diets containing nicotine. It seems safe to conclude that, in this case, insensitivity is caused by a failure of uptake.

The other insect studied was the tobacco hornworm (18). Biosynthetic C^{14}-nicotine was fed, and a far more satisfactory account of its disposal was therefore possible than in the metabolic experiments described above, which used unlabeled nicotine. The results were most interesting: 90% of an oral dose was excreted in 4 hours, and excretion was total in 1 day. This massive loss was not merely a matter of deficient uptake; nicotine injected into the body cavity was excreted even faster; an amazing 83% was recovered from feces in 15 minutes! Parallel work with larvae fed on unlabeled tobacco plants showed that the only alkaloid excreted was nicotine, judged by infrared analysis. These findings, coupled with the observation above that houseflies excrete only 10% of applied nicotine in 18 hours, strongly support the authors' contention that the insensitivity of tobacco hornworms to nicotine is caused by an ultrarapid excretion mechanism. Nevertheless, it would be most interesting to study excretory rates in a nicotine-sensitive lepidopterous larva, because gross inspection suggests that the rate of defecation in such larvae is very rapid in comparison to that of an adult housefly.

The above series of studies constitute a unique and satisfying account of the numerous ways in which different species can adapt to meet a single problem, that of utilizing a plant which contains a potent insecticide. Some species have "learned" to metabolize the insecticide; an aphid which is sensitive to ingested nicotine feeds in such a way that it avoids ingesting it; and the tobacco hornworm has developed an astonishingly effective excretory mechanism.

REFERENCES

1. Beard, R. L., *J. Econ. Entomol.* **42**, 292 (1949).
2. Bowman, E. R., Turnbull, L. B., and McKennis, H., *J. Pharmacol. Exptl. Therap.* **127**, 92 (1959).
3. Grollman, A., "Pharmacology and Therapeutics," p. 282. Lea and Febiger, Philadelphia, Pennsylvania, 1954.
4. Guthrie, F. E., Campbell, W. V., and Baron, R. L., *Ann. Entomol. Soc. Am.* **55**, 42 (1962).
5. Guthrie, F. E., Fingler, R. L., and Bowery, T. G., *J. Econ. Entomol.* **50**, 821 (1957).
6. Hansberry, R., Middlekauff, W. W., and Norton, L. B., *J. Econ. Entomol.* **33**, 511 (1940).
7. Harlow, P. A., *Ann. Appl. Biol.* **46**, 55 (1958).
8. Hucker, H. B., Gillette, J. R., and Brodie, B. B., *J. Pharmacol. Exptl. Therap.* **129**, 94 (1960).
9. Kamimura, H., Matsumoto, A., Miyazake, Y., and Yamamoto, I., *Agr. Biol. Chem.* (*Tokyo*) **27**, 684 (1963).
10. Langley, J. N., and Dickinson, W. L., *J. Physiol.* (*London*) **11**, 265 (1890).
11. McIndoo, N. E., *J. Agr. Res.* **55**, 909 (1937).
12. McKennis, H., Turnbull, L. B., and Bowman, E. R., *J. Am. Chem. Soc.* **81**, 3951 (1959).
13. Menusan, H., *J. Econ. Entomol.* **41**, 302 (1948).
14. Miller, A. W., and Larson, P. S., *J. Pharmacol. Exptl. Therap.* **109**, 218 (1953).
15. Negherbon, W. O., "Handbook of Toxicology, Insecticides," Vol. 3, 854 pp. Saunders, Philadelphia, Pennsylvania, 1959.
16. O'Connor, A., M.S. Thesis, Cornell Univ., Ithaca, New York, 1964.
17. Popadopoulos, N. M., and Kiatzios, J. A., *J. Pharmacol. Exptl. Therap.* **140**, 269 (1963).
18. Self, L. S., Guthrie, F. E., and Hodgson, E., *J. Insect Physiol.* **10**, 907 (1964).
19. Self, L. S., Guthrie, F. E., and Hodgson, E., *Nature* **204**, 200 (1964).
20. Tsujimoto, A., *Nippon Yak'urigaku Zasshi* **53**, 553 (1957).
21. Waite, M. B., *Yearbook Agr.* (*U.S. Dept. Agr.*) p. 453 (1925).
22. Welsh, J. H., and Gordon, H. T., *J. Cellular Comp. Physiol.* **30**, 147 (1947).
23. Yamamoto, I., *Advan. Pest Control Res.* **6**, 231 (1965).
24. Yamamoto, R., Yamamoto, I., and Kamimura, H., *Proc. 5th Intern. Pesticide Congr., London*, 1963.
25. Yeager, J. F., and Munson, S. C., *J. Agr. Res.* **64**, 307 (1942).
26. Yeager, J. F., and Munson, S. C., *Science* **102**, 305 (1945).

CHAPTER 9

Rotenoids

Primitive people around the world have been interested for untold years in fish poisons to aid their hunting. In 1848, T. Oxley (11) suggested that a Malayan fish poison, extracted from "tuba-root," might be a good insecticide. Tuba root is derived mainly from the leguminous plant *Derris elliptica*. Since those early days, a variety of native roots, including the above and other *Derris* species from Malaya, a variety of *Lonchocarpus* species from South America, and *Tephrosia* species from East Africa, have been shown to contain insecticidal rotenone and related compounds. The crude materials are quite often used directly, and known as derris dust or, if from South America, as "cubé root."

The structure of rotenone was elucidated in 1932 independently by four separate groups in the United States, England, Japan, and Germany. Its structure is as follows.

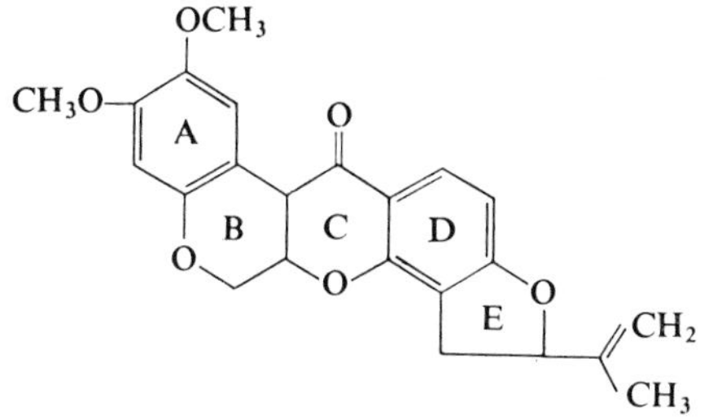

OCH_3 CH_3O A B C D E O O O O CH_2 CH_3

Rotenone

The letterings are unofficial, and are used to clarify the presentation of the following related compounds, whose formulas, apart from the ring actually shown, are identical with rotenone.

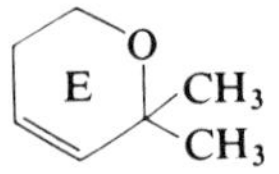

Deguelin 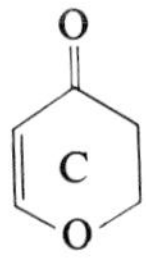 | 7,8-Dehydrorotenone 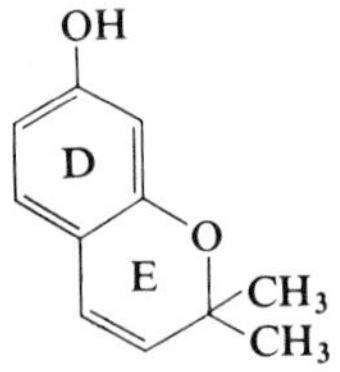 | Toxicarol 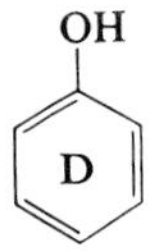 | Sumatrol

Rotenone is invariably found along with these, and up to as many as 13 other derivatives. The relative amounts in crude preparations vary tremendously; the rotenone content may be only a few percent, and yet the almost noninsecticidal toxicarol is often a major constituent (up to 60%). Deguelin is commonly a major constituent, and has about one-fourth the insecticidal activity of rotenone. Sumatrol has little insecticidal action; it is often absent, but in some samples can constitute 15% of the weight.

To add to the complexity, rotenone decomposes on exposure to heat or light; the main breakdown occurs by oxidation to the noninsecticidal 7,8-dehydrorotenone. Consequently, the effectiveness of rotenone on a plant surface lasts only a few days.

Finally, the rotenoids exhibit optical activity, and all except deguelin occur in the levorotatory form.

Rotenone has quite low toxicity for warm blooded vertebrates; it is very toxic to some insect species, but not to others (Table 9.1).

TABLE 9.1

TOXICITY OF ROTENONE[a]

Organism	Route	LD_{50}(mg/kg)
Rat	Oral	132
Guinea pig	Oral	200
	Intraperitoneal	15
Chicken	Oral	996
Honeybee	Oral	3
Milkweed bug	Topical	25
American cockroach	Topical	2000
	Oral	1000
	Injected (males)	5
Japanese beetle	Topical	25
	Injected	40

[a] From Negherbon (10).

Mode of Action

Until fairly recently, information on the mode of action of rotenone was confined to a recital of symptoms, such as (in insects) slowing of heart beat, depression of respiratory movements, a decrease in oxygen consumption, and eventual flaccid paralysis. In the 1930's, it was accurately noted, however, that unlike the majority of organic insecticides, rotenone had no specific action upon either peripheral (12) or central (8) nerves. Similarly, in mammals, effects upon respiration were observed: a stimulation followed by profound depression (1). In 1936, Tischler (12) proposed that a blockade in oxygen utilization was causal in poisoning.

In recent years, Fukami and his colleagues in Japan have examined Tischler's suggestion at the biochemical level, using cockroach muscle preparations. Let us here pause to review briefly the biochemistry of oxygen utilization.

The central theme of "energy production" in living organisms rotates around the synthesis of ATP (adenosine triphosphate) from ADP (adenosine diphosphate). This simple phosphorylation reaction requires energy; the reverse reaction releases energy, and bodily processes (movement, nerve transmission, solute pumping, etc.) are designed to utilize ATP, whose synthesis is therefore of utmost importance. The synthesis of ATP from ADP is an outcome of the oxidation of compounds (e.g., glutamate, pyruvate, and succinate), which in turn are derived from ingested sugars and starches. The overall reaction involves (1) conversion of these compounds (substrates) to oxidized forms, and (2) the concurrent reduction of oxygen to water. But (1) and (2) are linked through a complex chain of oxidation–reduction reactions, and a vital by-product of the operation of this chain is the phosphorylation of ADP to ATP.

One substrate, succinate, is linked into this chain (which is known as the pathway of oxidative phosphorylation) through some side reactions.

Because the system shown in part in Fig. 9.1 is the prime source of ATP for the body, its disruption in any way could have the effect of cutting off the body's energy source. One similar way of disrupting it is suffocation, which blocks the whole process by preventing the final step, oxygen utilization.

Now let us return to the work of Fukami's group. Their early observations (2,3) led them along a false trail; they found that muscle tissue from rotenone-poisoned cockroaches was deficient in its ability to oxidize succinate completely with consequent oxygen utilization ("succinoxidase activity") although the enzyme succinic dehydrogenase, SD in Fig. 9.1, was not inhibited. This suggested a blockade existing somewhere below SD in Fig. 9.1. And their finding that normal cockroach muscle, poisoned *in vitro* with $5 \times 10^{-5} M$ rotenone, showed inhibition of endogenous respiration* might suggest blockade of the

* Oxidation of the substrates naturally present, including glutamate, pyruvate, and succinate.

cytochromes, which are common to all the substrates of oxidative phosphorylation. Furthermore (13), muscle from rotenone-poisoned locusts showed a mild deficiency in its ability to synthesize ATP through oxidative phosphorylation.

Fukami's group found a hotter scent when they noted in 1957 that rotenone *in vitro* was a potent inhibitor of glutamic acid oxidation (6). They describe this elsewhere (4) as "glutamic dehydrogenase inhibition," but in fact they were measuring glutamate-stimulated uptake of oxygen, and therefore the whole pathway between glutamate and oxygen, with several enzymes as well as glutamic dehydrogenase (Fig. 9.1). Their massive examination of 35 analogs of rotenone revealed a good correlation between blockade of glutamate oxidation and toxicity to the azuki bean weevil (5), giving apparent support to the view (6) that rotenone acts by blocking glutamic dehydrogenase

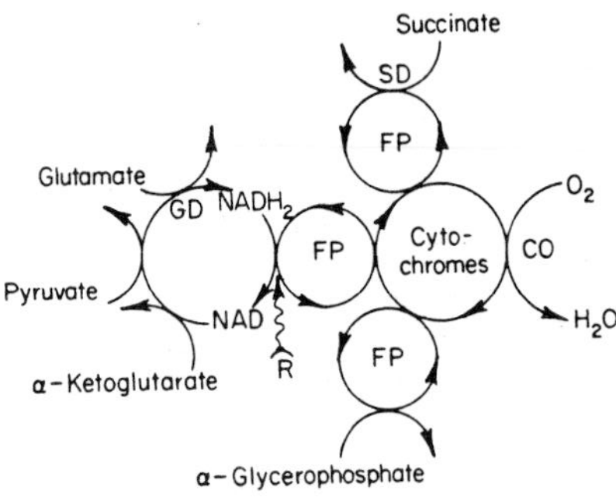

FIG. 9.1. The electron transport pathways for substrate oxidation with reduction of O_2 to H_2O. The coupling-in of the simultaneous conversions of ADP to ATP is not shown. CO=cytochrome oxidase, FP=flavoprotein, GD=glutamic dehydrogenase, SD=succinic dehydrogenase. Rotenone blocks at R.

In 1961 Lindahl and Oberg (9) observed that the oxidation by rat liver mitochondria of pyruvate, but not of succinate, was blocked by $1.5 \times 10^{-6} M$ rotenone. Rather than suggesting blockade at the dehydrogenase level, they suggested blockade at R in Fig. 9.1, i.e., at the point of coupled oxidation of $NADH_2$ and a flavoprotein. The view was supported by spectral measurements, and even more strongly by the observation that methylene blue could reverse the blockade caused by rotenone. It is well known that methylene blue permits the oxidation of $NADH_2$ back to NAD, thus eliminating the requirement for all the system to the right of NAD in Fig. 9.1. A consequence of the blockade at R is of course that oxidation of all substrates which are oxidized via the NAD system (such as glutamate, α-ketoglutarate, and pyruvate) is blocked by rotenone, but oxidation of succinate is not. These facts explain the phenomena observed above by Fukami. However, Fukami has now (4) extended Lindahl and Oberg's elegant proof to the case of American cockroach muscle, with the same conclusion. Perhaps the most direct proof is the potent blockade of $NADH_2$ oxidation.

The puzzle is not entirely solved yet. Why is rotenone of low toxicity to most mammals, but of high toxicity to insects, fish, and, strangely enough, pigs (7)? Differences in rates of degradation offer an attractive possible answer. And why do low doses of rotenone, given to American cockroaches, give rise to muscle tissue deficient in ability to oxidize succinate? Further work is needed.

Metabolism

It is astonishing to have to report that no information is available on the metabolism of rotenone by insects or mammals.

REFERENCES

1. Ambrose, A. M., and Haag, H. B., *Ind. Eng. Chem.* **28**, 815 (1936).
2. Fukami, J., "Japanese Contributions to the Study of the Insecticide-resistance Problem. Effects of Rotenone on the Succinoxidase System in the Muscle of the Cockroach." Inst. Insect Control, Kyoto Univ., Japan, 1957.
3. Fukami, J., "Japanese Contributions to the Study of the Insecticide-resistance Problem. Effects of Rotenone on Respiration in the Muscle of the Cockroach, Periplaneta americana L." Inst. Insect Control, Kyoto Univ., Japan, 1957.
4. Fukami, J., *Nogyo Gijutsu Kenkyusho Hokoku Byori Konchu* **13**, 33 (1961).
5. Fukami, J., Nakatsugawa, T., and Narahashi, T., *Nippon Oyo Dobutsu Konchu Gaku Zasshi* **3**, 259 (1959).
6. Fukami, J., and Tomizawa, C., "Japanese Contributions to the Study of the Insecticide-resistance Problem. Effects of Rotenone on the *l*-glutamic oxidase System in the Insect." Inst. Insect Control, Kyoto Univ., Japan, 1957.
7. Kingscote, A. A., Baker, A. W., McGregor, J. K., and Dixon, S. E., *Ann. Rept. Entomol. Soc. Ontario* p. 37 (1951).
8. Klinger, H., *Arb. Physiol. Angew. Entomol. Berlin-Dahlem* **3**, 49, 115 (1936).
9. Lindahl, P. E., and Oberg, K. E., *Exptl. Cell. Res.* **23**, 228 (1961).
10. Negherbon, W. O., "Handbook of Toxicology, Insecticides", Vol. 3. Saunders, Philadelphia (1959).
11. Oxley, T., *J. Indian Archipelago E. Asia* **2**, 641 (1848).
12. Tischler, N., *J. Econ. Entomol.* **28**, 215 (1936).
13. Tomizawa, C., and Fukami, J., "Japanese Contributions to the Study of the Insecticide-resistance Problem. Biochemical Studies on the Action of Insecticides II. Oxidative Phosphorylation in the Flight Muscle of Locusta migratoria and the Influence of Insecticides." Inst. Insect Control, Kyoto Univ., Japan, 1957.

CHAPTER 10

Pyrethroids

This group of compounds enjoys a number of distinctions. Pyrethrin, a crude mixture of pyrethroids, is perhaps the oldest of the organic insecticides, yet 135 years after its introduction it has displaced some newer competitors, particularly in domestic use, because of its remarkably low toxicity for mammals (Table 10.1). It is the most spectacularly effective of all insecticides, in that if one scores a direct hit, knock-down is almost instantaneous; but it has the distressing property of permitting total recovery of the victim in some circumstances. Finally, we understand its mechanism of action less than that of any other group of compounds.

TABLE 10.1

TOXICITY OF PYRETHROIDS (MIXED PYRETHRINS I AND II)[a]

Organism	Route	LD_{50} (mg/kg)
Rat	Oral	820
Guinea pig	Oral	1500
Squash bug	Topical	7
Milkweed bug	Topical	8
Japanese beetle	Topical	40
Yellow mealworm	Topical	35
Housefly	Topical	57
Aedes aegypti mosquito	Topical	1

[a] Data from Negherbon (11).

In the early 1800's, a Mr. Jumtikoff of Armenia discovered that certain Caucasian tribes used ground flowers of a plant as an insecticide. In 1828, his son began making and selling large quantities of this material, called "pyrethrum." Various species of the genus *Chrysanthemum* (which name has displaced the earlier generic name *Pyrethrum*) yield a useful product, but in 1840 the species *cinerariaefolium* was found to be the most effective, and has since displaced other species. For years Yugoslavia was the primary producer of the flowers, but Japan moved into the ascendent in about 1915, to yield to Kenya in about 1940. Since 1950, synthetic pyrethroids have been made commercially on a large scale.

The commonest form in which pyrethroids are used is as an extract of pyrethrum, obtained by extracting the ground flowers with any one of a variety of solvents, such as methanol or acetone, to obtain a solution of pyrethroids along with waxes and pigments. The latter are then removed by cleanup methods, such as passage through a charcoal column followed by distillation of the solvent, to leave the material called "pyrethrin." This contains a mixture of esters, as described below. The flower heads can contain from 0.7 to 3% of pyrethrin, depending on the strain.

The account of the elucidation of the composition of pyrethrin is complex. It has been well reviewed (6,7), and one need here only comment on the major contribution made by Staudinger and Ruzicka in 1924 (12). We now know that pyrethrin contains esters of two different alcohols which we may call L_1 and L_2, with two different acids, which we may call C_1 and C_2. One could in principle have four esters: L_1C_1, L_1C_2, L_2C_1, and L_2C_2. This is precisely what one finds. The two acids are quite similar to each other, both containing a triangular ring (cyclopropane). One acid contains a free carboxyl group, and the other has one free and one esterified carboxyl group.

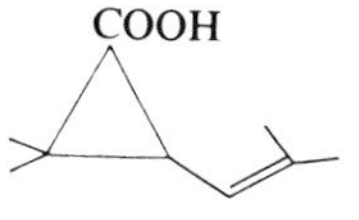

COOH

Chrysanthemic acid

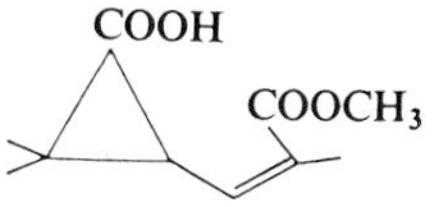

COOH COOCH$_3$

Pyrethric acid
(chrysanthemum dicarboxylic acid monomethyl ester)

The two alcohols also resemble one another, for both contain a five-membered ring to which is attached a ketone oxygen as well as the alcoholic OH, so that their chemical names contain "-one" as well as "-ol-":

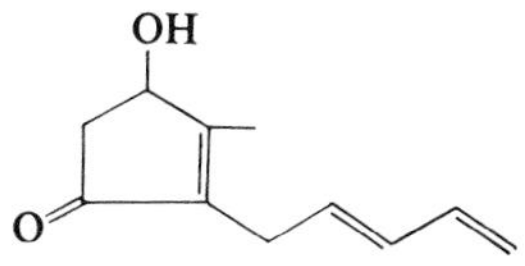

OH O

Pyrethrolone

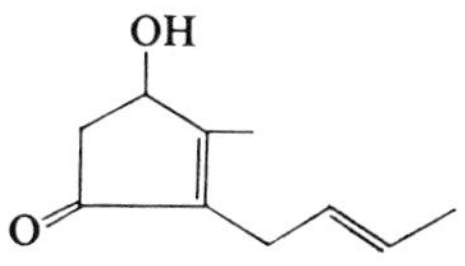

OH O

Cinerolone

Because pyrethric acid, pyrethrolone, and cinerolone all contain a vinyl group (C═C) with four different attachments, they all can have *cis* or *trans* positional isomers. The terms refer to the situation of the major substituents on the vinyl group.

trans Form

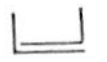

cis Form

In the above formulas, pyrethric acid has been drawn as the *cis* isomer, and the alcohols as the *trans* isomers. It will be recalled that *cis* and *trans* isomers frequently differ markedly, e.g., in melting point, crystalline form, and solubility. Furthermore, if one attempts to build models of these compounds, each can be made in two mirror-image forms (the acids have two ring carbons each with four different substituents, the alcohols have one). Consequently, there are optical isomers, *d*- and *l*-forms, of each positional isomer.

The standard classification of pyrethroids ignores the isomer situation. The esters containing pyrethrolones are called pyrethrin I if the acid is chrysanthemic acid, and pyrethrin II if the acid is pyrethric acid. The esters containing cinerolone are called cinerin I if the acid is chrysanthemic acid, and cinerin II if the acid is pyrethric acid. But no one of these four entities is singular because of the multiple isomers possible for each acid and each alcohol.

To the above list of four natural pyrethroids must now be added the two best-known synthetic pyrethroids: allethrin and cyclethrin, both of which are esters of chrysanthemic acid. The alcoholic parts are allethrolone in the case of allethrin, and a cyclopentenyl analog of allethrolone in the case of cyclethrin.

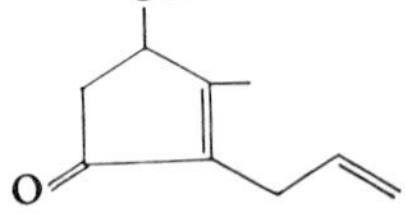

OH
O

Allethrolone
(alcohol of allethrin)

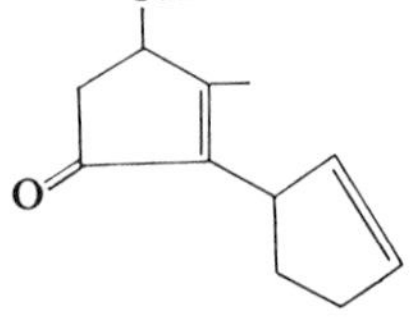

OH
O

Alcohol of cyclethrin

One can see that cinerin I, pyrethrin I, and the two above synthetics are all closely related chemically, differing only in the nature of the side chain on their alcoholic rings; and even there, different side chains all begin with:

These synthetic compounds were first prepared about 1950, and their commercial importance has been growing ever since. They are more stable in storage than the natural compounds. Allethrin is the more potent synthetic when used alone, but cyclethrin is the better when used along with synergists (6), which, as will become apparent, is the usual practice.

The efficacy of the pyrethroids can be much improved by applying them along with certain other compounds which, by themselves, are virtually

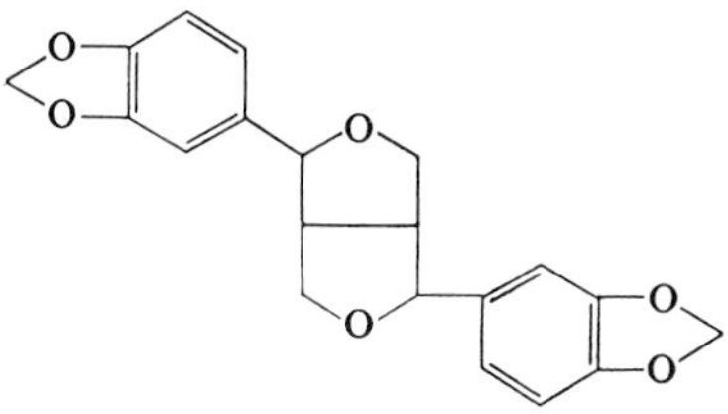

Sesamin

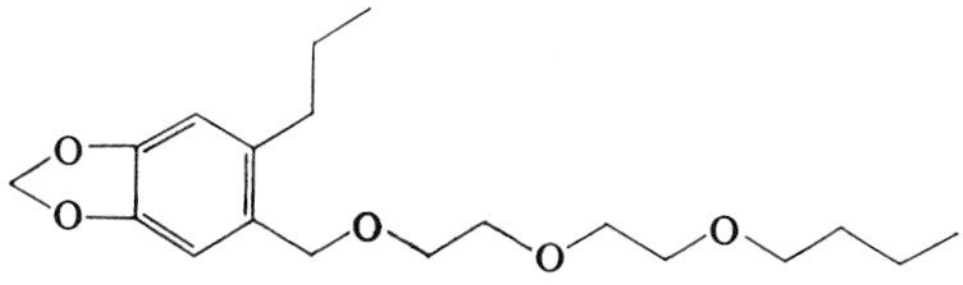

Piperonyl butoxide

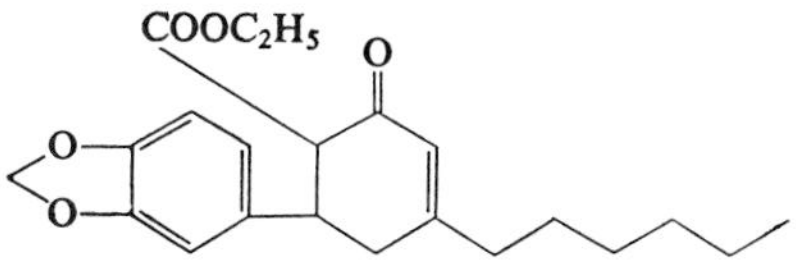

$COOC_2H_5$

Piperonyl cyclonene (minor component)

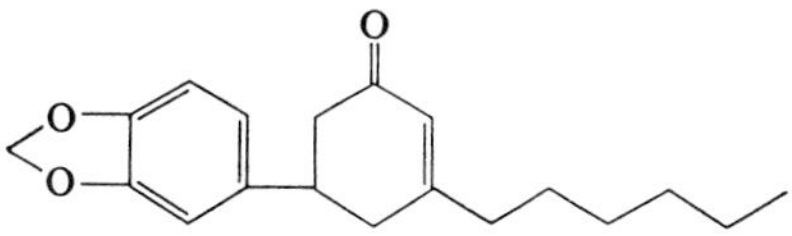

Piperonyl cyclonene (major compound)

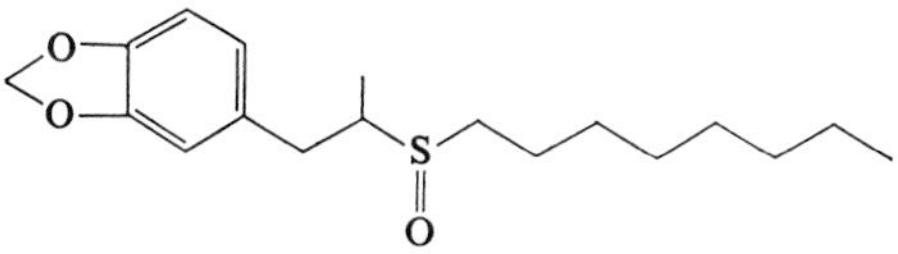

Sulfoxide

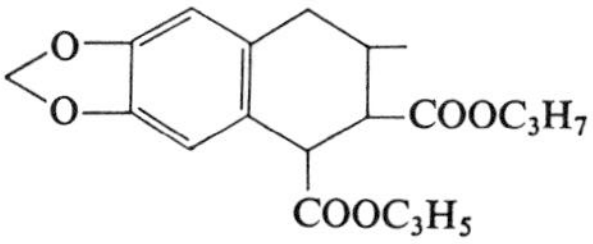

$COOC_3H_7$

$COOC_3H_5$

n-Propyl isome

FIG. 10.1. Some common pyrethrin synergists.

inactive. This is an example of synergism, a phenomenon which we can apply to cases where the toxicity of two compounds together is greater than that expected from the sum of their effects when applied separately. Synergism is therefore greater-than-additive, or one might say greater-than-expected, toxicity.* The pyrethrin synergists were the first important set of synergists; in

* Some authorities prefer rather different definitions. Pharmacologists may use the term "potentiation" for the phenomenon described above as synergism, and use "synergism" to mean a simple additive effect. Some entomologists reserve synergism for the case where at least one of the pair of compounds involved has no effect by itself, as in the case of the common pyrethrin synergists (8). For additional usages see Chapter 14.

Chapter 18 it will be shown that they, along with a few other compounds, frequently synergize organophosphates and carbamates as well. The well-known pyrethrin synergist, sesame oil, was introduced in 1940, and shown in 1942 to owe its effectiveness to its content of sesamin (4). A few years later, several analogs of piperonal were found to be excellent pyrethrin synergists, and the well-known compounds piperonyl butoxide and piperonyl cyclonene were a result. All of these synergists contain the methylenedioxyphenyl group; their detailed formulas are shown in Fig. 10.1.

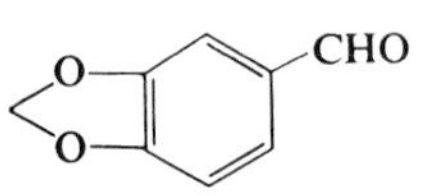

CHO

Piperonal

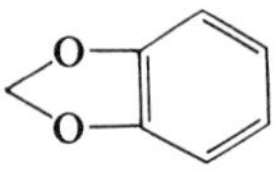

Methylenedioxyphenyl group

All workers agree on the rapidity of penetration of pyrethrins through insect cuticles; for example, in houseflies about 46% of a 20 μg/g dose of allethrin penetrated in 4 hours (5). It is also agreed that this rapidity can be substantially reduced by synergists, although the extent of the effect is variously given; for example, 13% with piperonyl butoxide and allethrin in houseflies (5). Although this retardation is a factor in synergism, blockade of metabolism is undoubtedly a more important factor.

Mode of Action

As mentioned in the opening of this chapter, the mechanisms of pyrethrin toxicity and of its remarkable selectivity remain a mystery. Many facts have been accumulated, and some will be reviewed here, with the hope that experiments yet to be done will be more revealing. Other facts and speculations have been reviewed by Metcalf (7).

Pyrethrins cause a rapid paralysis, an effect consistent with effects upon nerves (central or peripheral) or muscle.

Two fine studies by Narahashi have greatly enlarged our knowledge of pyrethroid action at the cellular level (9,10). He applied low concentrations of allethrin, typically $3 \times 10^{-6} M$, to the abdominal nerve cords of American cockroaches, and examined with intracellular electrodes in the giant axons the precise nature of the interference produced. Two separable effects were noted: the negative after-potential was first greatly increased, more than doubling in 3 minutes, then rapidly declining to zero in 6 minutes; and the action potential was progressively reduced to zero in 6 minutes. The resting potential was hardly affected (see p. 17 for explanation of these potentials). By lowering the allethrin concentration by two-thirds, the effect upon the action potential could be almost eliminated, and that upon the negative after-potential, which was now clearly revealed, was magnified to an amazing 6-fold increase. Finally, a very temperature-sensitive phenomenon was noted: at temperatures of 26.5°C or higher, allethrin ($10^{-6}M$) caused the nerve to fire repetitively in response to a single stimulus. This repetitive response was not made up of approximately equal spikes, as in the effect of DDT, but of rapidly diminishing spikes (Fig. 10.2). At 26°C or below, the first spike was followed not by a train of spikes, but merely by a damped oscillation in the resting potential; there is thus a critical temperature below which the repetitive response disappears.

In the case of the repetitive spikes caused by DDT, there was evidence that the observed concurrent modification of the negative after-potential was due to modification of potassium permeability. This possibility was ruled out for the case of allethrin poisoning, because high potassium concentrations had little effect on the unusually slow decay of the negative after-potential in allethrin poisoning; nor did high potassium mimic the allethrin effect.

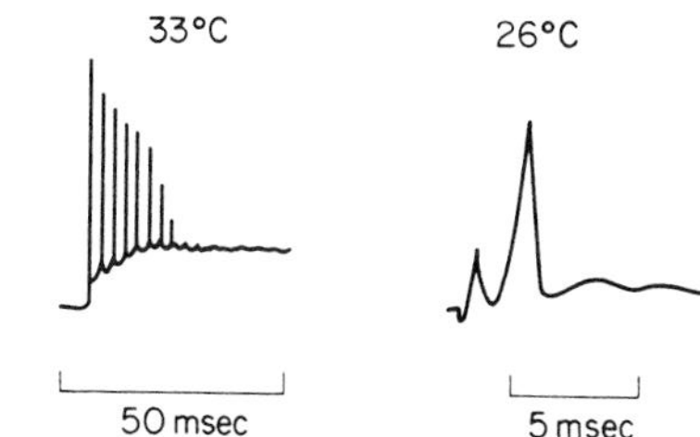

FIG. 10.2. Action potentials of the American cockroach exposed to 3×10^{-7} g/liter allethrin at two temperatures. Redrawn from Narahashi (9).

Another possibility to consider was that allethrin owed its effects to a modification of the sodium permeability. However, the prolongation of the negative after-potential was also produced by allethrin in a sodium-free system when the nerve was artificially depolarized. Consequently, interference with either potassium or sodium is probably not the cause of allethrin action.

Narahashi's informed guess about the mechanisms of allethrin action was that some unknown substance, perhaps a metabolite or perhaps chloride ion, accumulates inside or (less likely) outside the poisoned nerve. The only evidence is that with repetitive and rapid stimulation the negative after-potentials accumulate, although exponentially rather than linearly. It is as if after each stimulus, another portion of substance is produced and adds its effect to the total.

Metabolism

Any biochemist who inspected the formula of a pyrethroid would guess that a major metabolic route should be hydrolysis of the ester group. The hypothesis is so attractive that it has often been virtually assumed in the past, although the only evidence (reviewed below) was indirect. The latest work, of extreme reliability, has made it clear that, contrary to expectation, such hydrolysis is of very little importance indeed.

The earliest work on the metabolism of pyrethrin was done in 1939 when Woke (14), using a bioassay for pyrethrin, observed degradation caused by macerated armyworm tissues, especially in fat body. In 1950, Chamberlain (2) speculated that "lipase," because of its probable existence in fat body, and "because of the presence of a labile ester linkage in the pyrethrin molecule," was the probable degrading enzyme. (In fact, however, lipases act preferentially on lipid substrates, and the lability of the ester bond is chemical rather than biochemical.) Chamberlain then prepared acetone powders from whole American cockroaches and houseflies, which he referred to as lipase preparations, and which he did indeed show to contain a lipase, although numerous other enzymes were presumably present. These preparations did in fact produce acid material (judged by CO_2 production in bicarbonate buffer) from pyrethrin, suggesting that ester hydrolysis had occurred. Chamberlain speculated, on good grounds, that pyrethrin synergists might act by blocking pyrethrin degradation. Piperonyl butoxide, when added to the preparation, caused some inhibition of acid production, but a huge concentration (0.03M) caused only a little inhibition (25%). Furthermore, several other compounds, such as benzaldehyde, were inhibitory, yet are not synergists. But in favor of his hypothesis, piperonyl butoxide and benzaldehyde were about as good as inhibitors of acid production from pyrethrin caused by roach extracts as of hydrolysis of lipids by rat pancreatic lipase.

This careful study certainly suggested that insects had pyrethrin-hydrolyzing enzymes, but of course left open the question of how much degradation *in vivo* is caused by hydrolysis. Only radioisotopes could readily answer this question. The first such studies by Zeid *et al.* (15) used biosynthesized C^{14}-pyrethrin, which unfortunately was shown later (13) to contain about 24% of nonpyrethroid impurities. For instance, Zeid's finding with the cockroach that 3–12% of the dose appeared as $C^{14}O_2$ was not confirmed later with houseflies (13), when it was argued that the nonpyrethroids had given the $C^{14}O_2$. Paper chromatography was used by Zeid to resolve the radioactive metabolites; there were qualitative indications of hydrolysis "of a large portion" of the pyrethroids, but no R_f's were provided, nor any quantitative data. The research certainly kept alive the view of hydrolysis as a major route, but in retrospect the evidence was skimpy at best.

Later work (13) from Winteringham's group in England used chromatographically purified biosynthetic C^{14}-pyrethrins, and also synthetic C^{14}-allethrin labeled in known places in the alcohol portion. Extensive metabolism of both was shown in houseflies, e.g., 86% in 48 hours. This metabolism was profoundly blocked by piperonyl cyclonene. The biosynthetic pyrethrin, which was labeled in the acid and alcohol portions, did not give rise metabolically to chrysanthemic acid, as one should find (along with pyrethric acid) if enzymic hydrolysis had occurred; yet C^{14}-allethrin did give metabolite(s) chromatographing like allethrolone, a finding compatible with enzymic hydrolysis in this case. No $C^{14}O_2$ expiration was observed. The routes of metabolism therefore remained as puzzling as ever.

Bridges (1), extending this study, found some discrepancy between the amount of degradation in homogenates and in whole flies: in 5 hours, homogenates degraded 7% of the dose, but whole flies degraded 35%. Preparations of Chamberlain's "lipase" had very little effectiveness. Allethrin was metabolized about as fast as natural pyrethrins, and the rate was twice as fast in females as in males.

Parallel work in the United States with allethrin labeled with C^{14} in its acid moiety also showed that there was no ester hydrolysis in intact houseflies (5). Some other unknown metabolite, more polar than allethrin, was shown by means of paper chromatography.

To complete the swing of the pendulum, Chang and Kearns have recently shown definitively that hydrolysis plays very little role in degradation of pyrethrins by intact houseflies (3). Using randomly labeled C^{14}-pyrethrin I and C^{14}-cinerin I, and employing column chromatography on Florisil and silicic acid, they observed 96% degradation 4 hours after topical application! The degradation was virtually identical for pyrethrin I and cinerin I, and led to five metabolites as well as some chrysanthemic acid; this latter never exceeded 2.6% of the applied dose. Three of these five products, representing about half of the degradation products, were esters of chrysanthemic acid, so that the metabolic alteration was of the alcoholic portion.

Topical sesamex reduced the degradation of either compound more than 90%, and furthermore reduced the penetration of either by more than 50%. These effects taken together seem to account completely for the synergism of sesamex.

REFERENCES

1. Bridges, P. M., *Biochem. J.* **66**, 316 (1957).
2. Chamberlain, R. W., *Am. J. Hyg.* **52**, 153 (1950).
3. Chang, S. C., and Kearns, C. W., *J. Econ. Entomol.* **57**, 397 (1964).
4. Haller, H. L., LaForge, F. P., and Sullivan, W. N., *J. Org. Chem.* **7**, 185 (1942).
5. Hopkins, T. L., and Robbins, W. E., *J. Econ. Entomol.* **50**, 684 (1957).
6. Martin, H., "The Scientific Principles of Plant Protection", 4th Ed., 359 pp. Arnold, London, 1959.
7. Metcalf, R. L., "Organic Insecticides," 392 pp. Wiley (Interscience), New York, 1955.
8. Metcalf, R. L., Fukuto, T. R., Wilkinson, C., Fahmy, M. H., Abd El-Aziz, A., and Metcalf, E. R., *J. Agr. Food Chem.* **14**, 555 (1966).
9. Narahashi, T., *J. Cellular Comp. Physiol.* **59**, 61 (1962).

10. Narahashi, T., *J. Cellular Comp. Physiol.* **59**, 67 (1962).
11. Negherbon, W. O., "Handbook of Toxicology," Vol. 3, "Insecticides." Saunders, Philadelphia, 1959.
12. Staudinger, H., and Ruzicka, L., *Helv. Chim. Acta* **7**, 177, 201, 212, 236, 245, 377, 406, 412, 448 (1924).
13. Winteringham, F. P. W., Harrison, A., and Bridges, P. M., *Biochem. J.* **61**, 359 (1955).
14. Woke, P. A., *J. Agr. Res.* **58**, 289 (1939).
15. Zeid, M. M. I., Dahm, P. A., Hein, R. E., and McFarland, R. H., *J. Econ. Entomol.* **46**, 324 (1953).

CHAPTER 11

Fluorine Compounds

This chapter will deal with organic compounds of fluorine and with sodium fluoride, both of which are of rather small economic importance in terms of present world usage, but of considerable fundamental interest with respect to their modes of action. Their inclusion in a single chapter is purely on chemical grounds, and there is no reason to believe that biologically the organic and inorganic compounds of fluorine have anything in common.

Fluoro-organics

Fluoroacetate, FCH_2COOH, and certain amidic derivatives of it, have been of recurrent interest as insect control agents; present interest is especially strong in Japan. But the earliest fluoro-organic insecticides are credited to Schrader (see ref. 10), who reported in 1935 that the following derivatives of fluoroethanol were aphicidal:

$(FCH_2CH_2O)_2SO$ $(FCH_2CH_2O)_2CH$

$(FCH_2CH_2O)_2CO$ $(FCH_2CH_2OCH_2CH_2O)_2CH_2$

These compounds were successful in combating *phylloxera* in Germany (25), although they were fairly soon displaced by the even more successful organophosphates.

However, the better publicized interest in fluoro-organics began about 1951; for instance, David and Gardiner (8) then reported that sodium fluoroacetate was systemically active in plants against the bean aphid, i.e., when applied either to leaves or roots, it made other parts of the plant toxic because of its translocation through the plant. It was reported to be extremely effective, but its extreme hazard was pointed out. Undoubtedly this hazard explains the lack of extensive insecticidal use of fluoroacetate itself, although under the name of "1080" it continues to be widely used as a rodenticide.

In 1949, fluoroacetamide, FCH_2CONH_2, was patented as an insecticide (26) and in 1958 its value as a systemic insecticide was described (9). Thereafter it has been used, especially in Britain* (under the name Tritox) and Japan, on a commercial scale. There has also been interest in aromatic and aliphatic analogs of fluoroacetamide.

Toxicity

Table 11.1 shows that fluoroacetate varies remarkably in its mammalian toxicity; the rat is 100 times less sensitive than the dog. The few insects for which values are known show moderate to low sensitivity, and the celebrated case of the frog's astonishing insensitivity will be discussed below.

TABLE 11.1

Toxicity of Fluoroacetate and Fluoroacetamide[a]

	Fluoroacetate		Fluoroacetamide	
Species	LD_{50} (mg/kg)	Route	LD_{50} (mg/kg)	Route
Dog	0.06	iv	—	—
Cat	0.2	iv	—	—
Guinea pig	0.35	ip	—	—
Rat	5	ip	—	—
Mouse	18	ip	85	ip
Man	2–10	Oral	—	—
Frog	150	sc	—	—
Housefly	21	Injected	9.5	Injected
American cockroach	43	Injected	32	—

[a] Data from Pattison (25) and Matsumura and O'Brien (17).

The potency of fluoroacetate and its amide has encouraged synthesis of many analogs. Pianka and Polton (29) prepared a variety of fluoroacetamide derivatives (Table 11.2), of which several were as good as fluoroacetamide against particular insects, and had lower toxicity in rats.

* It appears to have been discontinued in Britain recently.

TABLE 11.2

TOXICITY OF FLUOROACETAMIDE DERIVATIVES[a]

Compound	Rat oral LD_{50} (mg/kg)	Percent kill[b]		
		Bean aphid (contact)	Spider mite (contact)	Bean aphid (systemic)
FCH_2CONH_2	17	88(10)	36(100)	51(100)
$FCH_2CONHCH_2OH$	23	67(30)	95(1000)	88(250)
$FCH_2CONHCH_2OCH_3$	15	56(30)	32(100)	95(100)
$FCH_2CONHCH_2O\text{-cyclo-}C_6H_{11}$	35	89(10)	87(100)	16(100)
$FCH_2CONHCH_2OCH_2CH_2Cl$	20	91(10)	95(1000)	100(250)
$FCH_2CONHCHCCl_3$ with $SC(S)N(CH_3)_2$ on CH	350	9(10)	36(100)	3(250)
$FCH_2CONHCH_2OCH_2CH_2OH$	16	80(30)	69(100)	59(100)

[a] From Pianka and Polton (29).
[b] Numbers in parentheses represent ppm.

MODE OF ACTION

During the Second World War, the belligerents were much concerned with the possible use of toxicants as warfare agents. Of special concern were those compounds for which no antidote was known, and fundamental studies were initiated to explore their mechanism of action and to try to find antidotes. One such compound was fluoroacetic acid, first synthesized in 1896, and found in 1943 to be the active principle of a poisonous South African plant, *Dichapetalum cymosum* or gibflaar. As a consequence primarily of the fine work of Sir Rudolph Peters and his colleagues, the biochemical basis of fluoroacetate poisoning was discovered (7,27,28).

Lethal doses of fluoroacetate cause symptoms only after a delay of 20–60 minutes, when clonic and especially tonic convulsions ensue, the body temperature declines markedly, the heart rate increases, and death ensues. High citrate levels are found in many tissues, but especially in heart and kidney.

After a disheartening search among 24 enzymes it was concluded the fluoroacetate was not a direct enzyme inhibitor; it was not until 1949 that it was established that fluoroacetate is a latent inhibitor, requiring metabolic conversion (or "lethal synthesis"* as Peters calls it) to a derivative which was

* Clearly this "lethal synthesis" is the analog of "activation" in phosphorothionates (p. 63). The latter term is not used here because of the risk of confusion with acetate activation, i.e., condensation of CoA with acetate, via the acetate-activating enzyme.

the actual cause of the citrate accumulation. In the following few years it was shown that the activation product was fluorocitric acid. The lethal synthesis therefore requires formation, presumably by acetate-activating enzyme, of the CoA derivative, fluoroacetyl CoA, followed by condensation with oxalacetate, presumably catalyzed by condensing enzyme, to give fluorocitrate.

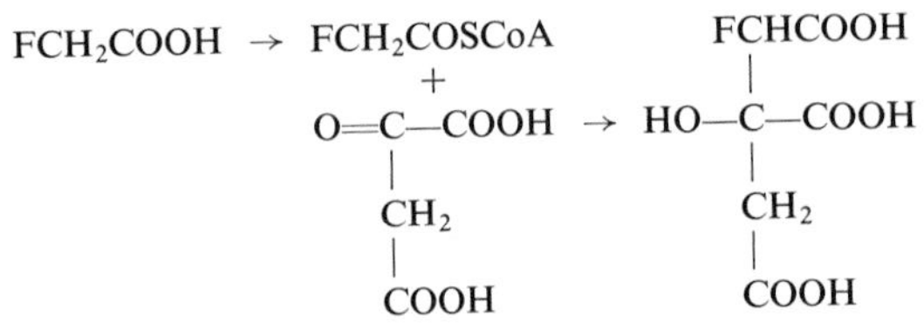

$$FCH_2COOH \rightarrow FCH_2COSCoA + O{=}C(COOH)CH_2COOH \rightarrow HO{-}C(FCHCOOH)(COOH)CH_2COOH$$

```
FCH2COOH → FCH2COSCoA                FCHCOOH
                +                       |
           O=C—COOH      →      HO—C—COOH
              |                         |
             CH2                       CH2
              |                         |
             COOH                      COOH
```

It is remarkable that neither acetate-activating enzyme nor condensing enzyme are blocked by the foreign substrate, whereas the next enzyme in sequence, aconitase, is profoundly sensitive to fluorocitrate, and is blocked by it. Because citrate is normally metabolized by aconitase, the citrate levels in poisoned rats accumulate, as described above. It is still not clear whether death is caused by the "jamming" of the Krebs citric acid cycle, with the resulting severe disruption of energy-producing reactions, hence the drop in body temperature, or whether the accumulation of citrate is the major factor, either directly or indirectly, for instance, by complexing calcium and thereby reducing free calcium levels at vital areas.

There is no excellent antidote for fluoroacetate poisoning. Acetate, which one might hope would compete with fluoroacetate at the activating enzyme, is of use in a few species only (3,35). However monoacetin, i.e., glyceryl monoacetate, has fairly general effectiveness (7):

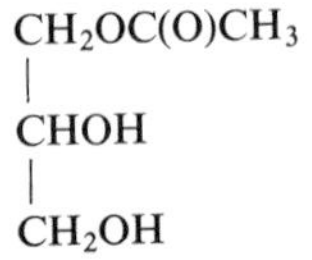

```
CH2OC(O)CH3
 |
CHOH
 |
CH2OH
```

Monoacetin

In addition, the convulsions induced by fluoroacetate can be treated symptomatically with barbiturates (25).

There is evidence that fluoroacetate kills insects by the same mechanism, for the visible symptoms (convulsions followed by prostration) and citrate accumulation have been found in American cockroaches (17). Probably fluoroacetamide kills mammals and insects by prior hydrolysis to fluoroacetate, so that, for this compound, lethal synthesis is actually a three-step process. The evidence is that fluoroacetamide gives rise to fluoroacetate in cockroaches;

and in both mice and cockroaches, massive citrate accumulations are found after the use of fluoroacetamide, as after fluoroacetate poisoning (17).

From Table 11.1 one can calculate the selective toxicity, cockroach/mouse, to be 0.4 for fluoroacetate and 2.6 for fluoroacetamide. There is some evidence that the hydrolysis of fluoroacetamide to fluoroacetate occurs faster in cockroaches than in mice, and that this is the cause of the better selectivity (17). It is probable that the various *N*-substituted derivatives of fluoroacetamide, such as those shown in Table 11.2, are also hydrolyzed to fluoroacetate, although there is a faint possibility that cleavage could occur with simultaneous introduction of coenzyme A, when the product would be fluoroacetyl CoA.

The above account has, for clarity's sake, presented matters rather straightforwardly. Yet many anomalies exist, and many curious facts remain unexplained. Why is the frog so remarkably insensitive to fluoroacetate, even though the compound causes accumulation of citrate in its heart even more than in mammals? Why is *Dichapetalum cymosum* not poisoned by its own fluoroacetate? Why does liver show such small citrate increases, although, paradoxically, the frog does show such an increase: 100 mg/kg of fluoroacetate increases the level from about 100 to 900 μg/g in 6 hours (19)? Why do purified pigeon-liver preparations, which contain both acetate-activating enzyme and condensing enzyme, not convert fluoroacetate to fluorocitrate (5)? Why does yeast convert fluoroacetate to fluoroacids (perhaps fluorobutyric and fluorohexanoic acids) other than fluorocitrate (2), and is it possible that such compounds play a role in poisoning of animals? Another compound whose significance is not known is fluoroacetoacetate, shown to be produced on treatment of perfused rat liver with fluoroacetate (18). Synthetic fluorocitrate is far less effective than the biosynthesized compounds, and it has been shown to contain many components; so far, no pure compound has been prepared which is as effective as the biosynthetic product, so some doubt still remains whether the latter really is fluorocitrate.

Until some of these questions are answered, there must still be an element of doubt about the precise mechanism of action of fluoro-organics.

Sodium Fluoride

This compound has long been of some importance for baits for cockroaches, earwigs, and ants. Its phytotoxicity and easy weathering have prohibited use on plants, although for a time compounds such as barium fluosilicate ($BaSiF_6$), sodium silicofluoride (Na_3SiF_6), and cryolite (Na_3AlF_6) enjoyed a little use for plant protection, acting on the principle of slow release of fluoride (as in the parallel case of the arsenicals, p. 192), but they compared unfavorably with arsenates (24) and cannot possibly compete with newer compounds. The use of fluosilicates in aerogels is discussed on p. 199.

Toxicity and Symptomology

Table 11.3 shows that sodium fluoride has rather low toxicity to insects and vertebrates equally. For man, sodium fluoride kills at about 70 mg/kg (14). An unexpected interaction between fluoride and organophosphates has been reported (32): an oral dose of 17 mg/kg of sodium fluoride had little effect on parathion poisoning but decreased the LD_{50} of demeton 5-fold. The effects of fluorides upon fish have been examined: rainbow trout are killed within 48 hours by 4 ppm of fluoride and carp by 83 ppm. Death was preceded by sluggishness, then convulsions and death in a state of rigor. Curiously enough, rainbow trout eggs were killed only at more than 200 ppm of fluoride (23).

TABLE 11.3

Toxicity of Sodium Fluoride[a]

Species	Route	LD_{50} (mg/kg)
Frog	sc	400
Mouse	Oral	80
Rat	Oral	200
Guinea pig	Oral	250
Dog	Oral	75
Bombyx silkworm	Oral	130
Differential grasshopper	Oral	110
American cockroach	Oral	350

[a] Data from Negherbon (22).

Fluorides have been shown (4) to have an effect upon embryonic development, at least in chicken eggs: 50 mg of sodium fluoride (a high dose) caused 30% mortality and the survivors showed gross deformations (i.e., teratogenic effects). In tissue culture preparations also, high concentrations are needed to depress cell reproduction, as measured with leukemic lymphoblasts: there was no effect at $3 \times 10^{-4} M$, and 50% inhibition required $1.5 \times 10^{-5} M$ sodium fluoride (1).

The symptoms of acute fluoride poisoning in man include salivation, stomach pains, vomiting, diarrhea, convulsions, and death by respiratory or heart failure (14). These are also the symptoms of acute poisoning of nonhuman animals (11). Chronic poisoning produces deleterious effects upon teeth and bones (11).

In insects, the symptoms involve hyperexcitability, followed by torpor and a slow decline to death. A severe necrosis of the midgut epithelium is observed after death (6).

Mechanism of Action

In the older literature, fluoride was thought to act on the integrity of cell walls by precipitating their calcium (36). In view of the epithelial disintegration of the gut described above for orally poisoned insects, this view might seem tenable. But in fact fluoride is active topically, even when insects are prevented from ingesting it during cleaning operations (33). Furthermore, as argued on p. 118, it is likely that the severe effects in gut epithelium represents an extreme response to a high local concentration, but that the lethal effects are less localized. The description below of the insensitivity of nerve to fluoride also speaks against an effect on the structure of cell walls. In vertebrates, also, the symptoms of oral poisoning are 2-fold: those which result from direct effects upon the gastrointestinal tract (vomiting, diarrhea) and those caused by fluoride absorbed from the gut and generally distributed (convulsions, lowered blood pressure). Undoubtedly, it is the latter effects which lead to death.

Neither in insects nor in mammals is the precise sequence of events leading to death fully understood, although one can enumerate many enzymes inhibited by fluoride, and the interesting direct effect upon heart muscle has been explored (see below).

Fluoride forms complexes with and inhibits a great number of metal-containing enzymes, including those containing iron, calcium, and magnesium (see review, ref. 12). The magnesium-containing enzymes include numerous phosphatases and phosphorylases, including especially ATPase, whose inhibition can give interesting effects, as discussed below. Alkaline phosphatases are rather insensitive, but acid phosphatases are particularly sensitive. Yet both acid and alkaline pyrophosphatases of potato are inhibited about 90% by $10^{-3} M$ fluoride (21); erythrocyte pyrophosphatase was 50% inhibited by only $2 \times 10^{-5} M$ fluoride (20). Other metalloenzymes affected include succinic dehydrogenase, enolase, phosphoglucomutase, cytochrome oxidase, peroxidase, and catalase. There are metalloenzymes with little sensitivity to fluoride, and these include uricase, carbonic anhydrase, and nitrate reductase.

It is therefore abundantly clear that fluoride might exert its lethal action on any one of a large number of key enzymes, and it becomes clear why it has not been possible to pinpoint precisely the fatal lesion; indeed, it is probable that no one is of unique importance. If one considers the human LD_{50} of 70 mg/kg, and if this were distributed equally through the body, the concentration of it would be almost 2mM, which is more than enough to produce large effects on those enzymes described above as sensitive. In fact, 1mM fluoride *in vitro* profoundly affects utilization of a variety of substrates (e.g., 37).

It has been claimed (13) that when sodium fluoride is administered orally to rats, or applied to rat kidney slices, fluorocitric acid is produced, and that aconitase is therefore the target for inorganic fluoride poisoning. This claim, although implausible, deserves further study.

Fluoride has no ill effect upon axonic transmission; indeed 40m*M* potassium fluoride was the best of the potassium halides for preserving the activity of perfused squid axons (34) perhaps because of ATP preservation through ATPase inhibition. If one assumes that the fundamental impulse-generating mechanism of vertebrate nerves has a similar insensitivity, then the convulsive effects of fluoride in intact animals are probably interpretable as induced by an energy deficit caused by effects on carbohydrate metabolism.

The effects of fluoride upon heart muscle are puzzling, as are those of several other inhibitors (malonate, arsenate, fluoroacetate) which cause a prolonged increase in the force of contraction, in spite of blockade of one aspect or another of metabolism. The overall effect (at low concentrations only) is stimulation. Fluoride at 4m*M* almost doubles the contraction of rat ventricle strips, while halving the utilization of glucose, with but little effect upon oxygen uptake or ability to utilize pyruvate (31). It is possible that fluoride is here exerting its well-known role as a phosphatase inhibitor, a role that has been specifically shown in rat heart for the case of ATPase inhibition (16). In this way we have a paradoxical case of an inhibitor which actually improves the efficiency of a physiological system.

When considering fluoride effects, one must always consider the possibility of precipitation of calcium fluoride as the primary factor, with consequent decrease of calcium with its various effects. By contrast, Loewi (15), noting that the effects of fluoride on heart somewhat resemble the effects of excess calcium, suggested that calcium fluoride becomes deposited on the cell membrane, giving local excess calcium. But Reiter (30) points out that whereas high calcium increases the *rate* of contraction, fluoride only alters the *extent*. A different mechanism is therefore operative, and Reiter suggests interference with the ATP-requiring calcium-uptake system which is discussed in more detail on p. 203.

These stimulating effects of moderate fluoride concentration on heart muscle are replaced by total abolition of contraction if one uses high fluoride levels, such as 0.1*M* (30).

REFERENCES

1. Albright, J. A., *Nature* **203**, 976 (1964)
2. Aldous, J. G., *Biochem. Pharmacol.* **12**, 627 (1963).
3. Annison, E. F., Hill, K. J., Lindsay, D. B., and Peters, R. A., *J. Comp. Pathol. Therap.* **70**, 145 (1960).
4. Bertran, E. C., *Anales Inst. Invest. Vet.* (*Madrid*) **13**, 11 (1963).
5. Brady, R. O., *J. Biol. Chem.* **217**, 213 (1955).

6. Brown, A. W. A., "Insect Control by Chemicals," Wiley, New York, 1951.
7. Chenoweth, M. B., *Pharmacol. Rev.* **1**, 383 (1949).
8. David, W. A. L., and Gardiner, B. O. C., *Ann. Appl. Biol.* **38**, 91 (1951).
9. David, W. A. L., and Gardiner, B. O. C., *Nature* **181**, 1810 (1958).
10. Geary, R. J., *J. Agr. Food Chem.* **1**, 880 (1953).
11. Greenwood, D. A., *Utah State Agr. Coll., Monograph Ser.* **4**, No. 2 (1956).
12. Hewitt, E. J., and Nicholas, D. J. D., *In* "Metabolic Inhibitors" (R. M. Hochster and J. H. Quastel, eds.), Vol. 2, Chapt. 29. Academic Press, New York, 1963.
13. Kurayuki, Y., *Osaka Shiritsu Daigaku Igaku Zasshi* **9**, 397 (1960).
14. Lindbeck, W. L., Hill, I. B., and Beeman, J. A., *J. Am. Med. Assoc.* **121**, 836 (1943).
15. Loewi, O., *J. Pharmacol. Exptl. Therap.* **114**, 90 (1955).
16. Maley, G. F., and Plant, G. W. E., *J. Biol. Chem.* **205**, 297 (1953).
17. Matsumura, F., and O'Brien, R. D., *Biochem. Pharmacol.* **12**, 1201 (1963).
18. Miura, K., and Hori, T., *Agr. Biol. Chem. (Tokyo)* **25**, 94 (1961).
19. Miura, K., Uchiyama, T., and Honda, K., *Agr. Biol. Chem. (Tokyo)* **25**, 83 (1961).
20. Nagana, B., and Menon, V. K. N., *J. Biol. Chem.* **174**, 501 (1948).
21. Nagana, B., Raman, A., Venugopal, B., and Sripathi, C. E., *Biochem. J.* **210**, 149 (1954).
22. Negherbon, W. O., "Handbook of Toxicology, Insecticides," Vol. 3. Saunders, Philadelphia, Pennsylvania, 1959.
23. Neuhold, J. M., and Sigler, W. F., *Trans. Am. Fisheries Soc.* **89**, 358 (1960).
24. Norton, L. B., *Ind. Eng. Chem.* **40**, 691 (1948).
25. Pattison, F. L. M., "Toxic Aliphatic Fluorine Compounds," Elsevier, New York, 1959.
26. Payne, N. M. C., U.S. Patent 2,469,349, May, 1949.
27. Peters, R. A., *Bull. Johns Hopkins Hosp.* **97**, 21 (1955).
28. Peters, R. A., *Advan. Enzymol.* **18**, 113 (1957).
29. Pianka, N., and Polton, D. J., *J. Sci. Food Agr.* **16**, 330 (1965).
30. Reiter, M., *Experienta* **21**, 87 (1965).
31. Rice, L. I., and Berman, D. A., *Am. J. Physiol.* **200**, 727 (1961).
32. Rice, W. B., and Lu, F. C., *Acta Pharmacol. Toxicol.* **20**, 39 (1963).
33. Sweetman, H. L., *Can. Entomologist* **73**, 31 (1941).
34. Tasaki, I., and Takenaka, T., *Proc. Natl. Acad. Sci. U. S.* **52**, 804 (1964).
35. Tourtellotte, W. W., and Coon, J. M., *J. Pharmacol. Exptl. Therap.* **101**, 82 (1951).
36. Trappmann, W., *Z. Pflanzenkrankh. Pflazenschutz* **48**, 514 (1938).
37. Tsao, M. U., Teagan, S. J., Borondy, P. E., and Hogg, J. F., *Metab. Clin. Exptl.* **14**, 246 (1965).

CHAPTER 12

Lindane and Other Hexachlorocyclohexanes

In 1942, it was discovered independently in England and France that the product then called benzene hexachloride was highly insecticidal. This product was a mixture of isomers produced by chlorinating benzene with six atoms of chlorine; but since the aromatic character of the ring disappears, it is entirely incorrect to call the product benzene hexachloride, a name which should be reserved for a quite different compound. Unfortunately, the use of the term benzene hexachloride and its abbreviation, BHC, is still quite common in the literature, but should be abandoned in favor of the term hexachlorocyclohexane (HCH).

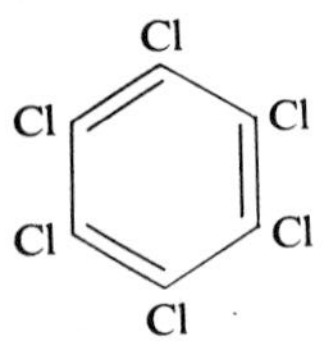

Benzene hexachloride

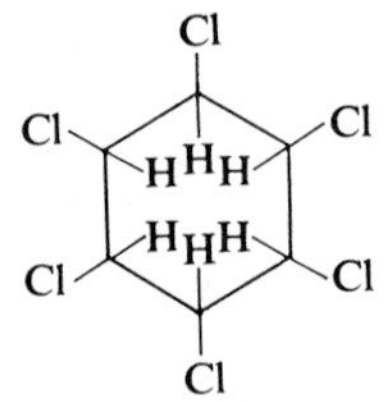

1,2,3,4,5,6,-Hexachlorocyclohexane (HCH)

If one makes models of HCH, he will find two kinds of isomerism possible. One kind is ring isomerism. The cyclohexane ring itself (whether substituted or not) can exist in two forms, picturesquely called the "boat" and "chair" forms.

The chair form is more stable, i.e., requires less energy to make and produces less on degradation, and is therefore the usual form. A second kind of isomerism involves the substituents. Of the two bonds available for substitution on each carbon atom, one of them lies approximately in the plane of the ring and is called the planar or equatorial (e) bond; the other sticks out from the plane of the ring, not unlike the axis around which a disk may rotate, and is called the axial bond. In HCH, each chlorine could be attached either equatorially or axially, so there are a series of isomers. One, called the β isomer, contains all its chlorines equatorially, and can be coded as eeeeee. At first thought one might imagine that numerous other isomers might exist, but it should be recalled that in fact the positions are disposed around a ring rather than in a straight line, so that aeeeea is the same molecule as aaeeee. Furthermore, some pairs of possible isomers are mirror images of one another, and so are enantiomorphs (optical isomers) rather than geometric isomers.

Only five isomers have been found in HCH:

Alpha (α): aaeeee
Beta (β): eeeeee
Gamma (γ): aaaeee
Delta (δ): aeeeee
Epsilon (ϵ): aeeaee

The α form exists as two enantiomorphs. The isomers differ greatly in insecticidal activity. Soon after HCH was first made, the γ isomer was found to be by far the most active, and indeed van Asperen found that the α and δ isomers actually antagonized the toxicity of the γ isomer for American cockroaches (1). For most insects, the γ isomer, commonly called lindane, is between 100 and 1000 times more toxic than any of the other isomers (27). In technical HCH, lindane is between 8 and 15% of the total (27), but it is be coming increasingly common to use pure lindane in place of crude HCH.

Lindane has a higher vapor pressure (9.4×10^{-6} mm at 20°C) than the cyclodienes or DDT, and consequently was used for some years in vapor dispensers. It is chemically stable except in alkaline solution, when it dehydrochlorinates.

Toxicity

Table 12.1 shows that lindane is a rather wide-spectrum insecticide, with LD_{50} values typically between 1 and 10 mg/kg. For mammals it has a low oral toxicity.

TABLE 12.1

TOXICITY OF LINDANE[a]

Species	Route	LD_{50} (mg/kg)
Aedes aegypti mosquito (male)	Spray	3
Housefly (male)	Spray	2
American cockroach	Topical	5
German cockroach	Topical	3.8
Milkweed bug	Topical	32.5
Differential grasshopper	Topical	3.4
Rat	Oral	125
Mouse	Oral	86
Guinea pig	Oral	127
Rabbit	Oral	200

[a] Data from Metcalf (27) and Negherbon (29).

Mode of Action

In view of the mystery surrounding the mode of action of the other, more widely used, chlorinated hydrocarbons, the reader should not be surprised to learn that we know painfully little about lindane's action. Probably it is a neuroactive agent which acts in a way not unlike DDT. In support of this view: (a) the gross symptoms of poisoning involve tremors, ataxia, convulsions, and prostration (31); (b) stimulated respiration (probably a consequence of excessive nervous and hence muscular activity) occurs, very much as for DDT, with a similar time course but to a greater extent (Fig. 6.4); (c) acetylcholine levels in the nerves of poisoned insects are substantially increased, as with DDT (details on p. 118); (d) excessive electrical activity is seen in poisoned axons, as with DDT; but there are differences in detail. Whereas DDT gives rise to multiple spikes of 250–700 μV height, lindane produces only sets of spikes, 2 to 4 in number, and only 50–100 μV in height (23); (e) lindane's toxicity shows a negative temperature coefficient, but numerically smaller than that of DDT. The decrease in toxicity to cockroaches caused by raising the temperature 17°C was 19-fold for DDT, but only 2.5-fold for lindane (17).

Mullins (28) attempted in 1955 to explain the marked variation in neural activity caused by the various HCH isomers on the basis of varying abilities to "fit" into a hypothetical lattice in the axonic membrane. He noted that the ϵ and η isomers were inactive, the β was a weak depressant, the δ a strong depressant, the α a weak excitant, and lindane a strong excitant. He suggested that one might consider the lattice to resemble the spaces seen when one looks, end-on, at a pile of cylinders packed in the tightest possible way (hexagonal array). The spaces are then the hypothetical pores in the membrane lattice, and Mullins suggests that compounds are excitatory if they fit tightly into these pores. Compounds which are too large to enter should have no effect. Compounds which can fit tightly might well distort the membrane structure and produce (by an unknown mechanism) excitability. Compounds which are small enough to enter, but then can only bind at one or two places

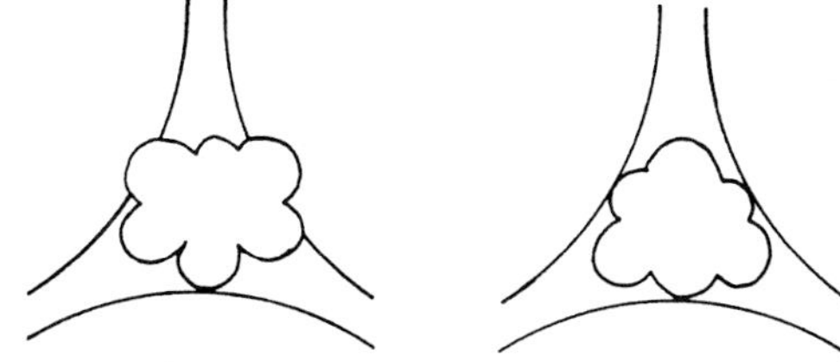

FIG. 12.1. Mullins' model of HCH in a membrane lattice. Two spaces are shown; each is formed from the gap between three cylinders of 40 Å diameter, separated from each other by 2 Å. The HCH isomers, shown in plane orientation, are the δ (left) and γ (right). Redrawn from Mullins (28).

of contact, would block the pores but not distort the membrane, and thus (again by an unknown mechanism) lessen excitability, i.e., act as narcotics (p. 22). Mullins found that if he considered a lattice made up of 40-Å cylinders which were held apart at their area of potential contact by a 2-Å space (Fig. 12.1), the resultant pore sizes were such that in the plane orientation (i.e., pushing the HCH isomer in with its flat face in the plane of the pore) the γ isomer fitted neatly, and the other known configurations (α, β, δ, ϵ) were too large. All of the isomers could be pushed in, in an end-on orientation, but then none fitted snugly to the pore walls. Mullins also showed that DDT, if pushed into these pores in an end-on position, fitted rather snugly, and was therefore prepared to extend the argument to DDT activity; the inactive 2-chloro-DDT, for instance, cannot be correctly oriented.

The Mullins hypothesis has never been disproved. But until some experimental evidence is forthcoming to show that lindane does indeed bind to some vital surface and alter its properties, the hypothesis remains entirely speculative.

There has been a celebrated case of a false trail in the search for lindane's mode of action. Inositol is hexahydroxycyclohexane, i.e., the hydroxy analog of hexachlorocyclohexane. In 1954, Slade (33) proposed that lindane had the same configuration as myoinositol, one of the isomers of inositol.

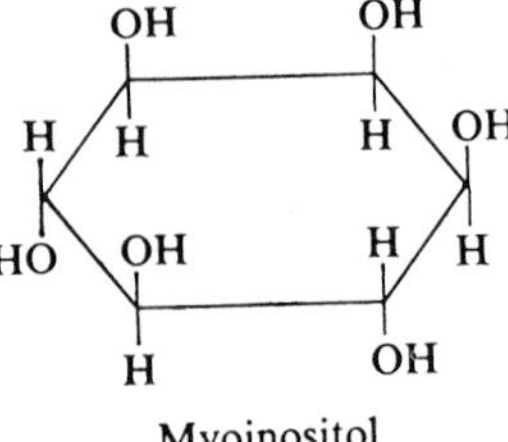

Myoinositol

The proposal was biologically interesting because myoinositol is required in the diet of mammals and fungi. Acting on this cue, Kirkwood and Phillips (21) showed in 1946 that growth of the yeast *Saccharomyces cerevisiae* was inhibited by several hexachlorocyclohexanes and especially by lindane; in the case of lindane only, this inhibition could be overcome by adding myoinositol. These findings constituted quite good evidence that lindane was acting as an antimetabolite for myoinositol, and seemed confirmed by the demonstration that an unusual strain of the yeast, which did not require myoinositol, was also insensitive to lindane. Similarly, the myoinositol-requiring fungus *Nematospora gossypii* had its growth stopped by lindane (not by α- or β-HCH), and this effect was reversed by myoinositol (9); a similar case was shown for the fungus *Neurospora crassa* (37). Furthermore, in *N. crassa* there is also a strain which requires inositol and one which does not; both showed growth inhibition by lindane, but only in the inositol-requiring strain did inositol reverse inhibition (16). As for insects, inositol delayed the time-to-death from lindane poisoning in the German cockroach (34) and antagonized growth retardation by lindane in the rice moth larva (30). At the enzyme level, it has been claimed (24), but more authoritatively denied (10,12,32), that α-amylase contains inositol and is inhibited by lindane.

In spite of the impressive evidence marshalled above in favor of the hypothesis that lindane is an antimetabolite for myoinositol, the current view is that it is incorrect.

The first doubts were based upon the view that inositol is not a dietary requirement for insects. But Forgash showed in 1958 and later that the American cockroach does require 80 ppm of myoinositol in its diet for normal growth and development (13,15). Against the hypothesis, however, are two kinds of evidence. First, extensive work in two independent laboratories has shown that δ-HCH and not lindane is the true structural analog of myoinositol (3,4,18,38). Second, it has been shown for rabbits (25), *Culex fatigans* and

Aedes aegypti mosquito larvae (36), thrips (26), and American cockroaches (11) that the acute toxicity of lindane is unaffected by myoinositol. The most complete study on this failure of antagonism was in 1962 by Forgash (14). He found that dietary lindane caused exactly the same chronic effects upon American cockroaches in the presence of a normal subsistence level of inositol (80 ppm) or in a huge excess of it (e.g., 66,000 ppm); this was true both at low lindane doses (0.03% of diet) which caused growth depression, or at high doses (0.13% of diet) which caused high mortalities in the course of two months. In addition, δ-HCH was entirely without action under any conditions. Other reports show that a 5-fold excess of inositol in the diet did not effect the chronic toxicity of dieldrin to rats (10), nor did inositol affect the inhibition by lindane of cell division in *Psammechinus microtuberculatus* or *Sphoerochinus granularis*.

In summary, lindane is not a structural analog of myoinositol. Although lindane acts like an antimetabolite of myoinositol for many fungi, the bulk of the evidence suggests that it does not so act for insects or for mammals. Finally, the reports above suggest that lindane is a neurotoxicant whose effects are normally seen within hours, and it is therefore unlikely that it acts as an antimetabolite of a growth factor.

Metabolism

In 1954 it was shown that lindane was fairly rapidly converted by mice into unknown products (2). Ten years later (22) the state of knowledge was only a little better: Cl^{36}-lindane was used to show that 60% of the urinary radioactive products were inorganic (presumably as chlorides and related anions), suggesting extensive breakdown. The breakdown was probably mediated by the well-known liver microsomal system, for pretreatment of the animals with phenobarbital, which induces development of microsomes (p. 212), markedly increased breakdown.

Sternburg and Kearns (35) suggested in 1956 that houseflies could dehydrochlorinate lindane to pentachlorocyclohexene (PCC):

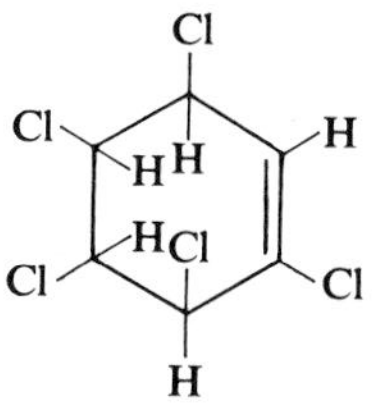

The evidence was essentially that the product on nitration behaved like PCC. However, it was later shown (6,8), using the isotope dilution technique, that negligible PCC was produced.

In 1959, Bradbury and Standen (7) showed that housefly homogenates, in the presence of reduced glutathione, converted lindane to a material which could be hydrolyzed by alkali to thiophenols,* suggesting that at least one of the CCl groups had been converted to CSR, permitting later hydrolysis to CSH. The nature of R was unknown. Intact resistant houseflies convert lindane

$$C_6H_5Cl + HS{-}R \longrightarrow C_6H_5S{-}R + H^+ + Cl^- \longrightarrow C_6H_5SH + HOR$$

similarly, and release four or more moles of chloride per mole of lindane (5).

Ishida and Dahm (19,20) described in 1965 some properties of the HCH-metabolizing enzymes, using HCH disappearance, assayed by gas chromatography, as the index of enzyme activity. Activity was in the soluble fraction of whole insects, and associated with proteins in the molecular weight range of 54,000. A very specific requirement for glutathione was described: other SH

TABLE 12.2

DISTRIBUTION OF ACTIVITY IN DEGRADING LINDANE AND ANALOGS[a]

Species or tissue	Units per mg N			
	Lindane (γ-HCH)	α-HCH	δ-PCC	γ-PCC
Housefly adults (female)	38	158	6390	560
Drosophila melanogaster adults (mixed sexes)	0	0	990	23
Stable fly adults (mixed sexes)	0	13	0	63
American cockroach adults (female)	0	14	—	44
German cockroach adults (mixed sexes)	0	0	—	23
Honey bee adults (female)	0	0	—	0
Rat liver	0	0	—	19
Rabbit liver (female)	0	3.2	227	13
Rabbit kidney (female)	0	1.1	79	2.7

[a] Data from Ishida and Dahm (19).

* It is not clear whether the hydrolysis product was a thiophenol, implying that ring aromatization had occurred, or a thiolcyclohexyl compound.

compounds were inactive or even inhibitory. Such a specificity is reminiscent of the similar finding with DDT (p. 128) and indeed the enzyme system dehydrochlorinated DDT, and DDT and lindane were competitive inhibitors of each other. It is quite likely, there, that the enzymes which act on DDT and lindane are identical; both are inhibited by "WARF antiresistant" (p. 129).

The lindane-degrading preparations also degraded other HCH isomers tested, in the order $\alpha > \gamma > \delta$: but the β-isomer was not degraded. PCC was rapidly degraded, and the authors suggested that this might account for the virtual absence of PCC residues in lindane-treated insects. There was great variation in the activity found in various insects and in mammalian tissues (Table 12.2), and also in various developmental phases of houseflies; but no correlation of enzyme activity with toxicity was found.

REFERENCES

1. Asperen, K., van, *Bull. Entomol. Res.* **46**, 837 (1956).
2. Asperen, K., van, and Oppenoorth, F. J., *Nature* **173**, 1000 (1954).
3. Bastiansen, O. O., Ellefsen, O., and Hassel, O., *Research* (*London*) **2**, 248 (1949).
4. Bijvoet, J., *Rec. Trav. Chim.* **67**, 777 (1948).
5. Bradbury, F. R., *J. Sci. Food Agr.* **8**, 90 (1957).
6. Bradbury, F. R., and Standen, H., *J. Sci. Food Agr.* **9**, 203 (1958).
7. Bradbury, F. R., and Standen, H., *Nature* **183**, 983 (1959).
8. Bridges, R. G., *Nature* **184**, 1337 (1959).
9. Buston, H. W., Jacobs, S. E., and Goldstein, A., *Nature* **158**, 22 (1946).
10. Doisy, E., and Bocklage, E., *Proc. Soc. Exptl. Biol. Med.* **74**, 613 (1950).
11. Dresden, D., and Krijgsman, B. J., *Bull. Entomol. Res.* **38**, 575 (1948).
12. Fischer, E., and Bernfeld, P., *Helv. Chim. Acta* **32**, 1146 (1949).
13. Forgash, A. J., *Ann. Entomol. Soc. Am.* **51**, 406 (1958).
14. Forgash, A. J., *J. Econ. Entomol.* **55**, 308 (1962).
15. Forgash, A. J., and Moore, R. F., *Ann. Entomol. Soc. Am.* **53**, 91 (1960).
16. Fuller, R. C., Barratt, R. W., and Tatum, E. L., *J. Biol. Chem.* **186**, 823 (1950).
17. Guthrie, F. E., *J. Econ. Entomol.* **43**, 559 (1950).
18. Hassel, O., *Research* (*London*) **3**, 504 (1950).
19. Ishida, M., and Dahm, P. A., *J. Econ. Entomol.* **58**, 383 (1965).
20. Ishida, M., and Dahm, P. A., *J. Econ. Entomol.* **58**, 602 (1965).
21. Kirkwood, S., and Phillips, S., *J. Biol. Chem.* **163**, 261 (1946).
22. Koransky, W., Portig, J., Vohland, H. W., and Klempan, I., *Arch. Exptl. Pathol. Pharmakol.* **247**, 49 (1964).
23. Lalonde, D. I. V., and Brown, A. W. A., *Can. J. Zool.* **32**, 74 (1954).
24. Land, R., and Williams, R., *Arch. Biochem.* **19**, 329 (1948).
25. McNamara, B. P., and Krop, S., *J. Pharmacol. Exptl. Therap.* **92**, 140 (1948).
26. Metcalf, R. L., *J. Econ. Entomol.* **40**, 522 (1947).
27. Metcalf, R. L., "Organic Insecticides." Wiley (Interscience), New York, 1955.
28. Mullins, L. J., *Science* **122**, 118 (1955).
29. Negherbon, W. O., "Handbook of Toxicology, Insecticides," Vol. 3. Saunders, Philadelphia, Pennsylvania, 1959.
30. Sarma, P. S., *Current Sci.* (*India*) **19**, 315 (1950).

31. Savit, J., Kollross, J. J., and Tobias, J. M., *Proc. Soc. Exptl. Biol. Med.* **62**, 44 (1946).
32. Schwimmer, S., and Balls, A. K., *J. Biol. Chem.* **179**, 1063 (1949).
33. Slade, R. E., *Chem. Ind.* (*London*) **40**, 314 (1945).
34. Srivastava, A. S., *Science* **115**, 403 (1952).
35. Sternburg, J., and Kearns, C. W., *J. Econ. Entomol.* **49**, 548 (1956).
36. Thorp, J. M., and de Meillon, B., *Nature* **160**, 264 (1947).
37. Tirunarayanan, M., and Sarma, P. S., *J. Sci. Ind. Res.* (*India*) **12B**, 251 (1953).
38. Van Vloten, G. W., Kruissink, C. A., Strijk, B., and Bijvoet, J. M., *Nature* **162**, 771 (1948).

CHAPTER 13

Various Compounds

In this chapter we will consider a variety of compounds whose practical importance is rather small, and which do not form a part of the major groups of insecticides which today account for most theoretical and economic interest. Nevertheless, each compound has significant practical use, and for each we know a good deal about its mechanism of action. Compounds which do not meet these two criteria, such as the sabadilla alkaloids, phenothiazines, and the "amaroids" or quassia extracts, will not be discussed in this book.

Arsenicals

Many inorganic materials have been employed in insect control, including compounds of mercury, boron, thallium, arsenic, antimony, selenium and fluoride. The only such element used on a large scale now is arsenic, which in the form of lead arsenate is still a common pesticide, and in the years prior to 1960 was used more in the United States than were pyrethrins, rotenoids, or lindane, although well below the amounts of DDT, cyclodienes, or organophosphates.

Arsenic occurs in two valence forms, the trivalent form giving arsenious acid $As(OH)_3$ and its salts (called arsenites) and the pentavalent giving arsenic acid $O{=}As(OH)_3$ and its salts (called arsenates). The arsenites are generally more soluble and insecticidal, but also more phytotoxic. The material "Paris green" was used in the United States in 1867 and thereafter; it suffers from its hazard to plants and animals and from the inconstancy of different preparations, so that now it is used primarily in baits. In consists of a complex compound between cupric acetate $(CH_3COO)_2Cu$ and three molecules of cupric arsenite

$Cu(AsO_2)_2$, although a ratio nearer to 1:2 is obtained with some methods of preparation (35)

The lead and calcium salts of arsenic acid are by far the commonest forms in use today, and the salt called "acid lead arsenate" is most used. This preparation is primarily plumbic hydrogen arsenate, $PbHAsO_4$. A less common material called "neutral lead arsenate" or (paradoxically) "basic lead arsenate" is sometimes described as triplumbic arsenate $Pb_2(AsO_4)_2$, but in fact is a mixture of unknown compounds whose average composition approaches this formula (35).

By adding an excess of lime to arsenic acid, one gets a material known as calcium arsenate, which again is not a single compound but "mixtures of indefinite basic calcium arsenates and calcium hydroxide" (35). It is almost certainly *not* tricalcium arsenate, as its name would suggest. The basic calcium arsenates consist of compounds such as $[Ca_3(AsO_4)_2]_3Ca(OH)_2$.

The varied (and variable) forms of arsenic insecticides are due in part to the multitude of possible salts that arsenic acids can form, in part to the empirical approach to preparation, and in part to another factor altogether: that the toxic material itself is undoubtedly the arsenate or arsenite ion, which is an indiscriminate toxicant rapidly lost by weathering. The aim of arsenic formulation is to apply it as a material which will itself be of low toxicity (especially to plants) and with persistence on a plant surface, but will release soluble toxic ions, preferably not until ingestion by insects (41), for the arsenicals are classic "stomach poisons," i.e., compounds whose action follows oral ingestion. One might hope indeed to find arsenicals which lose arsenic slowly by weathering, but rapidly in the gut, for a study in 1929 (20) showed that the toxicity of a series of arsenites and arsenates was unrelated to simple water-solubility, but was closely correlated with their solubility at pH 9, an alkaline pH often encountered in insect gut.

One might well imagine that in the course of seeking this uneasy balance of solubility, one produces materials much of whose potential toxicity is never realized. And indeed, studies with labeled arsenicals show that most of what is ingested passes through the gut unchanged; for example, of a dose of lead arsenate administered to silkworms, one study in 1931 showed 90% passed through (7) and another in 1941 showed 55%, with only 2% retained in the insect tissues (42); the remainder was retained in the gut or regurgitated.

Toxicity and Symptoms

Table 13.1 shows that lead arsenate is of moderate to low toxicity for a variety of insects and mammals. Accidental poisoning in man is common; in 1956, 35% of accidental deaths associated with pesticides were caused by arsenicals (24).

TABLE 13.1

TOXICITY OF LEAD ARSENATE[a]

Species	Route	LD_{50} (mg/kg)
Differential grasshopper	Oral	3000
American cockroach (male)	Oral	150
Imported cabbageworm larva	Oral	90
Southern armyworm larva	Oral	290
Rat	Oral	825
Dog	Oral	500
Rabbit	Oral	125

[a] Data from Negherbon (40).

Symptoms in man and other mammals include abdominal pain and vomiting, and a precipitous fall in blood pressure leading to a state of shock. The fall is caused by increased dilation and permeability of the capillaries. In lethal cases, death may be delayed for up to 14 days, and is preceded by vomiting and profuse diarrhea, due to direct effects upon the alimentary tract. In sublethal cases, a polyneuritis may be seen, with pain and tenderness in the limbs (24,40).

In insects poisoned by arsenic, eating stops, regurgitation occurs (in lepidoptera), activity is steadily reduced, and an inexcitability of increasing completeness terminates in death (40).

MODE OF ACTION

The inhibitory effects of arsenicals have been recently reviewed at length (62). The uncomfortable variation in the nature of arsenicals, described above, is only added to when we consider mode of action. Three factors, partially separable, may be involved: (1) uncoupling of oxidative phosphorylation by arsenolysis; (2) combination with various enzymic SH groups and especially in pyruvic oxidase; and (3) gross protein precipitation. Probably the actual toxicant is arsenite ion except in arsenolysis (see below); in the case of arsenate poisoning, reduction to the arsenite is a prerequisite for development of the biochemical lesion.*

Arsenic resembles phosphorus in several ways because they are both in the same group in the periodic table of elements, so that their outermost, most

* It would seem that the major evidence for this statement is the inactivity of arsenate *in vitro*, although somewhat more direct evidence exists for some organo-arsenicals (61). Yet arsenate acts directly as an uncoupler of oxidative phosphorylation (10).

reactive, electronic shells are identical. For instance, both form two series of acids of the type $X(OH)_3$ and $O{=}X(OH)_3$, where X can be arsenic or phosphorus. Now phosphorus occupies a unique place in intermediary metabolism, since the commonest energy storehouse is the P—O—P bond of ATP. Arsenic (as arsenite, or in some cases as arsenate) can substitute partially for phosphorus in some reactions, with results that can be devastating. The best established reaction is so-called arsenolysis, which can take place instead of phosphorolysis, with the unfortunate result that whereas phosphorolysis yields a precious mole of ATP, arsenolysis does not. In general terms, if we write BH for oxidizable substrate, B for its oxidation product, and BP for phosphorylated oxidation product, then a fairly common metabolic step involves (*a*) simultaneous oxidation and phosphorylation of B, using inorganic phosphorus as the phosphorus source and simultaneously reducing NADP to $NADPH_2$:

$$BH + NADP + P_{inorg} \rightarrow BP + NADPH_2$$

Then (*b*) the BP is cleaved with simultaneous formation of ATP from ADP:

$$BP + ADP \rightarrow B + ATP$$

Thus the overall reaction has two usable products, $NADPH_2$ in step (*a*) and ATP in step (*b*). For an actual example, BH might be glyceraldehyde 3-phosphate, then BP would be 1,3-diphosphoglycerate, and B would be 3-phosphoglycerate. The enzyme of step (*a*) would then be glyceraldehyde phosphate dehydrogenase, and of step (*b*), phosphoglycerate kinase.

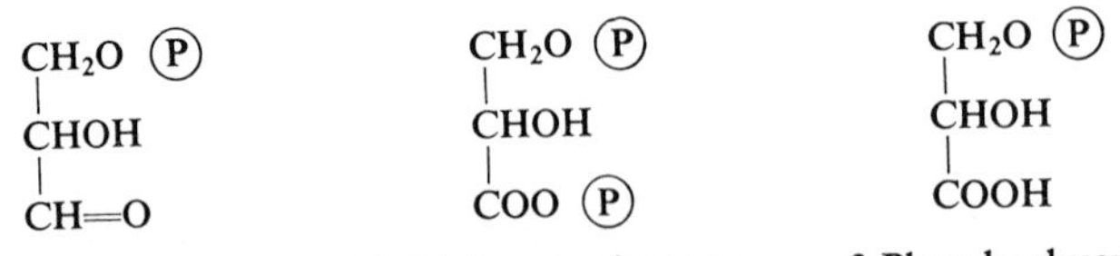

Glyceraldehyde 3-phosphate	1,3-Diphosphoglycerate	3-Phosphoglycerate
CH_2O Ⓟ	CH_2O Ⓟ	CH_2O Ⓟ
|	|	|
CHOH	CHOH	CHOH
|	|	|
CH=O	COO Ⓟ	COOH

where the circled P represents the phosphoryl group $P(O)(OH)_2$.

Arsenite interferes in the above reactions by substituting for phosphate in step (*a*):

$$BH + NADP + As(OH)_3 \rightarrow BAs(OH)_2 + NADPH_2$$

But the $BAsOH)_2$ is far less stable than the corresponding phosphate BP, which "ought" to have been formed, and it hydrolyzes spontaneously and wastefully with no ATP formation.

$$BAs(OH)_3 + H_2O \rightarrow B + As(OH)_3$$

Consequently, the overall reaction has gone, as far as B is concerned, just as well with arsenite as with phosphate; but the other products with phosphate are $NADPH_2$ and ATP, whereas with arsenite only $NADPH_2$ is produced.

Another arsenolytic reaction is sucrose hydrolysis by bacterial sucrose phosphorylase (12); but there is no guarantee that arsenolysis occurs in all such cases, for in the maltose phosphorylase reaction, arsenite cannot replace phosphate (61). Nevertheless, the ability of arsenate or arsenite to cause arsenolysis is used as a criterion for determining whether an intermediate phosphorylation step is involved. For instance, α-ketoglutarate is oxidized to succinate with concurrent ATP synthesis; the demonstration of arsenolysis showed that a phosphorylated intermediate was involved (53).

An extremely important example of arsenolysis is the ability of arsenite and arsenate to uncouple phosphorylation. At comparable concentrations (about $5 \times 10^{-3} M$) arsenate reduces oxidative phosphorylation about 50% and arsenite reduces it about 95% (10,31). Oxidative phosphorylation (discussed further on p. 161) is of course the major energy-producing step of the cell, and involves production of three ATP molecules for every $NADPH_2$ molecule it oxidizes; the mechanism probably involves triple repetition of steps (*a*) and (*b*) above. Arsenite therefore permits easy oxidation of $NADPH_2$, but without concurrent ATP synthesis, which is of course the whole purpose of oxidative phosphorylation.

Now let us consider a second mechanism of arsenic toxicity: its ability to combine with enzymic SH groups. In 1909 Ehrlich had suggested that therapeutic arsenicals, such as mapharsen, react with SH groups. Perhaps the most

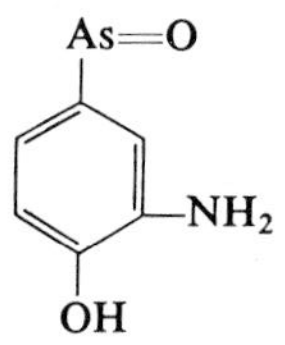

As=O
NH_2
OH

Mapharsen
(Mapharside, arsenoxide, oxophenarsine)

conclusive proof of a reaction with SH is the work of Peters (44) upon another organic arsenical, the warfare agent lewisite, $ClCH{=}CHAsCl_2$. Peters was able to show that the primary effect of lewisite was on the pyruvic oxidase enzyme system, and one may presume the actual sensitive item therein is the lipoic acid (or thioctic acid) which, in the form of lipothiamine pyrophosphate, is a vital component. The work of Peters' group culminated in the development in 1946 of an antidote for lewisite, called British anti-lewisite or BAL or 2,3-dimercaptopropanol or dimercaprol (57).

BAL	Lipoic acid
CH_2SH	CH_2SH
|	|
$CHSH$	CH_2
|	|
CH_2OH	$CHSH$
	|
	$(CH_2)_4COOH$

However, from the fact that organic arsenicals are used as therapeutic agents as well as for warfare purposes, one might guess that different arsenicals attack different enzymes, and such is the case. For instance, 10m*M* arsenite has no effect on aconitase *in vitro*, whereas 0.04m*M* diphenylchloroarsine inhibits it 70%. The same is qualitatively true for isocitric dehydrogenase. The inhibitory effects are reversed by typical monothiol* reagents such as glutathione (44). There are numerous other SH enzymes of importance, such as lactic dehydrogenase, α-glycerophosphate dehydrogenase, and cytochrome oxidase, and susceptibility to at least some arsenicals, in low concentrations, is found in all of them. Webb (62) lists 22 pages of enzymes sensitive to arsenic. Typically, glutathione provides moderate protection, whereas BAL gives great protection.

Finally, inorganic arsenicals can cause gross coagulation of proteins at sufficiently high concentrations, as will be discussed below with respect to insecticidal action. It seems most probable that this effect is also on SH groups, but in this case instead of involving a particular SH group in an enzyme's active site, it involves the sulphur bonds which play an important role in maintaining the native configuration of most proteins.

With these three mechanisms (arsenolysis, anti-SH-enzymes, and protein coagulation) in mind, let us turn to the question of the cause of poisoning by inorganic arsenate and arsenite in vertebrates and in insects. Definitive answers, in a word, are absent. In vertebrates, the commonest hazard is from soluble forms in low concentrations, so that gross protein effects are probably unimportant. From the work on lewisite it would seem that pyruvic oxidase is the most arsenic-sensitive enzyme, but arguing from data obtained with organic compounds may be dangerous. A corollary of pyruvic oxidase inhibition would be increased pyruvate levels in blood. Alternatively, if arsenolysis was the primary factor, mitochondria of poisoned animals should show uncoupled oxidative phosphorylation. I am not aware of studies of either of these factors in poisoned vertebrates.

* Glutathione has a single SH group; BAL has two strategically located ones.

Arsenite-poisoned animals show profound decreases in blood sugar and liver glycogen, and to a lesser extent in muscle glycogen. Thus in normal mice the values for these three are, respectively, 149, 5.5, and 0.33 mg %. In mice given 19 mg/kg of sodium arsenite, these values after 5 hours were 59, 0.2, and 0.18 mg %. It is likely that these decreases owe in part to uncoupling of oxidative phosphorylation and in part to direct enzyme inhibition. An interesting feature is that high altitudes exacerbate arsenite toxicity; a dose that normally kills 5% of mice kills 70% at altitudes of 20,000 feet (4).

Brain homogenates from guinea pigs show small responses in their glucose metabolism with $5 \times 10^{-4} M$ arsenate, but this concentration of arsenite inhibits oxygen uptake 80% (suggesting that a major effect is *not* uncoupling, which stimulates respiration in this preparation). Experiments with C^{14}-glucose suggested that the normal glycolytic route was 90% blocked, whereas the alternative pentose-shunt pathway was unaffected (27).

When one turns to the situation in insects, similar uncertainty prevails, which is worsened by the variable nature of the insecticidal preparations often used and confused by the fact that the amount of soluble arsenic produced may be the factor that dominates toxicity. Unfortunately, at the very time when the greatly increased knowledge of organic arsenicals was published after the war, the newly discovered organic insecticides captured the attention of insecticide workers and the arsenicals were much neglected, as Norton sadly commented in 1948 (41). In Brown's view (6), the "main site of action ... is the midgut tissue," and he classifies inorganic arsenicals under "necrotic poisons". Now it is certainly the case that prominent features of arsenic poisoning of insects include effects upon midgut epithelium, as shown by several workers starting with Parfentjev in 1929 (43) and more recently by Chadbourne and Rainwater in 1953 (8). The effects, seen in many species, involve increased mitosis at low doses, vacuolation, pycnosis of the nuclei* [which in some species may extend into the muscular wall of the midgut (8)] at higher doses, and total loss of patches of epithelium with heavy doses. Another microscopic change is in the hemocytes, which are reduced in number by 80% in some cases (18) or enlarged in size in others (59).

I find it hard to accept Brown's view on this matter. Massive necrotic effects have been reported for other insecticides which are undoubtedly not primarily "necrotic poisons." Thus DDT causes vacuolization of the midgut epithehal cells of the bee (52) and loss of the midgut epithelium in silkworms (21), and parathion causes changes in secretory glands of the gut (29). I have always felt that these disintegrations were secondary phenomena for DDT and parathion, and that the same is true of the arsenicals. It seems implausible to argue that an effect on the midgut, however massive, is a primary cause of death if one considers how lively an American cockroach remains for a day or two after

* Condensation and shrinkage to a structureless, intensely staining clump.

his whole gut and fat body have been removed. It seems more plausible that the gut, which is exposed to very high concentrations, is profoundly affected, but that the fatal lesion is biochemical rather than "necrotic."

The symptoms of insect poisoning involve progressive inactivity, beginning with reduced spontaneous movement, proceding through loss of the righting reflex, and terminating in death without convulsions (37). These symptoms are quite unlike those of the specific neuroactive agents (anticholinesterases, fluoro-organics, nicotine), and quite similar to respiratory poisons such as rotenone. *In vitro* tests suggest that insect SH-enzymes have, as one would expect, a sensitivity to arsenicals, as discussed above for vertebrates; thus arsenite inhibits α-ketoglutarate dehydrogenase of bee (28), and arsenate is arsenolytic for glyceraldehyde 3-phosphate in houseflies (9). Glutathione protects American cockroaches against arsenate (19), but does not protect yellow mealworms against arsenite, although BAL is highly protective in this regard (2). These facts all suggest that arsenicals kill by virtue of their arsenolytic action or inhibition of respiratory SH enzymes. In view of the fact (17), known since 1926, that arsenite reduces oxygen consumption of whole Japanese beetles and Colorado potato beetles, the arsenolytic mechanism is improbable, for one would expect the uncoupling aspect of arsenolysis to lead to enhanced oxygen consumption. Finally, respiratory SH enzymes are inhibited *in vitro* by arsenites, for example, in muscle and fat body in codling moth, midgut of a grasshopper, muscle of American cockroach, embryos of another grasshopper, and other tissues (6). All these findings lead to the conclusion that inorganic arsenicals kill primarily by virtue of their inhibition of respiratory enzymes.

An effect of arsenates upon fecundity of a variety of flies, including the housefly, apple maggot, and two *Drosophila* species, was described (45) in 1963. Adults were fed calcium or sodium arsenate at a high but sublethal dose, either by incorporating arsenates, up to 0.5%, in a synthetic diet, or by feeding the insects on treated plants. With apple maggots, 69% laid no eggs at all at the highest dose tested. The mechanism of the sterilization was that ovarian development was impaired; males were unaffected. This phenomenon could be an important factor in insect control.

Silica Aerogels

Some of the most primitive insecticides were common materials, essentially inert chemically: ashes, road dust, and soot. Later, commercial materials were used, such as alumina (Al_2O_3), talc ($3MgO \cdot 4SiO_2H_2O$), and pyrophyllite ($Al_2O_3 \cdot 4SiO_2H_2O$), but rapidly these became vehicles for more potent materials.

In 1959, Ebeling and Wagner (14) made the surprising statement that in attempts to control termites in houses, long-lasting control was obtained only when dusts were applied, and that it was the dust vehicle itself that was effective, not the insecticide. The silica aerogels were particularly effective in this regard.

Silica gels are amorphous powders made up of SiO_2 and formed by reacting sodium silicate with sulfuric acid, and washing out soluble products. The gels of very low density and high porosity are called aerogels. In order to improve the flow characteristics, ammonium fluosilicate is sometimes added during the preparation of the aerogel, and the particles are said to be positively charged in consequence, and much better insecticidally.

The times-to-death of 50% of insects placed on a silica gel film were: ants, 10 minutes; *Drosophila melanogaster*, 19 minutes; German cockroaches, 92

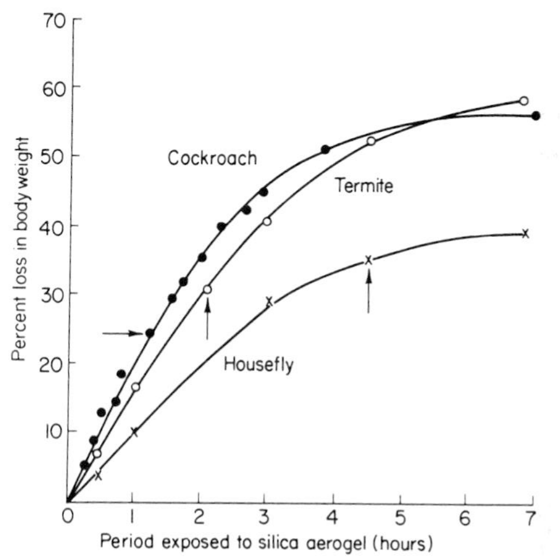

FIG. 13.1. Loss in body weight of insects exposed to silica aerogel SG67. Arrows show times for 100% mortality. Redrawn from Ebeling and Wagner (14).

minutes; drywood termites, 152 minutes; and houseflies, 185 minutes (14). Death is associated with heavy water loss, and it seems most probable that this loss is the cause of death, for insects which differ manyfold in their time-to-death all die at a similar level of water loss, that is when 28–35% of their weight is lost (Fig. 13.1).

Insects, by virtue of their small size, have an extremely large surface-to-volume ratio, and therefore (with the exception of those which live in wet or moist environments) face special problems with respect to prevention of evaporative loss of water from their surface. One important mechanism of such prevention involves secretion of a layer of wax or grease, commonly coated with a shellaclike "cement layer." These two layers, along with an underlying zone of hydrophilic protein, constitute the epicuticle, representing only 5% of the whole cuticle. The other 95% (the procuticle) lies under the epicuticle, and is made up of chitin and protein impregnated with phenolic polymers (49).

Disruption of the epicuticular wax (from here on, the term "wax" will be used for the waxy or greasy layer) by abrasion causes heavy water loss, followed by death by desiccation, as has been known since 1931 (64). It has been widely held that certain finely divided powders which kill insects by desiccation do so by a physical abrasion of the wax, involving movement of cuticle with respect to the powder (63). Ebeling (13) has argued that in at least some cases, such gross movement is not necessary, and that powder particles, resting upon the waxy surface film or an insect or upon a synthetic film, can cause profound disruption. For instance silica aerogel, deposited by settling onto a beeswax film on a glass slide, steadily became impregnated with the wax, without any movement of the aerogel. This effect, which involves true migration of wax molecules, can be seen readily with dyed wax, and is even apparent in photographs of undyed material. The surprising extent of migration was compatible with direct measurements of C^{14}-stearic acid, which diffused on a mica surface at the rate of 5.3×10^{-8} cm^2 sec^{-1} (50).

Sixteen powders of varying types were compared (clays, silica aerogels, carbon, sand, carborundum, etc.), and it was found that only those effective in wax adsorption were highly insecticidal, i.e., killed within a few hours. These most-adsorptive powders were also the least abrasive, judged by their ability to abrade vinyl plastic. The features favoring high adsorption were large surface area per unit weight, and large pore sizes, over 20 Å, presumably to permit entry of the large wax molecules.

One might expect that high humidity would greatly decrease the effectiveness of these "desiccating insecticides." But in fact, so long as the insects are left in contact with the aerogel or other powder, large losses of water from their bodies occur even at 100% relative humidity; thus German cockroaches lost 42% of their weight in 24 hours during exposure to a nonfluorinated silica aerogel. In some insects and powders, one can see knockdown as well as subsequent death. One particular gel (ALI) caused knockdown of German cockroaches in two minutes; Ebeling attributes this to "a state of shock," a term picturesque but not well defined in insects.

Ebeling and Wagner (14) were of the opinion that the fluorides in the fluorinated silica aerogels "have added to dust desiccation the factor of toxication," the implication being that fluoride poisoning occurs in addition to the dehydration effect, and indeed that the gel, by disrupting the lipoidal layer, permits ready access of the water-soluble fluorides. However, there is no evidence that the mechanism of action of fluorinated and unfluorinated gels is different, and in view of the fact that the dust particles actually become coated with wax displaced from the epicuticle, it is hard to imagine that water-soluble materials are released from the particles.

Ryanodine

Ryanodine is the active principle of various *Ryania* species, but especially from the South American plant *Ryania speciosa* Vahl. The toxicity of certain impure extracts called "ryanine" or "ryanatine" was described in 1928 by Nakari and Sano (38), who suggested that these materials were toxic to frogs, mice, cats, rabbits, and dogs, but not fish. This pattern contrasts interestingly with that of rotenone, which is toxic to fish but not to warm-blooded vertebrates (see p. 160).

The ground-up stems of *Ryania speciosa* are used as an insecticidal preparation, commonly under the name Ryanex. It has enjoyed for many years a small but steady usage, and appears to be considered rather effective, expensive, and of low hazard.

In 1948 the isolation of the pure alkaloid, ryanodine, was described by Rogers *et al.* (51). The structure of ryanodine itself is not known, but the dehydrated product, anhydroryanodine was characterized in 1962 by Canadian workers (3):

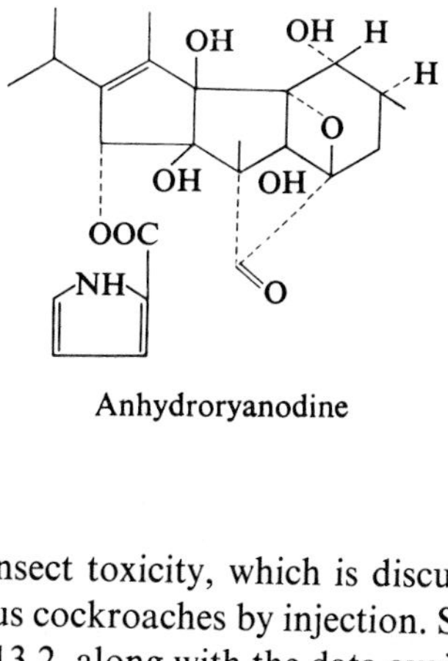

OH OH H H O OH OH OOC NH O

Anhydroryanodine

Toxicity

The limited data on insect toxicity, which is discussed below, suggests an LD_{50} of 5 μg/g for various cockroaches by injection. Some additional data for insects is given in Table 13.2, along with the data available for mammals. It is evident that ryanodine is at least 20 times more toxic to mammals than to the insects studied. This fact contrasts with the vague impression in many quarters which suggests that "natural" insecticides are in some way safer to use than synthetics.

Mechanism of Action

The mechanism of action of ryanodine was first described in 1948 by Edwards *et al.*, who worked primarily with insects (15). With the American cockroach, the giant roach *Blaberus cranifer*, and the pupa of the moth *Platipamia cecropia*, they observed gigantic increases in oxygen consumption,

TABLE 13.2

TOXICITY OF RYANODINE[a]

Animal	Route	LD_{50} (mg/kg)
Dog	iv	0.075
Cat	ip	0.070
Rabbit	iv	0.025
Guinea pig	ip	0.250
Rat	ip	0.325
Mouse	ip	0.260
German cockroach (male)	Topical	5
Milkweed bug	Topical	25

[a] Data approximated from Procita (47) and Heal (25).

reaching almost 10 times normal in 25 minutes, whereupon (in the cockroaches) a flaccid paralysis set in. Whereas in insects a dose of about 5 μg/g (approximately the LD_{50}) gave progressive sluggishness and flaccid paralysis with eventual death, the same dose in the frog gave, after initial flaccid paralysis, complete rigor in 3 hours. Such a rigor is the most striking feature in mammalian poisoning, as we shall see.

In this very first paper on ryanodine, Edwards *et al.* accurately located the point of action of ryanodine. They showed that the effect was *directly on the muscle*, which they proved by noting that action potentials in the muscle, or in central or peripheral nerve, were unaffected, and furthermore that direct electrical stimulation of the muscle (i.e., not via the nerve) fail to elicit a contraction. It is apparently the contractile response alone that is affected. They speculated that the effect was upon energy metabolism, perhaps an interference with ATP synthesis, with or without interference with phosphagen*; but later work disproves these speculations.

The pharmacology of ryanodine to mammals was first described in detail by Procita (48) in 1958, and since then has been fairly widely studied. Procita reported that early symptoms of poisoning involves rigidity of leg muscles, profuse salivation with vomiting and defecation, then a progressive rigidity of the musculature with final respiratory failure and death. The final cause of death was due to circulatory failure (probably due to an effect on heart muscle)

* Phosphagens are the phosphorylated compounds that can rapidly replenish the ATP supply, and act as an "instant reserve." It is usually held that creatine phosphate is the primary phosphagen for vertebrates, and that arginine phosphate is primary for insects and many other invertebrates.

in the anesthetized dog, but to paralysis of respiratory muscles in the anesthetized cat. Application of 50 μg into the artery supplying the cat's tibialis anticus muscle produced sustained contracture (47).

Not all muscles respond to ryanodine; sea urchins are insensitive, mammalian uterine and bladder muscle is insensitive, cardiac muscle undergoes progressive failure, whereas skeletal muscle contracts irreversibly. These variations bear no relation to phosphagen type or amount (23).

There is ample evidence that ryanodine affects muscle directly. At $5 \times 10^{-9} M$, it finally abolishes the contractile force of spontaneously beating cat auricles, with little effect on the rhythmicity. The effect was not reversible by washing (26).

The molecular basis for the ryanodine effect is not clear. So-called "ryanodine rigor" is unlike that caused by iodoacetate, for, as observed in frog muscle, it does not involve depletion of ATP (54). A modest increase of Ca^{++} permeability was found in frog muscle treated with high levels (1 mg/ml) of ryanodine; but nicotine showed a similar effect, yet undoubtedly acts differently, by affecting the neuromuscular junction (1). Nevertheless, the negative inotropic effect (muscle-weakening effect) of $10^{-8} M$ ryanodine on toad ventricular muscle could be reversed by ethylenediaminetetraacetic acid, a chelating agent, suggesting that Ca^{++} or similar cations may be involved (39). In frog muscle, it has been claimed (5) that ryanodine increases Ca^{++} efflux but not influx; iodoacetamide acts similarly, and in this way these compounds differ from other rigor-producing agents, such as noracetylcholine dodecaiodide, which increase Ca^{++} influx and efflux.

More recent work has concerned itself with a phenomenon observed in muscle homogenates which may be crucial in the relaxation phase of muscle action: an ATP-dependent Ca^{++} uptake in which ATP is hydrolyzed concomitantly with the uptake. It was shown (16) that ryanodine at $10^{-4} M$ substantially increases the ATP hydrolysis per mole of Ca^{++} taken up. Ryanodine did not decrease Ca^{++} uptake when excess ATP was present, but when ATP was made rate limiting, ryanodine reduced Ca^{++} uptake 33%. A later development of this view was the demonstration (58), again in a rabbit muscle preparation, that ryanodine diminishes the *affinity* of the microsomal fraction for Ca^{++}, but not the amount bound under saturating conditions. A simplified version of the hypothesis indicated by these experiments is that there is a so-called "relaxing system" which strips Ca^{++} from contracted muscle, and leads to a relaxed state. Ryanodine may interfere with this system, and hence produce prolonged contracture.

An extensive study of ryanodine effects upon cockroach and locust muscle was performed in 1962 by Usherwood (60). Even at $10^{-9} M$, effects were seen; at $10^{-3} M$ the muscle was highly excitable and produced spontaneous waves of depolarization, an effect which Usherwood attributed to diminished K^{+}

conductance. In late poisoning, however, these effects were reversed, and excitability was much diminished.

It would seem, therefore, that ryanodine, like chlorinated hydrocarbons, is a membrane disrupter rather than an antienzyme; but that, unlike chlorinated hydrocarbons, its effect is specific for the excitable membrane of muscle. However, one cannot exclude the possibility that the actual target is the quasi-enzymic ATPase ion-transport system, as postulated for other alkaloids (46). None of the above hypotheses has accounted for the extreme increase in respiratory rate described by Edwards *et al.* (p. 201) and unless this is shown to be a secondary effect of the muscle response, which is unlikely because it *preceded* the paralysis, one must continue to suspect that ryanodine can interfere with metabolism, even though that effect may be unrelated to the effects on muscle.

DNOC and Dinex

DNOC is an abbreviation for 4,6-dinitro-*o*-cresol, more correctly called 2-methyl-4,6-dinitrophenol. It is a compound of venerable age, whose use has dwindled for some time. It was introduced in 1892 as the active component of a product Antinonnin, designed for control of the nun moth (11). It was then used as the potassium salt, but since that time the free phenol has been more popular and is used in an oil base.

OH
H_3C NO_2
NO_2

DNOC

The period of greatest interest in DNOC was in the 1930's and 1940's, particularly for ovicidal use. In 1937 it was reported that what is now called dinex (formerly DNOCHP), in which the methyl of DNOC is replaced by cyclohexyl, was more active ovicidally. These compounds have been largely displaced by newer insecticides, but DNOC still finds great use as a herbicide (35).

Dinitro-*o*-cresol was at one time of great interest for locust control (22) and is still of major importance for control of red locusts (a pest of dwindling importance) and remains of secondary importance for control of the more important desert locust (33). The LD_{50} of DNOC for locusts compares very favorably with that of other compounds; the LD_{50} for *Eyprepoenemis plorans*, for instance, was 11.6 $\mu g/g$ for DNOC, compared with 3.0 for lindane, about 20 for diazinon, and 40 for dimethoate. Nevertheless, the effectiveness obtained with DNOC in locust control in 1945 has been improved 300-fold by the use of organophosphates, against which the high cost is the only objection (34).

Toxicity and Symptoms

The data of Table 13.3 show that DNOC and dinex have essentially similar toxicities for rats and a variety of insects. They are fairly toxic, with LD_{50}'s lying in the range 10–70 $\mu g/g$.

TABLE 13.3

Toxicity of DNOC and Dinex[a]

	DNOC			Dinex		
Species	Route	Form[b]	LD_{50} ($\mu g/g$)	Route	Form[b]	LD_{50} ($\mu g/g$)
Honey bee	Oral	S	18	—	—	—
American cockroach	Topical	F	20	—	—	—
Bombyx silkworm	Oral	F	49	Oral	C	20
Imported cabbageworm	—	—	—	Oral	F	73
Migratory locust	Topical	F	10	—	—	—
Rat	Oral	F	30	Oral	F	65
Dog	Intraperitoneal	F	10	—	—	—
Goat	Oral	F	100	—	—	—
Pigeon	Intramuscular	F	5	—	—	—

[a] Data from Metcalf (36) and Negherbon (40).
[b] S=sodium salt; C=calcium salt; F=free phenol.

The symptoms of DNOC poisoning in man and other mammals occur very rapidly and include nausea, gastric distress, sweating, flushed skin, fever (of 6°–10°F) with a marked increase in basal metabolic rate, then collapse and coma, with death or complete recovery within 1–2 days. Metabolism of DNOC is slow, and cumulative poisoning is therefore possible (24,40).

DNOC affects insects relatively rapidly, causing hyperactivity, convulsions, paralysis, and death, often within an hour. A notable increase in oxygen consumption is well established, for instance, a 10-fold increase for the *Tribolium castaneum* beetle in 1 hour (32). Nerve transmission in cockroach legs is rapidly and profoundly affected; spontaneous discharges are produced for 15 minutes, followed by a steady decrease in activity and blockade in 45 minutes (30).

Mechanism of Action

DNOC and dinex are representative of the large group of dinitrophenols which uncouple oxidative phosphorylation (for review, see Slater, 55). Most of the work on such compounds has been done with mammalian tissues, but the effects on insect preparations, where studied, have proved almost identical (56); this fact, taken with the essential equitoxicity of DNOC for insects and mammals, strongly suggests that its action is identical in each, that there are no enormous differences in its rate of metabolic removal, and that the target is of similar importance for both.

The topic of oxidative phosphorylation has already been reviewed briefly in the discussion on the action of rotenone (p. 161) and arsenate (p. 195), both of which interfere with it by different mechanisms; DNOC interferes by a mechanism similar to arsenate. Whereas rotenone blocks the system which reduces a flavoprotein with concurrent $NADH_2$ oxidation (see Fig. 9.1), arsenate and dinitrophenols act on the system which reoxidizes the reduced flavoprotein, with concurrent phosphorylation of ADP to ATP. However, whereas rotenone acts upon a particular flavoprotein (flavoprotein FP of Fig. 9.1), arsenate and dinitrophenols are not known to act on any one specific flavoprotein or cytochrome. All that one can say is that they act somewhere on the rather long chain of intermediates which link $NADPH_2$ oxidation with reduction of O_2 to H_2O. Furthermore, whereas rotenone *blocks*, arsenate and dinitrophenol *uncouple*. An analogy would be in the two ways that the progress of an automobile with a manual transmission can be disrupted: if one is driving along and steps on the brake, one stops the wheels and hence the engine, gears, and drive shaft must stop. This is blockade. In a similar way, rotenone, by blocking $NADPH_2$ oxidation, blocks all the reactions which lead to $NADPH_2$ production. But if in this same automobile the drive shaft breaks, progress stops but the engine continues to run; one has uncoupled the engine from the wheels. Similarly arsenate and dinitrophenols uncouple the oxidation of $NADPH_2$ from the useful phosphorylation of ADP to ATP, permitting the $NADPH_2$-producing reactions to proceed, but without a useful outcome. In many cases they may actually stimulate substrate utilization and oxygen uptake, but without concurrent ADP phosphorylation. This is measurable as a decrease in the so-called P:O ratio, which is the ratio of moles of ADP phosphorylated to atoms of oxygen utilized.

Whereas arsenates very probably uncouple by arsenolysis (p. 195), the precise mechanism of dinitrophenol uncoupling is unknown. One possibility is that it catalyzes the hydrolysis of some unknown high-energy intermediate which is crucial to the coupling of flavoprotein oxidation to ADP phosphorylation. If FP is oxidized and FPH is reduced flavoprotein, one might have

$$\begin{array}{ccccc} \text{FPH} & \searrow\!\!\swarrow & \text{A+B} & \nwarrow\!\!\nearrow & \text{ATP} \\ \text{FP} & \swarrow\!\!\searrow & \text{AB} & \nearrow\!\!\searrow & \text{ADP+P} \end{array}$$

where A—B would be the unknown intermediate. If dinitrophenols caused hydrolysis of A—B, one would observe continuous oxidation of FPH without ADP phosphorylation, i.e., uncoupling. Alternatively, dinitrophenols might interfere by causing hydrolysis of the ATP as fast as it is formed, or perhaps of some other phosphorylated compound whose equilibrium is tied to the ATP–ADP equilibrium.

The differences between mechanisms of arsenate and dinitrophenol uncoupling are reflected in various ways. Higher concentrations of arsenate are required and the uncoupling is usually incomplete and progressive.

All these agents which interfere with ATP synthesis lead to the same outcome: a deficiency of the precious ATP, which is the immediate energy source for all energy-requiring functions, including nerve and muscle action. However, there is room for a good deal of variation in the organs which are most affected, because of differences in the distribution of the compounds within the body.

REFERENCES

1. Ahmed, K., and Lewis, J. J., *J. Pharm. Pharmacol.* **13**, 383 (1961).
2. Anderson, A. D., and Patton, R. L., *J. Econ. Entomol.* **46**, 423 (1953).
3. Babin, D. R., Forrest, T. P., Valenta, Z., and Wiesner, K., *Experientia* **18**, 549 (1962).
4. Berry, L. J., and Smythe, D. S., *Am. J. Physiol.* **197**, 37 (1959).
5. Bianchi, C. P., *J. Cellular Comp. Physiol.* **61**, 255 (1963).
6. Brown, A. W. A., *J. Insect Pathol.* **1**, 65 (1963).
7. Campbell, F. L., and Lukens, C., *J. Econ. Entomol.* **24**, 88 (1931).
8. Chadbourne, D. S., and Rainwater, C. F., *J. Econ. Entomol.* **46**, 44 (1953).
9. Chefurka, W., *Enzymologia* **18**, 209 (1957).
10. Cooper, C., and Lehninger, A. L., *J. Biol. Chem.* **219**, 489 (1956).
11. Cooper, W. F., and Nuttall, W. H., *Ann. Appl. Biol.* **1**, 273 (1915).
12. Doudoroff, M., Barker, H. A., and Hassid, W. Z., *J. Biol. Chem.* **170**, 147 (1947).
13. Ebeling, W., *Hilgardia* **30**, 531 (1961).
14. Ebeling, W., and Wagner, R. E., *J. Econ. Entomol.* **52**, 190 (1959).
15. Edwards, G. A., Weiant, E. A., Slocombe, A. G., and Roeder, K. D., *Science* **108**, 330 (1948).
16. Fairhurst, A. S., and Jenden, D. J., *Proc. Natl. Acad. Sci. U.S.* **48**, 807 (1962).
17. Fink, D. E., *J. Agr. Res.* **33**, 993 (1926).
18. Fisher, R. A., *Ann. Entomol. Soc. Am.* **29**, 335 (1936).
19. Forgash, A. J., *J. Econ. Entomol.* **44**, 870 (1956).
20. Fulmek, L., *Fortschr. Landwirtsch.* **4**, 209 (1929).
21. Grandori, L., and Reali, G., *Boll. Zool. Agrar. Bachicolt. Univ. Studi Milano* **16**, 1 (1950).
22. Gunn, D. L., ed., "Locust Control by Aircraft in Tanganyika." Antilocust Res. Center, London, 1948.
23. Haslett, W. L., and Jenden, D. J., *J. Cellular Comp. Physiol.* **57**, 123 (1961).

24. Hayes, W. J., "Clinical Handbook on Economic Poisons." U.S. Dept. Health, Educ. Welfare, Communicable Disease Center, Atlanta, Georgia, 1963.
25. Heal, R. E., *Agr. Chem.* **4**, 37 (1949).
26. Hillyard, I. W., and Procita, L., *J. Pharmacol. Exptl. Therap.* **127**, 22 (1959).
27. Hoskin, F. C. G., *Biochim. Biophys. Acta* **40**, 309 (1960).
28. Hoskins, D. D., Cheldelin, V. H., and Newburgh, R. W., *J. Gen. Physiol.* **39**, 705 (1956).
29. Jochum, F., *Hoefchen Briefe* (English Ed.) **9**, 289 (1956).
30. Lalonde, D. I. V., and Brown, A. W. A., *Can. J. Zool.* **32**, 74 (1954).
31. Lehninger, A. L., *J. Biol. Chem.* **178**, 625 (1949).
32. Lord, K. A., *Ann. Appl. Biol.* **36**, 113 (1949).
33. MacCraig, R. D., *World Rev. Pest Control* (*London*) **2**, Pt. 1, 7 (1963).
34. MacCraig, R. D., and Yeates, M. N. D. B., *J. Sci. Food Agr.* **12**, 861 (1961).
35. Martin, H., "The Scientific Principles of Crop Protection." Arnold, London, 1959.
36. Metcalf, R. L., "Organic Insecticides." Wiley (Interscience), New York, 1955.
37. Munson, S. C., and Yeager, J. F., *Ann. Entomol. Soc. Am.* **38**, 634 (1945).
38. Nakari, S., and Sano, T., *Yakugaku Zasshi* **48**, 1102 (1928).
39. Nayler, W. G., *Am. J. Physiol.* **204**, 975 (1963).
40. Negherbon, W. O., "Handbook of Toxicology, Insecticides," Vol. 3, Saunders, Philadelphia, Pennsylvania, 1959.
41. Norton, L. B., *Ind. Eng. Chem.* **40**, 691 (1948).
42. Norton, L. B., and Hansberry, R., *J. Econ. Entomol.* **34**, 431 (1941).
43. Parfentjev, J. A., *Trans. 4th Intern. Entomol. Congr., 1928* p. 853 (1929).
44. Peters, R. A., *Bull. Johns Hopkins Hosp.* **97**, 1 (1955).
45. Pickett, A. D., and Patterson, N. A., *Science* **140**, 493 (1963).
46. Portius, H. J., and Repke, K., *Arzneimittel-Forsch.* **14**, 1073 (1964).
47. Procita, L., *J. Pharmacol. Exptl. Therap.* **117**, 363 (1956).
48. Procita, L., *J. Pharmacol. Exptl. Therap.* **123**, 296 (1958).
49. Richards, A. G., "The Integument of Arthropods." Univ. of Minnesota Press, Minneapolis, Minnesota, 1951.
50. Rideal, E. K., and Tadayon, J., *Proc. Roy. Soc.* (*London*) **A225**, 537 (1954).
51. Rogers, E. F., Konivsky, F. R., Shavel, J., and Falkers, K., *J. Am. Chem. Soc.* **70**, 3086 (1948).
52. Salkeld, E. H., *Can. Entomologist* **83**, 39 (1951).
53. Sanadi, D. R., Gibson, D. M., Ayengar, P., and Jacob, M., *J. Biol. Chem.* **218**, 505 (1956).
54. Seraydarian, M. W., Jenden, D. J., and Abbott, B., *J. Pharmacol. Exptl. Therap.* **135**, 374 (1962).
55. Slater, E. C., *In* "Metabolic Inhibitors" (R. M. Hochster and J. H. Quastel, eds.), Vol. 2, Chap. 32. Academic Press, New York, 1963.
56. Slater, E. C., and Lewis, S. E., *Biochem. J.* **58**, 207 (1954).
57. Stocken, L. A., and Thompson, R. H. S., *Biochem. J.* **40**, 535 (1946).
58. Takanji, M., Nakano, I., Taniguchi, M., and Sasaki, J., *Japan J. Physiol.* **15**, 42 (1965).
59. Tareev, A. I., and Nenjukov, D. V., *Zashchita Rast. ot Vreditelei i Boleznei* **3**, 39 (1931).
60. Usherwood, P. N. R., *Comp. Biochem. Physiol.* **6**, 181 (1962).
61. Vallee, B. L., Ulmer, D. D., and Walker, W. E. C., *Am. M. A. Arch. Ind. Health* **21**, 132 (1960).
62. Webb, J. L., "Enzyme and Metabolic Inhibitors," Vol. 3. Academic Press, New York, 1966.
63. Wigglesworth, V. B., *Nature* **153**, 493 (1944).
64. Zacher, F., and Kunicke, G., *Arb. Biol. Reichsanstalt Land-Forstwirtsch. Berlin-Dahlem* **18**, 201 (1931).

CHAPTER 14

Synergism, Antagonism, and Other Interactions

This topic [reviewed in part by Hewlett (31) in 1960] is one which some years ago seemed to be of importance for a few classes of compounds only, particularly pyrethroids. It is now apparent that for most members of most classes of toxicants, other compounds exist which can influence their toxicity. Furthermore, a few compounds turn up again and again as synergists or antagonists for very diverse compounds. The reason undoubtedly lies in those amazingly versatile little structures, the microsomes, which mediate so many important metabolic reactions, all of which can be played upon by these few compounds.

The term synergism will be used in the way defined on p. 167. The term antagonism will be used for the precisely opposite phenomenon, in which the toxicity of two compounds applied together is less than that expected from the sum of their effects when applied separately. Thus if one applied one-half the LD_{50} of compound A plus one-half of the LD_{50} of B, then one would predict, if their effects were simply additive (for instance, in the extreme case, where A and B were the same compound), that a mortality of 50% would be encountered. If the above combination gave a mortality significantly less than 50%, antagonism had occurred; if the mortality were significantly greater than 50%, synergism had occurred. Often one of the compounds involved is nontoxic; the term "cotoxicity coefficient" (77) or "synergistic ratio" (82) then becomes useful; it is defined as the increase in toxicity caused by the nontoxic compound, and is given by measuring the value of LD_{50} of toxicant alone/LD_{50} of mixture. If this value is greater than one, synergism has occurred and the nontoxic compound is a synergist. If the value is less than one, antagonism has occurred and the nontoxic compound is an antagonist.

Unfortunately the use of words such as synergism and antagonism is not uniform. Some (31) reserve synergism for the case where one member of the pair of compounds is nontoxic, although others use "activation" for this situation. Others speak of antagonism (31) or "negative synergism" (5) if the activity of the mixture is less than that of the more active constituent. The term "potentiation" was often used to describe greater-than-additive toxicity in pairs of organophosphates; my preference is either to avoid the term or to reserve it for a special case of synergism, that is, where the mechanism has clearly been shown to owe to an increase in the toxicity of compound B caused by compound A, so that A may be called a potentiator. Other terms, such as "dissimilar joint action," "dependent joint action," and the like, are also in use (45), but I trust that the two simple terms, synergism and antagonism, will serve to describe all these phenomena in an operational way; further elucidation of mechanism is then an experimental rather than a semantic problem. For those who prefer more theoretical and mathematical treatments of the topic, there are several excellent reviews (5,31,45,69,80). We shall use the term "moderators" to include both synergists and antagonists.

We will deal with two quite different interactions, inductive and noninductive. The inductive cases, which have only recently been understood, involve increases in the level of an enzyme system induced by administering a compound, usually over several days or more. When the induced enzyme is important in determining the toxicity of some other agent, the lethal dose of that agent will of course be modified by such prior induction. The noninductive effects are better known, and may involve various interactions, including inhibition by one compound of an enzyme which breaks down another, or interferences with storage, binding, or the effect upon a target.

Inductive Effects

Several references have been made in this book to the remarkably diverse reactions performed by liver microsomes; when studied *in vitro*, these microsomal reactions require oxygen and reduced pyridine nucleotide; sometimes $NADH_2$ (reduced nicotine adenine dinucleotide; formerly DPNH) is preferred, sometimes $NADPH_2$ (reduced nicotine adenine dinucleotide phosphate; formerly TPNH). Nicotinamide is sometimes added, in order to block enzymic breakdown of the nucleotide (33), particularly in crude preparation. A requirement for Mg^{++} was indicated in the earlier work. In place of reduced nucleotide, one may use the oxidized form along with a reducing system, of which the simplest is the soluble fraction of the liver, which has oxidizable substrates and nucleotide-linked enzymes.

In Table 14.1 is a list of a few of the many diverse reactions catalysed by such microsomal preparations, which include oxidations, reductions, hydroxyla-

TABLE 14.1

SOME DRUG REACTIONS CATALYZED BY LIVER MICROSOMES[a]

Reaction	Substrate		Product
Deamination	$C_6H_5CH_2CH(CH_3)NH_2$ Amphetamine	$\xrightarrow{b}$	$C_6H_5CH_2C(=O)CH_3$ Phenylacetone
O-Dealkylation	$CH_3C(O)NH-C_6H_4-OC_2H_5$ *p*-Ethoxyacetanilide	$\longrightarrow$	$CH_3C(O)NH-C_6H_4-OH$ *p*-Hydroxyacetanilide
N-Dealkylation	$C_6H_5CH(OH)CH(CH_3)NHCH_3$ Ephedrine	$\xrightarrow{b}$	$C_6H_5CH(OH)CH(CH_3)NH_2$ Norephedrine
	$C_6H_5NHCH_3$ *N*-Methylaniline	$\xrightarrow{c}$	$C_6H_5NH_2$ Aniline
Sulfoxidation	2-Chloro-10-[$C_3H_6N(CH_3)_2$]phenothiazine (S, N, Cl) Chlorpromazine	$\xrightarrow{c}$	Corresponding sulfoxide (S=O), N–$C_3H_6N(CH_3)_2$, Cl
Side-chain oxidation	Hexobarbital (N–CH_3, OH, N, O, H_3C, cyclohexenyl)	$\xrightarrow{b}$	Same with oxo-cyclohexenyl (C=O on ring), N–CH_3, OH, N, O, H_3C

[a] From Nether (54) and Gillette (29). [b] Reactions inhibited by SKF 525A.
[c] Reactions known to be insensitive to SKF 525A.

tions, hydrolyses, dealkylations, and sulfoxidations. It is inconceivable that a single enzyme could perform all these reactions, and there have therefore been numerous attempts to fractionate microsomes, but all without success. But the various reactions differ in their nucleotide requirement: in their susceptibility to inhibition by SKF 525A (discussed more fully below, see p. 221), as shown in the table; in the ratio of their activities in various species (25); and in their cross-inductive pattern, as we shall shortly see. These facts are evidence that more than one enzyme is involved in microsomal systems.

In 1956, it was shown that a single injection of the carcinogen 3,4-benzpyrene into rats markedly increased the activity of the microsomal enzymes (9). Since then, a great variety of drugs and insecticides which can be metabolized by microsomes have been shown to have this same ability to increase the activity of microsomes so that they metabolize not only the compound itself, but also numerous other compounds. Usually the inducing compound is administered daily for several days. The effect is indeed a true induction: it is known that there is an actual increase in the amount of enzyme and not simply a change in its properties (65). Furthermore, in the case of induction by phenobarbital, and undoubtedly this is true for the other cases, it has been shown (67) with the electron microscope that the induction involves a massive increase in the smooth membranes, which when broken in homogenization, are one of the principal components of microsomes.

That it is the smooth membrane fraction which is involved is shown not only by microphotographs, but by the demonstration that the rough fraction has its protein, lipid, RNA, and phosphorus contents little changed by phenobarbital induction (increases of 1.1, 1.5, 0.9, and 1.1 times, respectively), whereas these components of the smooth fraction undergo almost a doubling (increases of 1.9, 2.3, 1.6, and 1.7 times, respectively). In this particular experiment, the corresponding changes in drug-degrading ability were 1.8 times for hexabarbital, 3.6 times for chloramphenicol, and 2.5 times for procaine. Clearly, the increases in quantities of constituents are of the same order as the increases in ability to degrade drugs (66).

In view of the nonspecificity of the microsomal system, it is perhaps not surprising to find that induction is not specific; that is, compound A may induce activity toward compounds B and C. In dogs, metabolism of phenylbutazone (a uric acid solubilizing agent used for gout) can be doubled by injecting, for 1–4 months, daily doses of probenecid (another gout agent), phenobarbital, chlorcyclizine (an antihistamine), or, of course, phenylbutazone itself (7). In other words, cross induction is common; one drug may stimulate the metabolism of a different one though an inductive mechanism. But cross induction is not uniform; certain metabolic routes can be induced by compounds A, B, and C, but not by D, E, or F, even though D, E, or F may be effective inducers for other routes. For example, in rats phenobarbital and aminopyrine seemed to be rather general inducers, stimulating extra activity towards themselves and also to hexobarbital, 3-methyl-4-methylaminoazobenzene (MAB), and 3,4-benzpyrene. But 3,4-benzpyrene induced extra activity for itself and MAB, but not for hexobarbital or aminopyrine (10).

Soon after the first demonstration of microsomal induction, it was shown that insecticide metabolism, and therefore toxicity, can be modified by such induction. Murphy and DuBois (51) showed in 1958 that, 24 hours after a single dose of 25 mg/kg of 3-methylcholanthrene in rats, the ability of the liver to activate azinphosmethyl was greatly increased: the effect was greater in females (2.5-fold increase) than in males (1.3-fold). The effect increased with time-after-treatment, reaching a maximum at 6 days; it could be blocked by ethionine, which is an inhibitor of protein synthesis.

So far we have discussed cases where the inducer is a drug or a carcinogen. But numerous chlorinated insecticides are good inducers. Chlordane administration produces in rats an increased ability in their liver microsomes to metabolize hexobarbital (a barbiturate), chlorpromazine (a tranquillizer), or aminopyrine (30). Table 14.2 shows that 25 mg/kg daily for 3 days led to

TABLE 14.2

EFFECT OF 25 MG/KG OF CHLORDANE FOR 3 DAYS ON MICROSOMAL METABOLISM OF DRUGS BY RAT LIVER[a]

Drug being Metabolized	Percent increase in rate of metabolism on days after last chlordane treatment[b]				
	1 Day	8 Days	15 Days	22 Days	29 Days
Hexobarbital	94[c]	24[c]	16	23	29
Aminopyrine	282[c]	135[c]	117[c]	56	44
Chlorpromazine	63[c]	—	33	91[c]	−22

[a] Data calculated from Hart *et al.* (30).
[b] Values expressed as percent greater than the control value.
[c] These values were significantly greater than the control value at $P = 0.05$.

substantial increases in metabolizing action, and that the effects persisted for many days after dosing was stopped. It was shown that chlordane *in vitro* had no effect on these enzymic activities, so that the findings presented in Table 18.2 clearly represent inductive effects. Furthermore, administration of ethionine entirely prevented the chlordane effect. Chlorinated hydrocarbons also induce effects upon epoxidation of aldrin and heptachlor (28) because the feeding of DDT, DDE, Kelthane, or DDD was effective (in that order) in increasing these epoxidations by rat liver microsomes.

One would expect that these metabolic interferences would lead to influences upon drug effects or upon toxicity, and indeed that is the case. For toxicants, one may find that induction decreases the toxicity if the primary role of the microsomes is detoxification. Thus a dose of strychnine normally lethal to 70% of treated rats killed only 5% if they had been treated for 4 days with 70 mg/kg of the tranquillizer, phenaglycodol, daily; or 15% if they had been treated with 20 mg/kg of the barbiturate, thiopental, daily (36). Alternatively, one may find that induction increases toxicity if the primary role of the microsomes is activation. Thus a dose of schradan that normally kills 6% of treated rats killed 81% of those which had been treated as above with phenaglycodol, or 75% of those treated with thiopental (36).

Inductive effects upon liver microsomes are even greater upon newborn animals than upon adults. Table 14.3 shows that chlordane has only moderate

TABLE 14.3

EFFECTS OF CHLORDANE ON DRUG METABOLISM IN LIVERS OF ADULT AND NEWBORN RABBITS[a]

	Hexobarbital	Aminopyrine	p-Nitrobenzoic acid
Adults			
Control	2.86	3.24	0.61
Treated	4.25	2.85	2.73
% Increase	48	−12	348
Newborn			
Control	0.02	0.02	0.14
Treated directly	3.33	0.35	1.40
% Increase	16,600	1,650	900
Mother treated	0.58	0.08	0.45
% Increase	2,000	300	221

[a] Adults and newborn induced with 50 mg/kg of chlordane for 3 days. Mothers induced with 50 mg/kg daily for 5 days, starting 2 days after birth. Figures are units of drug metabolized per gram of liver in 2 hours. From Fouts and Hart (20).

inductive effects upon metabolism of hexobarbital, aminopyrine, and *p*-nitrobenzoic acid in adult rabbits. But its effect upon metabolism of these compounds in newborn rabbits is tremendous, whether it is administered directly to the newborn or to the nursing mother, although the effects are smaller in the latter case. Inspection of the table reveals that the reason for the larger percentage increase in the newborn is that untreated newborns have extremely low metabolic capacity in their microsomes.

The relatively recent understanding of the mechanism of inductive effects has permitted reevaluation of what seemed a puzzling finding of Canadian workers in 1954. They found (4,13) that feeding or a single injection of aldrin, chlordane, or lindane gave marked protection against parathion poisoning for rats, but only if the chlorinated compound was given some time before the parathion. The increases in the LD_{50} of parathion were 7.3-fold from aldrin (30 mg/kg), 5.5-fold from chlordane (200 mg/kg), and 2.5-fold from lindane (30 mg/kg). In the case of aldrin induction, effects were also found on tepp (whose toxicity was decreased 5-fold), but not on eserine. German workers (55) showed in 1958 that a single injection of α-hexachlorocyclohexane protected mice against paraoxon or schradan, but not against DFP or eserine.

Recently, such effects upon organophosphate poisoning have been examined again by Welch and Coon (81) using mice. The inducers were chlorcyclizine, cyclizine, phenobarbital, or SKF 525A,* and protection against malathion, parathion, EPN, tepp, and eserine was found (the eserine effect was not found in the experiments described above, where chlorinated hydrocarbons were the inducers). The effects were large: chlorcyclizine given subcutaneously at 25 mg/kg for 4 days increased the oral LD_{50} 5-fold for parathion, 2.5-fold for paraoxon, 3.9-fold for tepp, and 2.9-fold for eserine. In this study and in the Canadian work, it was noted that fairly substantial increases (up to 2-fold) in the aliesterase level of serum occurred after induction, and both groups have speculated that it is the enhanced aliesterase that gives protection by competing for the available anticholinesterase. A variant on this speculation is that the aliesterase might by the A-type, which hydrolyzes organophosphates, and hence its raised level would have a protective effect. However, a more plausible explanation would be that liver-degrading enzymes were induced by the pretreatments. Welch and Coon (81) found a small (15%) increase in liver paraoxonase, but they assayed this activity in the absence of reduced nucleotide. There is evidence that there exists a nucleotide-requiring paraoxonase in mice (57) in addition to the well-known phosphatases; it is this which one would expect to be subject to induction, but of course it must be assayed in the presence of reduced nucleotide.

The effects of chlorcyclizine induction upon schradan toxicity were later studied (39) in rats and mice. Two aspects were studied: short- and long-term effects. When given to mice, a single dose of chlorcyclizine (25 mg/kg) gave

* Later, the more familiar acute effects of SKF 525A will be discussed; in such cases, this agent inhibits microsomal action because it is a competitive substrate. Used chronically, it increases microsomal action because it is a substrate, and it thus induces microsomes.

substantial protection, so that a dose of schradan which normally gave 100% mortality had no effect; the protection was optimal at 3–12 hours after administration of the chlorcyclizine, and then waned. These effects are undoubtedly noninductive, and probably reflect direct competition with the activating system, as found in acute effects of SKF 525A (see p. 221). When inducing effects were sought by administering chlorcyclizine daily for 3 days, protection against schradan was found in rats but not in mice (paradoxically, after induction, the sleeping time from a fixed dose of hexobarbital was reduced in mice but not in rats). Work with liver slices from both acute and inductive experiments showed pronounced loss in ability to activate schradan. This finding is, in the case of inductive experiments, the opposite of that expected; but both the effect on liver and upon toxicity in the inductive experiments may have been due to the persistence of chlorcyclizine, so that an "acute effect" was obscuring an "inductive effect."

The implications of all these studies on induction are clear. A history of fairly high dosing with any one of a great variety of other drugs and toxicants can profoundly affect the response of a variety of other drugs and toxicants applied subsequently. One practical implication is that patients undergoing therapy with many drugs will show abnormal responses to accidental poisoning by insecticides. Probably the reverse phenomenon would be far rarer: it is unlikely that the extremely small doses of insecticides ingested normally as residues on foods are large enough to influence drug metabolism. But those exposed occupationally to persistently high intakes of insecticides might show abnormal drug responses. Since virtually every class of insecticide can be acted upon by liver microsomes, it is very probable that most insecticides could be inducers under appropriate circumstances, i.e., with sustained, fairly high levels of intake.

Noninductive Effects

If an interaction can be seen in acute experiments, for instance, by measuring the acute LD_{50} of the toxicant with and without the modifier, then the effect is probably noninductive, for enzyme induction in insects or mammals is a rather slow process, usually involving several days at least.

The classic example of synergism concerns the pyrethroids; indeed, the modern phase of the history and biology of pyrethroids is so intimately related to their synergism that this aspect has been reported in detail in Chapter 10, in which will be found (p. 167) the structures of the various modifiers which will be discussed below. It may be recalled that it was in 1940 that the first pyrethrin synergist (sesame oil) was patented. Since then, most researchers on insecticides have been alert to the possibility that, for other classes of compounds too, synergists might be found that would make inadequate compounds become excellent insecticides, or excellent compounds become superb insecticides. Naturally enough, the pyrethrin synergists themselves have been widely examined against other toxicants, and have proved to be quite effective. In 1954, Hoffman *et al.* (32) found that such compounds were quite good synergists for some, but not all, organophosphates with houseflies. Inspection of his data (Table 14.4) shows that the familiar pyrethrin synergists (the first

TABLE 14.4

INCREASE IN HOUSEFLY MORTALITY FROM ORGANOPHOSPHATES CAUSED BY SYNERGISTS[a]

Synergist	Malathion (5:25)	EPN (1:10)	Methyl parathion (1:10)	Coumaphos (5:25)	Diazinon (1:10)
Piperonyl cyclonene	−3	−20	−35	44	−10
Sulfoxide	−3	36	37	77	71
Piperonyl butoxide	1	77	48	80	73
n-Propyl isome	−3	16	−48	56	9
Di-*n*-butyl hexahydrophthalate	75	68	36	55	49
Ethyl *N*,*N*-diethylglutaramate	80	58	16	58	—
Mortality from organophosphate alone	3	22	51	20	23

[a] Applications were made to surfaces. Ratios in column headings indicate mg/ft^2 of toxicant:synergist. Figures are increases in percent mortality, except in bottom row, in which percent mortalities are shown. Data selected from Hoffman (32).

four compounds listed) were all valueless for malathion, and all good for coumaphos. For the other three organophosphates shown, sulfoxide and piperonyl butoxide were always good synergists, and piperonyl cyclonene was always bad, so bad that it seemed an antagonist. It should be noted that in studies such as this, where instead of LD_{50} one determines the percent mortality caused by a fixed dose of toxicant, the experiment must usually be designed to look either for synergism, by using a toxicant dose that causes a low mortality by itself, or for antagonism, by selecting a toxicant dose that causes a high mortality by itself. In neither case can the opposite phenomenon be readily demonstrated; for example, in the Hoffman experiment, antagonism is not readily observed.

One way of interpreting these puzzling variations is to postulate that the above modifiers all inhibit a metabolizing system, whose role is primarily to detoxify as far as some toxicants are concerned, so that in these cases the modifier acts as a synergist; but whose role is primarily to toxify (activate) as far as other toxicants are concerned, so that in these cases the modifier acts as an antagonist. For instance, perhaps for malathion the system acts primarily to activate, whereas for coumaphos it acts primarily to detoxify. One must consider the relative effects of and upon other tissues; dimethoate and malathion are both activated primarily in vertebrate liver, but malathion is detoxified by numerous tissues including liver (72), whereas dimethoate is detoxified only in liver (78). In such a case, if a modifier severely inhibited both activation and degradation in liver but had no effect elsewhere, then for dimethoate the detoxification blockade would be very significant, whereas for malathion the detoxification blockade would be negligible.

Bearing this sort of possibility in mind, let us briefly survey similarly mixed responses in a variety of cases. In 1960, Sun and Johnson compared various pyrethrin synergists, of which sesamex proved most potent, as modifiers for pyrethrin and other important insecticides. Table 14.5 shows that for both

TABLE 14.5

EFFECTS OF SESAMEX ON TOXICITY OF VARIOUS INSECTICIDES FOR HOUSEFLIES[a]

Synergistic action		Antagonistic action	
Compound	Cotoxicity coefficient[b]	Compound	Cotoxicity coefficient[b]
Pyrethrin	61		
Organophosphates			
Amiton	29	Parathion	0.63
Phosphamidon	15	Methyl parathion	0.14
Mevinphos	2.5	EPN	0.70
Dichlorvos	2.2		
Azinphosmethyl	1.8		
Schradan	1.6		
Chlorinated hydrocarbons			
Endrin	3.8	Aldrin	0.60
Isodrin	1.7	Heptachlor	0.57
Dieldrin	1.6		
Lindane	1.4		
Heptachlor epoxide	1.3		
DDT	1.2		

[a] Data selected from Sun and Johnson (77).
[b] Cotoxicity coefficient = LC_{50} of toxicant alone/LC_{50} of toxicant plus 1% sesamex.

organophosphates and chlorinated hydrocarbons, clear-cut examples of both synergism and antagonism could be found.

With respect to the very "mixed" effects upon organophosphates, a similar picture has emerged from studies on *Drosophila melanogaster* by Zschintzsch (84). Piperonyl butoxide (and to a similar extent sulfoxide; to a lesser extent piperonyl cyclonene and *n*-propyl butoxide) was synergistic for Potasan, coumaphos, phosphamidon, and under some conditions for trichlorofon, dichlorvos, and mevinphos. But they were antagonistic for Chlorthion and Thiometon [$(CH_3O)_2P(S)SC_2H_4SC_2H_5$]. The findings agree fully with the data on houseflies (Table 14.5). With parathion, malathion, diazinon, and EPN, it was possible to have synergism at low organophosphate concentrations and antagonism at high concentrations. In a study on chlorinated hydrocarbons (85), Zschintzsch and Fuchs showed in 1959 that, for *Drosophila*, piperonyl butoxide synergized lindane (and to a lesser extent dieldrin and DDT) and antagonized aldrin; these effects fully agree with the later findings on houseflies.

In the Sun and Johnson study, sesamex was shown to inhibit the epoxidation of aldrin to dieldrin in houseflies, suggesting an attractive explanation for the fact that sesamex synergizes dieldrin and antagonizes aldrin; perhaps the epoxidation is an activation, so that its blockade reduced aldrin's toxicity. The hypothesis is rendered more attractive by the observation that heptachlor is antagonized and heptachlor epoxide is synergized; but there is independent evidence that makes the hypothesis doubtful (p. 144).

We will see later on, in the case of organophosphates and DDT, cases in which resistance bestows a susceptibility to synergism; the explanation is that the resistance was due to the development of an enzyme which could be blocked by the synergist. But in the cyclodienes, the opposite has been shown (6); certain rather unusual cyclodienes were synergized by sesamex with susceptible houseflies (see p. 143), but these compounds were not synergized in a resistant strain. Presumably the resistance owed to some mechanism which was insensitive to sesamex.

There is a considerable probability (with only scanty evidence yet) that these varied effects of sesamex are the consequences of its inhibition of the amazingly versatile microsomal system of vertebrate liver and insects. A detailed example was provided recently (60) when it was shown that sesamex blocks the hydroxylation of naphthalene by housefly microsomes; very probably an analogous blockade of DDT hydroxylation occurs.

Sesamex can be extremely specific; it can synergize, for instance, the organophosphate Bidrin [which has a $C(O)N(CH_3)_2$ group] and its $C(O)NHCH_3$ analog, but not its $C(O)NH_2$ analog (44). Such a finding suggests that *N*-demethylation is a potent detoxification route.

An area in which pyrethrin synergists have proved particularly interesting is that of carbamate synergism. In 1958, Moorefield (47) found that the toxicity for houseflies of four different carbamates was synergized by a variety of compounds containing the methylenedioxyphenyl group. In 1959, Fuchs and Zschintzsch (23) reported that sulfoxide and *n*-propyl isome were synergists for Isolan and Pyrolan against *Drosophila melanogaster*. Once more the extreme variation in response is demonstrable, but in this case with respect to different organisms: Fuchs and Seume reported in 1957 that piperonyl butoxide *antagonized* the toxicity of eserine or Pyrolan for the water flea, *Daphnia Magna* (22). In 1961, Georghiou and Metcalf showed that octachlorodipropyl ether synergized a variety of carbamates against houseflies (26).

Later, Moorefield and Weiden (48) carried out a more extensive search for such carbamate synergists, and found, for each of the several cases studied, that the methylenedioxy ring

CH_2
O O

could not be replaced by various similar groups, such as the corresponding dimethoxy compounds

CH_3O OCH_3

An even more extensive study was that of Wilkinson *et al.* (82) in 1966 on structure–activity relations in these synergists, of which 62 were prepared and evaluated, many for the first time. The primary conclusion was that the planar methylenedioxyphenyl ring portion was vital, although replacement of one of its oxygens by sulfur was acceptable. Various nonplanar variants, or analogs with substitution upon the methylene or with ring opening, were all virtually inactive.

There is little doubt that the mechanism of this synergism is interference by the synergist with carbamate degradation. The first clue was the observation (24,46) that the toxicity of carbamates to normal houseflies was directly proportional to the anticholinesterase activity—if and only if the toxicity was measured on houseflies treated with piperonyl butoxide. It was argued that such a measurement then indicated "innate" toxicity, and that the departures from the "innate" toxicity (revealed only in the absence of piperonyl butoxide) were due to the variable degrees of metabolism of the different carbamates. The correctness (at least in part) of this argument was demonstrated directly for the case of *m*-isopropylphenyl methylcarbamate, when it was shown (27) that in resistant houseflies piperonyl butoxide partially blocked degradation of this carbamate. However, huge doses of piperonyl butoxide were employed (about 2500 mg/kg) and the blockade was even then incomplete; at about 50 hours,

92% of the carbamate was degraded without, and 60% with, piperonyl butoxide.

To conclude this section showing the diversity of action of modifiers, let us consider the effects of SKF 525A, or 2-diethylaminoethyl 2,2-diphenylvalerate hydrochloride.*

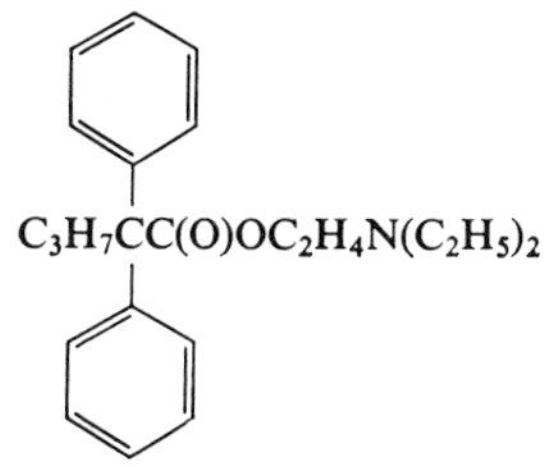

$C_3H_7CC(O)OC_2H_4N(C_2H_5)_2$

SKF525A

This compound, originally developed as an inhibitor of monoamine oxide, is now one of the best established inhibitors of the great variety of reactions catalyzed by microsomes in the presence of reduced nucleotide and oxygen. The first report (15) of its effects upon toxicant metabolism was in 1955 by Davison, who had previously been interested in monoamine oxidase. He showed that at moderate concentrations, such as $10^{-3}M$, SKF 525A could inhibit the activation (see p. 43) of parathion and schradan by rat liver both *in vitro* and *in vivo*. In 1957, this inhibition was also shown in liver for azinphosmethyl *in vitro* by Murphy and DuBois (49). In 1958, O'Brien and Davison (59) argued that if these inhibitions occurred *in vitro*, one would expect that SKF 525A would antagonize poisoning by these organophosphates, since activation is a necessary step in the poisoning process. Working with mice, they found that schradan was greatly antagonized by SKF 525A, so that its LD_{50} was increased 3.8-fold by 20 mg/kg of SKF 525A. By this time it was known that barbiturate breakdown is also mediated by liver microsomes, and breakdown is inhibited by SKF 525A as well as by iproniazid (another monoamine oxidase inhibitor) and 3-acetylpyridine. It was interesting to note (59) that the ability of these three agents to block barbiturate metabolism paralleled their ability to block schradan activation.

Up to this point, the basis for the experimental findings was clear. But it was puzzling to find that although SKF 525A gave modest protection against azinphosmethyl (increasing its LD_{50} about 2-fold), there was no protection against parathion. This puzzle was resolved in 1961 when it was shown with radioisotopes (57) that although activation (to paraoxon) was indeed inhibited

* Also known as the pentanoate rather then the valerate; or as β-diethylaminoethyl 3,3-diphenylpropylacetate hydrochloride.

by SKF 525A in mouse liver slices, yet activation was actually promoted by SKF 525A in the intact mouse. This unexpected finding was shown to be due to the fact that paraoxon degradation *in vivo* was blocked by SKF 525A. It appeared, then, that one could get blockade primarily of degradation for some compounds and primarily of activation for others. A clear-cut case is Amiton, which requires no activation, but whose degradation is catalysed by liver microsomes; consequently, its degradation is blocked (70) and its toxicity is profoundly synergized (56) by SKF 525A. Table 14.6 shows that, in both insects and mice, SKF 525A can either synergize or antagonize organophosphate poisoning, depending on compound and animal.

TABLE 14.6

VARYING EFFECTS OF SKF 525A ON ORGANOPHOSPHATE TOXICITY[a]

Synergistic action			Antagonistic action		
Compound	% Mortality alone	% Mortality with SKF 525A	Compound	% Mortality alone	% Mortality with SKF 525A
Phorate	30	90	Azinphosmethyl	83	0
Amiton	0	100	Dimethoate	70	0
EPN	15	40	Schradan	78	10
			Dimefox	20	0
			Mipafox	70	10

[a] Above data for mice for whom the toxicity of the following was little affected by SKF 525A: Chlorthion, coumaphos, dioxathion, diazinon, Dowco 109, ronnel, parathion, paraoxon, and tepp. Houseflies: SKF 525A doubled LD_{50} for diazinon and had no effect upon toxicity of coumaphos, dimethoate, Dowco 109, azinphosmethyl, or ronnel. Data all for 20 mg/kg of SKF 525A. From O'Brien and Davison (59) and O'Brien (57).

Recently, Anders (2) has provided evidence that SKF 525A is in fact a substrate for microsomal enzymes, and inhibits other microsomal activity by acting as a competitive substrate with low turnover. This finding is expected in view of the fact that chronically administered SKF 525A is an inducer of liver microsomes (p. 215).

We have seen that one line of interest in moderators sprang from pyrethrin synergists; another sprang from interference with microsomal systems. A quite different line of interest has its origin in reports in 1956 and 1957 by the FDA (United States Food and Drug Administration) that certain pairs of organophosphates showed unexpectedly high toxicity when fed to dogs or rats (3,21). The pair of compounds first reported has continued to be the most thoroughly explored, and the most clear-cut case of synergism: EPN with malathion. Thus one-tenth of an LD_{50} of malathion plus one-tenth of an LD_{50} of EPN gave 50% mortality in rats. In dogs, the effects were even greater: one-fortieth of the LD_{50} of malathion plus one-fiftieth of the LD_{50} of EPN gave 100% mortality. In the following years, several reports with such combinations in mice (68,71), rats (16), and dogs (83) were published. They have been reviewed in part elsewhere (56); only the outstanding conclusions will be given here.

The most-studied synergism of this type occurs with malathion as one member of the pair and EPN, TOCP, or a TOCP analog as the other member; for reasons given below, malathion is the compound synergized, and the others are the synergists. As Table 14.7 shows, in this class of synergism, as with others, one may find all possible effects if he studies enough pairs of compounds: some organophosphate pairs are synergistic, some additive, and some antagonistic. Fortunately, there was little basis for the original fear of what might be called a "synergism salad," i.e., that two plants, each bearing a harmless residue, could be toxic if eaten together. It was shown (83) at least for five pairs of compounds, that if the compounds were each at or below their permitted tolerance level, then no significant effects, such as overt symptoms of cholinesterase depression, were found in dogs.

The results of several independent groups (11,12,37,50,52,68,72) working with a variety of techniques, are in general agreement upon the mechanism of the interaction between malathion and EPN or TOCP. In brief, one can show that EPN or TOCP, *in vitro* or *in vivo*, can inhibit the enzyme (a carboxyesterase) which hydrolyzes malathion and its activation product malaoxon, at the $COOC_2H_5$ group. In mammals, this is the primary breakdown enzyme for malathion. This has been shown in numerous tissues, but especially in the liver, and in whole rats and dogs. The theory has been powerfully reinforced by findings with insects; normal houseflies and *Culex* mosquitoes use a phosphatase route rather than a carboxyesterase route for their principal malathion breakdown mechanism, and EPN does not synergize malathion's toxicity to them. But certain strains of housefly and *Culex* mosquitoes have developed resistance to malathion by achieving a high carboxyesterase level, and EPN and TOCP (and related compounds) synergize malathion's toxicity for these resistant strains (41,43,62,64). Furthermore, resistance of these housefly and mosquito strains can be largely overcome by replacing malathion with analogs having $COOCH_3$ in place of $COOC_2H_5$; presumably the carboxyesterase of the resistant insects is specific to $COOC_2H_5$ (14,42).

In spite of the convincing nature of the above evidence, there are certain anomalies. First, although carboxyesterase is inhibited by EPN, there was no demonstrable increase in production of the actual toxicant, malaoxon, in rat

TABLE 14.7

ORGANOPHOSPHATE SYNERGISM IN RATS AND MICE[a]

	Effect in rats[b]	Effect in mice[b]
Synergistic		
Malathion and EPN	SYN (100)	SYN (100)
Malathion and trichlorfon	SYN (100)	—
Azinphosmethyl and trichlorfon	SYN (100)	—
Acethion and EPN	—	SYN (80)
Dowco 109 and EPN	—	SYN (100)
Dimethoate and EPN	—	SYN (100)
Trans-Thionophosdrin	—	SYN (85)
Antagonistic		
Parathion and malathion	ANT (10)	—
Parathion and azinphosmethyl	ANT (10)	—
Trichlorfon and EPN	ANT (30)	ANT (0)
Trichlorfon and demeton	ANT (10)	—
Malathion and azinphosmethyl	ANT (10)	—
Demeton and azinphosmethyl	ANT (5)	—
Additive		
Parathion and EPN	ADD (45)	—
Parathion and trichlorfon	ADD (55)	—
Parathion and demeton	ADD (50)	—
Demeton and EPN	ADD (45)	—
Demeton and malathion	ADD (60)	—
Azinphosmethyl and EPN	ADD (60)	—
cis-Thionophosdrin	—	ADD (15)

[a] Data from DuBois (16) and Seume and O'Brien (72).

[b] SYN = synergism, ANT = antagonism, ADD = additive. In rats, the predicted mortality if no interaction occurred was 50%; in mice it was 10%. Parenthetic values are the observed mortalities.

tissues *in vitro* (72). Second, EPN should have the effect of reducing urinary excretion of malathion breakdown products, but in fact it somewhat increased it in the dog and had no effect in the rat (37). Third, it has been claimed that EPN and malathion display synergism under conditions in which metabolic interference is improbable, e.g., when EPN was given 45 minutes after malathion (34) or when the mixture was applied directly to the target site, specifically, at the neuromuscular junction and in the brain (35) [but there is evidence that the compounds used in these experiments were impure (58)]. Fourth, a quite different mechanism of synergism is suggested by experiments by

Fleisher *et al.* (18) showing that unmetabolized sarin is bound in many tissues, especially in lung, and that the binding in lung is blocked by EPN. Such a mechanism has not been examined for the case of EPN with other compounds than sarin.

The fact that substantial space has been devoted here to the anomalies in the carboxyesterase-inhibition theory of EPN synergism should not be taken to imply that this theory is probably wrong. On the contrary, its corollaries have been so generally proven that it is generally accepted; but the great challenge now is to explain the anomalies.

Why is it that only certain pairs of organophosphates are synergistic? Or, specifically, why do organophosphates differ in their ability to synergize malathion? The answer is (12) that although most organophosphates can inhibit carboxyesterase *in vitro*, it is only when the ratio of the inhibitory potencies for cholinesterase and for carboxyesterase is low (which is seldom the case) that one can substantially inhibit carboxyesterase *in vivo*; otherwise, the appropriate dose is more than enough to kill the animal by inhibiting all its cholinesterase. Looked at in this light, one might say that the special feature of EPN is not that it is such a good carboxyesterase inhibitor, but that it is such a bad cholinesterase inhibitor.

It is interesting that the two best-known organophosphate synergists, EPN and TOCP, are almost certainly not active as such, but require metabolic conversion. It is generally assumed that EPN, like all phosphorothionates, requires activation by conversion of P═S to P═O. As for TOCP, in spite of long-standing suspicions, it was not until 1961 that Casida *et al.* (8) proved that a series of reactions was involved in the conversion to the actual synergist *in vivo*; hydroxylation of a methyl group, followed by attack of the new hydroxyl upon the phosphorus, and ejection of a cresyl group, gives the indicated compound, which is the actual inhibitor.

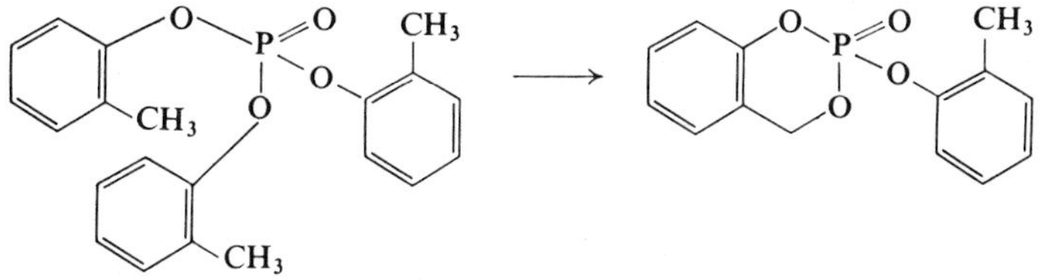

On page 58, the ability of certain organophosphates to cause demyelination is discussed; TOCP is the most familiar example of such a compound. It would seem, however, that there is no correlation between ability to demyelinate and to synergize malathion. Thus EPN is a good synergist but not a demyelinator (17). Nevertheless, in a large series of 68 organophosphates tested as malathion synergists against resistant houseflies and *Culex tarsalis* mosquitoes by Plapp and Tong (63), virtually all the good synergists were good demyelinating agents. This series demonstrated the excellence of some simply symmetrical compounds; the two best for housefly synergism were tripropyl phosphorotrithiolate $(C_3H_7S)_3PO$ and its tributyl analog $(C_4H_9S)_3PO$. It also suggested that there are differences in the nature of the carboxyesterase of resistant housefly, *Culex*, and mouse, for a different synergist was optimal for each of these species.

Before leaving the topic of malathion synergism, it should be noted that the carboxyesterase in human and rat liver which breaks down malathion, has been shown to be identical with the rather well-known liver enzyme, aliesterase (40).

The discovery that malathion's low toxicity to mammals was due to carboxyester cleavage suggested that other organophosphates containing a carboxyester group should have low toxicity for a similar reason; a corollary would be that such compounds would be subject to synergism by EPN and TOCP. Experiments with mice (71) showed that this was true in some, but not all, cases. Thus acethion, $(C_2H_5O)_2P(S)SCH_2COOC_2H_5$, and methyl methprothion, $(C_2H_5)_2P(S)SCH(CH_3)CH_2COOCH_3$, were synergized, but neither isomer of mevinphos was synergized. Even more interesting, the novel compound thionomevinphos (or thionophosdrin), $(CH_3O)_2P(S)OCH{=}CHCOOCH_3$, was synergized in the case of its *cis*, but not its *trans*, isomer. It was suggested, and this has never been verified, that susceptibility to synergism by EPN or TOCP must mean that carboxyesterase is involved in degradation, and therefore that mevinphos (*cis* or *trans*) and *trans*-thionomevinphos are not degraded in this way, but by, for instance, a phosphatase which is insensitive to EPN and TOCP.

The observation was made that dimethoate is synergized by EPN in mice (71), and therefore is was suggested that for it, and related compounds containing the carboxyamide $[C(O)NR_2]$ group, a case parallel to that found in carboxyester-containing compounds would hold; and indeed it was found (79) that, in insects and mammals the ability to block degradation of dimethoate was an excellent index of ability to synergize. Thus the synergizing and metabolism-blocking action of EPN was profound in mice, less in guinea pigs, and absent in houseflies (two strains) or milkweed bugs. But the ability of EPN to block dimethoate degradation was not simply linked with an effect upon carboxyamidase, as was found in the parallel case of carboxyesterase and malathion. Dimethoate in houseflies and milkweed bugs was degraded about 80% by phosphatase and 20% by amidase; EPN had negligible effect upon either pathway. In mouse liver, degradation was about equally caused by phosphatase and amidase; both were about equally sensitive to EPN. In guinea pig liver, phosphatase was almost the exclusive breakdown enzyme, and its was a good deal less sensitive to EPN than the carboxyamidase. It follows that whereas malathion carboxyesterases of insects and mammals are similar, at least with respect to sensitivity to EPN,* the dimethoate carboxyamidases differ in different organisms.

A complicated kind of interaction was demonstrated by Abdallah (1) between TOCP and either parathion or paraoxon applied topically to houseflies. Such a combination was synergistic if the two compounds were applied to different parts of the body; but if they were applied to the same part, antagonism was observed, presumably because of hindered penetration. In a similar way, sesamex somewhat reduced the cuticular penetration of the organophosphate, Bidrin (44).

The final example of noninductive synergism is one that occurs only in those resistant insects (houseflies or *Aedes aegypti* mosquitoes) which have developed resistance by virtue of developing the enzyme DDT-dehydrochlorinase. In these cases only, a specific inhibitor of that enzyme, called WARF antiresistant, is profoundly synergistic (61,74).

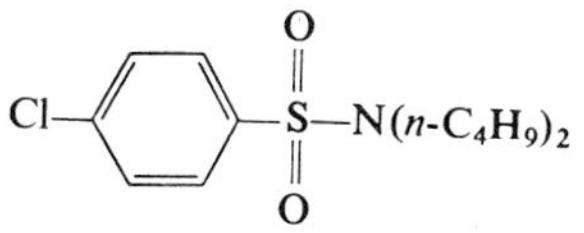

$$Cl-C_6H_4-S(=O)_2-N(n\text{-}C_4H_9)_2$$

WARF antiresistant
(*N*-di-*n*-butyl-*p*-chlorobenzenesulfonamide)

Unfortunately, repeated application of the synergist along with DDT soon led to profound resistance to the mixture (19).

One might reasonably ask how such a synergist was stumbled upon. It seems that the origins lie in the very numerous attempts to prepare compounds structurally enough like DDT that they would block its metabolism. The outcome of that search [reviewed in 1954 (76)] has been slight but, in the course of it, one of the many series having (like DDT) two phenyls attached to some bridge group was benzenesulfonanilide and its derivatives:

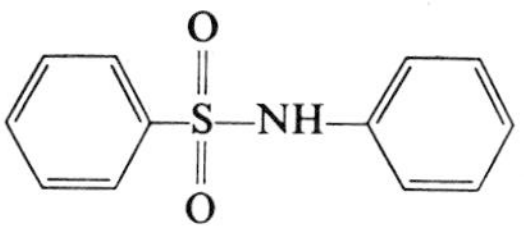

$$C_6H_5-S(=O)_2-NH-C_6H_5$$

This series, originally prepared in Italy (73) in 1953, was embroidered upon by Neeman *et al.* (53) in 1957 in order to improve solubility in organic solvents. The latter reported unpublished results of S. Cohen showing that at least one

* Kojima (38) has shown that mouse and cockroach carboxyesterases differ in other respects, e.g., relative activities toward malaoxon and acetoxon.

such derivative blocked DDT dehydrochlorinase *in vitro*. Presumably in the course of later studies, a bold chemist replaced the *N*-aromatic by *N*-alkyl groups, and the WARF family of compounds resulted.

There has been one report (75) of antagonism between two compounds with respect to their storage; probably the absence of other reports is a reflection of lack of investigation rather than of the rarity of the phenomenon. DDT was shown to depress the storage of dieldrin when both were fed to rats. For instance, feeding 10 ppm of dieldrin normally leads to deposition of 68 ppm in body fat, but if one simultaneously fed 5 ppm of DDT, the dieldrin in fat was depressed to 44 ppm, and 50 ppm of DDT in the diet depressed dieldrin storage to 11 ppm in body fat. These findings suggest that storage of chlorinated hydrocarbons is not a matter of simple solution in some large pool of fatty material, but involves fairly specific binding sites which are quite limited in capacity. This conclusion must be tempered with the thought that the findings might be interpreted in very different ways; for instance, the DDT might affect dieldrin metabolism.

REFERENCES

1. Abdallah, M. D., *Mededel. Landbouwhogeschool Wageningen* **63**, 1 (1963).
2. Anders, M. W., Private communication, 1966.
3. Anonymous, *Chem. Eng. News* **34**, 5398 (1956).
4. Ball, W. L., Sinclair, J. W., Crevier, M., and Kay, K., *Can. J. Biochem. Physiol.* **32**, 440 (1954).
5. Bliss, C. I., *Ann. Appl. Biol.* **26**, 585 (1939).
6. Brooks, G. T., and Harrison, A., *Biochem. Pharmacol.* **13**, 827 (1964).
7. Burns, J. J., Cucinell, S. A., Koster, R., and Conney, A. H., *Ann. N.Y. Acad. Sci.* **123**, 273 (1965).
8. Casida, J. E., Eto, M., and Baron, R. L., *Nature* **191**, 1396 (1961).
9. Conney, A. H., Miller, E. C., and Miller, J. A., *Cancer Res.* **16**, 450 (1956).
10. Conney, A. H., Davison, C., Gastel, R., and Burns, J. J., *J. Pharmacol. Exptl. Therap.* **130**, 1 (1960).
11. Cook, J. W., and Yip, G., *J. Assoc. Offic. Agr. Chemists* **41**, 407 (1958).
12. Cook, J. W., Blake, J. R., and Williams, M., *J. Assoc. Offic. Agr. Chemists* **40**, 664 (1957).
13. Crevier, M., Ball, W. L., and Kay, K., *Am. Med. Assoc. Arch. Ind. Health* **9**, 306 (1954).
14. Dauterman, W. C., and Matsumura, F., *Science* **138**, 69A (1962).
15. Davison, A. N., *Biochem. J.* **61**, 203 (1955).
16. DuBois, K. P., *A. M. A. Arch. Ind. Health* **18**, 488 (1958).
17. Durham, W. F., Gaines, T. B., and Hayes, W. J., *Am. Med. Assoc. Arch. Ind. Health* **13**, 326 (1956).
18. Fleisher, J. H., Harris, L. W., Prudhomme, C., and Bursel, J., *J. Pharmacol. Exptl. Therap.* **139**, 390 (1963).
19. Forgash, A. J., *J. Econ. Entomol.* **57**, 644 (1964).
20. Fouts, J. R., and Hart, L. G., *Ann. N.Y. Acad. Sci.* **123**, 245 (1965).
21. Frawley, J. P., Fuyat, H. N., Hagan, E. C., Blake, J. R., and Fitzhugh, O. G., *J. Pharmacol. Exptl. Therap.* **121**, 96 (1957).
22. Fuchs, W. H., and Seume, F. W., *Naturwissenschaften* **44**, 334 (1957).

23. Fuchs, W. H., and Zschintzsch, J., *Naturwissenschaften* **46**, 273 (1959).
24. Fukuto, T. R., Metcalf, R. L., Winton, M. Y., and Roberts, P. A., *J. Econ. Entomol.* **55**, 341 (1962).
25. Gaudette, L. E., and Brodie, B. B., *Biochem. Pharmacol.* **2**, 89 (1959).
26. Georghiou, G. P., and Metcalf, R. L., *J. Econ. Entomol.* **54**, 150 (1961).
27. Georghiou, G. P., and Metcalf, R. L., *J. Econ. Entomol.* **54**, 231 (1961).
28. Gillett, J. W., and Terriere, L. C., *Am. Chem. Soc. Div. Agr. Food Chem., Phoenix, Arizona*, 1966 Abstr. No. A18 (1966).
29. Gillette, J. R., *Proc. 1st Intern. Pharmacol. Meeting, Stockholm*, 1961, **6**, 235 (1962).
30. Hart, L. G., Shultice, R. W., and Fouts, J. R., *Toxicol. Appl. Pharmacol.* **5**, 371 (1963).
31. Hewlett, P. S., *Advan. Pest Control Res.* **3**, 27 (1960).
32. Hoffman, R. A., Hopkins, T. L., and Lindquist, A. W., *J. Econ. Entomol.* **47**, 72 (1954).
33. Jacobson, K. B., and Kaplan, N. O., *J. Biophys. Biochem. Cytol.* **3**, 31 (1957).
34. Karczmar, A. G., Awad, O., and Blachut, K., *Toxicol. Appl. Pharmacol.* **4**, 133 (1962).
35. Karczmar, A. G., Blachut, K., Redlon, S. A., Gothelf, G., and Awad, O., *Intern. J. Neuropharmacol.* **2**, 163 (1963).
36. Kato, R., *Arzneimittel-Forsch.* **11**, 797 (1961).
37. Knaak, J. B., and O'Brien, R. D., *J. Agr. Food Chem.* **8**, 198 (1960).
38. Kojima, K., "Studies on the Selective Toxicity and Detoxication of Organophosphorus Compounds." Inst. Agr. Chem. Toa Nayaku Co., Odawara, 1961.
39. McPhillips, J. J., *Toxicol. Appl. Pharmacol.* **7**, 64 (1965).
40. Main, A. R., and Braid, P. E., *Biochem. J.* **84**, 255 (1962).
41. Matsumura, F., and Brown, A. W. A., *J. Econ. Entomol.* **54**, 1176 (1961).
42. Matsumura, F., and Dauterman, W. C., *Nature* **202**, 1356 (1964).
43. Matsumura, F., and Hogendijk, C. J., *Entomol. Exptl. Appl.* **7**, 179 (1964).
44. Menzer, R. E., and Casida, J. E., *J. Agr. Food Chem.* **13**, 102 (1965).
45. Metcalf, R. L., "Organic Insecticides." Wiley (Interscience), New York, 1965.
46. Metcalf, R. L., Fukuto, T. R., and Winton, M. Y., *J. Econ. Entomol.* **53**, 828 (1960).
47. Moorefield, H. H., *Contrib. Boyce Thompson Inst.* **19**, 501 (1958).
48. Moorefield, H. H., and Weiden, M. H. J., *Contrib. Boyce Thompson Inst.* **22**, 425 (1964).
49. Murphy, S. D., and DuBois, K. P., *J. Pharmacol. Exptl. Therap.* **119**, 572 (1957).
50. Murphy, S. D., and DuBois, K. P., *Proc. Soc. Exptl. Biol. Med.* **96**, 813 (1957).
51. Murphy, S. D., and DuBois, K. P., *J. Pharmacol. Exptl. Therap.* **124**, 194 (1958).
52. Murphy, S. D., Anderson, R. L., and DuBois, K. P., *Proc. Soc. Exptl. Biol. Med.* **100**, 483 (1959).
53. Neeman, M., Mer, G. G., Cevilich, R., Modiano, A., and Zacks, S., *J. Sci. Food Agr.* **8**, 55 (1957).
54. Netter, K. J., *Proc. 1st Intern. Pharmacol. Meeting, Stockholm*, 1961 **6**, 213 (1962).
55. Neubert, D., and Schaefer, J., *Arch. Exptl. Pathol. Pharmakol.* **233**, 151 (1958).
56. O'Brien, R. D., "Toxic Phosphorus Esters." 434 pp. Academic Press, New York, 1960.
57. O'Brien, R. D., *Biochem. J.* **79**, 229 (1961).
58. O'Brien, R. D., *Ann. Rev. Entomol.* **11**, 369 (1966).
59. O'Brien, R. D., and Davison, A. N., *Can. J. Biochem. Physiol.* **36**, 1203 (1958).
60. Philleo, W. W., Schonbrod, R. D., and Terriere, L. C., *J. Agr. Food Chem.* **13**, 113 (1965).
61. Pillai, M. K. K., Abedi, Z. H., and Brown, A. W. A., *Mosquito News* **23**, 112 (1963).
62. Plapp, F. W., and Eddy, G. W., *Science* **134**, 2043 (1961).
63. Plapp, F. W., and Tong, H. H. C., *J. Econ. Entomol.* **59**, 11 (1966).
64. Plapp, F. W., Bigley, W. S., Chapman, G. A., and Eddy, G. W., *J. Econ. Entomol.* **56**, 643 (1963).
65. Remmer, H., *Proc. 1st Intern. Pharmacol. Meeting, Stockholm*, 1961 **6**, 235 (1962).

66. Remmer, H., and Merker, H. J., *Science* **142**, 1657 (1964).
67. Remmer, H., and Merker, H. J., *Ann. N.Y. Acad. Sci.* **123**, 79 (1965).
68. Rosenberg, P., and Coon, J. M., *Proc. Soc. Exptl. Biol. Med.* **97**, 836 (1958).
69. Sakai, S., "Insect Toxicological Studies on the Joint Toxic Action of Insecticides." Inst. Agr. Chem., Toa Nayaku Co., Odawara, 1960.
70. Scaife, J. F., and Campbell, D. H., *Can. J. Biochem. Physiol.* **37**, 297 (1959).
71. Seume, F. W., and O'Brien, R. D., *Toxicol. Appl. Pharmacol.* **2**, 495 (1960).
72. Seume, F. W., and O'Brien, R. D., *J. Agr. Food Chem.* **8**, 36 (1960).
73. Speroni, G., Losco, G., Santi, R., and Peri, C., *Chim. Ind.* (*Milan*) **69**, 658 (1953).
74. Spiller, D., *Science* **142**, 585 (1963).
75. Street, J. C., *Science* **146**, 1580 (1964).
76. Sumerford, W. T., *J. Agr. Food Chem.* **2**, 310 (1954).
77. Sun, Y. P., and Johnson, E. R., *J. Agr. Food Chem.* **8**, 261 (1960).
78. Uchida, T., Dauterman, W. C., and O'Brien, R. D., *J. Agr. Food Chem.* **12**, 48 (1964).
79. Uchida, T., Zschintzsch, J., and O'Brien, R. D., *Toxicol. Appl. Pharmacol.* **8**, 259 (1966).
80. Veldstra, H., *Pharmacol. Rev.* **8**, 339 (1956).
81. Welch, R. M., and Coon, J. M., *J. Pharmacol. Exptl. Therap.* **144**, 192 (1964).
82. Wilkinson, C., Metcalf, R. L., and Fukuto, T. R., *J. Agr. Food Chem.* **14**, 73 (1966).
83. Williams, M. W., Fuyat, H. N., Frawley, J. P., and Fitzhugh, O. G., *J. Agr. Food Chem.* **6**, 514 (1958).
84. Zschintzsch, J., *Arzneimittel-Forsch.* **11**, 579 (1961).
85. Zschintzsch, J., and Fuchs, W. H., *Naturwissenschaften* **46**, 354 (1959).

CHAPTER 15

Resistance

The official definition of resistance is: "Resistance to insecticides is the development of an ability in a strain of insects to tolerate doses of toxicants which would prove lethal to the majority of individuals in a normal population of the same species" (3). This formidable topic deserves a book rather than a chapter. In order to deal with it in a few pages, the discussion of its occurrence and its genetics will be very briefly mentioned, and our knowledge of its mechanism will be considered at some length. Two very fine reviews are available on the genetic aspects: one (22) by Crow in 1957 and the other (59) by Oppenoorth in 1965. Valuable reviews giving perspective on the occurrence of and mechanism of resistance have been published by Brown (15,17) since his *magnum opus* on the subject in 1958 (14).

Because of the frequency of their usage in the following pages, "R" will be used to refer to "resistant" and "S" to "susceptible" strains. Two other terms requiring definition are "behavioral resistance," which occurs when an insect strain develops the ability to avoid a lethal dose, rather than developing a physiological indifference to the dose; and "vigor tolerance," a term used to describe development of a modest and nonspecific ability to tolerate a variety of insecticidal or environmental stresses.

Resistance is seen normally in field operations as a progressive inability of a given compound, at a fixed application rate, to achieve control. It can be induced in the laboratory by insecticide "pressure," i.e., by treating successive generations with a dose large enough to kill (say) 90%, and breeding from survivors. It is preadaptive, that is to say, the insecticide does not induce any heritable changes, but merely selects and (over generations) makes more common the innate insensitivity found originally in only a few individuals. It is a case of pure Darwinian selection.

Resistance of insects to insecticides is not new; in 1914, Melander described resistance of San Jose scale to lime sulfur, and in 1916, Quayle reported resistance of California red scale to cyanide (53). Prior to 1945, 13 insect or tick species were reported as resistant to arsenicals, selenium, rotenone, cyanide, and other compounds (15). However, the problem on its present heroic scale concerns the newer synthetic insecticides. In 1942, DDT was patented, and in 1947 the first reports came in, from Italy and Sweden, suggesting that DDT was becoming less effective for housefly control (43). Since then the roster of insects and of insecticides involved in resistance has steadily lengthened. In 1960, the number of species involved was 137, and the organophosphates and several chlorinated hydrocarbons were implicated (15). Since then carbamate resistance has been repeatedly demonstrated.

An important factor is the pattern of cross resistance, i.e., the extent to which resistance induced by exposure to one compound extends to other compounds. The problems are 2-fold: within a class of compounds and between classes. The former problem will be discussed at appropriate places below. The problem of cross resistance between insecticide groups will now be discussed briefly, with special reference to the housefly, on which the most data is available. The facts will be presented as didactic generalizations, with qualifying comments where appropriate. For more details, the 1964 review by Winteringham and Hewlett (90) is recommended.

DDT-induced resistance extends to closely related compounds such as methoxychlor, but not to lindane, dieldrin, or nonchlorinated compounds. There may be vigor tolerance to such compounds as pyrethrins (90). The generalization appears to be valid for many insect species.

Lindane and the cyclodienes induce resistance to each other that does not extend to DDT or nonchlorinated compounds. Maximal resistance develops to the inducing compound itself, so that lindane-induced resistance is particularly marked for lindane, and less marked for dieldrin.

Organophosphates induce resistance relatively slowly and often to a less extreme extent than do chlorinated hydrocarbons, but severe cross resistance commonly extends to many other compounds, including chlorinated hydrocarbons and carbamates. Thus March (42) found that houseflies selected by parathion for 41 generations became 7-fold resistant to parathion, but over 3000-fold to DDT, 70-fold to methoxychlor, and 120-fold to lindane. When parathion selection was terminated, subsequent generations lost their parathion resistance, but retained resistance to DDT! Similarly, mosquitoes selected with malathion (18) or houseflies selected with diazinon (25) develop a resistance to DDT accompanied by the presence of DDT-dehydrochlorinase.

Carbamates may induce resistance to organophosphates and chlorinated hydrocarbons, but the extent of cross resistance is highly variable. Thus carbaryl selection of houseflies has induced modest resistance to DDT and parathion (33); but a different strain selected with phenyl dimethylcarbamate showed no resistance to the carbamate, little to DDT, but high resistance to dieldrin and toxaphene (51).

Resistance is therefore well established for the major groups of insecticides. One gets the impression that for every toxicant, resistance may occur; thus in 1963 Tahori (84) was able to develop 7-fold resistance to fluoroacetate in houseflies after 25 generations; simultaneously the flies developed cross resistance to DDT (67-fold resistance), methoxychlor (12-fold), lindane (26-fold), and especially dieldrin (400-fold), but practically no resistance to organophosphates or a carbamate (carbaryl).

Finally, resistance is worldwide in scope, particularly for the chlorinated hydrocarbons, which have been used in the remotest parts of the world. Reports of it come from Dahomey, Java, Nepal, Nicaragua, and Ethiopia, just as much as from such unexotic regions as California, Ontario, and England (15).

DDT Resistance

This is the most celebrated case of resistance; it was the first to be demonstrated on a large scale, and the first to be rather fully explained, at least in the case of the housefly.

It is now widely accepted (but not totally proved) that, in the housefly, resistance to DDT is usually caused by the high titer of DDT-dehydrochlorinase (see p. 128) which occurs in most R strains and is almost absent in S strains. The early work was almost exclusively from Kearn's laboratory in Illinois. It was in 1950 that it was first reported that R strains of houseflies could dehydrochlorinate DDT (66,83). At first, this enzymic ability was reported to exist only in R flies and only in their cuticle (83), but later work (54) showed that most tissues of R flies were active, and fat body especially so. In 1959, Lovell and Kearns (41) refined the techniques to permit assays on individual houseflies, and were then able to show by genetic procedures that dehydrochlorination and resistance were inseparably linked; they are inherited together and in the same proportions.

The enzyme DDT-dehydrochlorinase, once so difficult even to find, has now been purified and its properties have been studied; it was reviewed by Lipke and Kearns in 1960 (40). Some highlights of this achievement are as follows. Because of the excessively low solubility of DDT, effective assay was at first only achieved by adsorption of DDT onto glass microbeads, and later by solubilization of DDT by a special egg yolk lipoprotein. Ammonium sulfate fractionation of frozen, whole R houseflies, followed by methanol precipitation, carbonate extraction, heat treatment (48°C for 4 minutes), dialysis, cation-exchange chromatography, calcium phosphate gel treatment, and further methanol precipitation, gave a 5% yield of a three-component mixture of protein. The evidence is that the enzyme is a small globulin, of less than 80,000 M.W. and requires glutathione as a cofactor. Strangely enough, glutathione cannot be replaced by other familiar SH agents (cysteine, thiomalate, and so on). The enzyme is rather insensitive to SH inhibitors such as *p*-chloromercuribenzoate or *N*-ethylmaleimide. It can be inhibited *in vitro* by various compounds which synergize its toxicity *in vivo*, such as WARF antiresistant (p. 129) and bis(*p*-chlorophenyl)ethane,

Cl—C₆H₄—CH(CH₃)—C₆H₄—Cl

Bis(*p*-chlorophenyl)ethane

Finally, there is a fairly good correlation between dehydrochlorinase activity and DDT resistance for a variety of resistant strains of houseflies, as Fig. 15.1 shows.

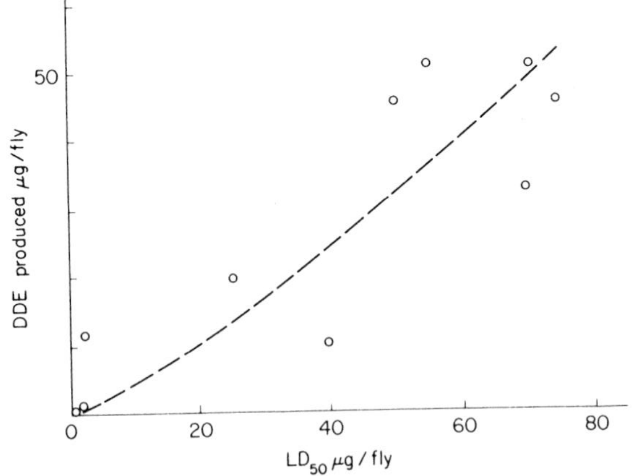

FIG. 15.1. Relationship of DDT-dehydrochlorinase activity to DDT resistance in houseflies. Drawn using data of Lipke and Kearns (40).

It is considered that the "development" of DDT-dehydrochlorinating ability is preadaptive, i.e., it represents the selection and "magnification," according to Darwinian principles, of a character already existent prior to DDT application. (This is the opposite of the inductive mechanisms discussed in Chapter 14.) Perhaps the best evidence on this point is that one can select for DDT resistance by means that do not employ DDT, and in such a case one finds high DDT-dehydrochlorinase activity. This classic experiment was performed in 1957 by Kerr and his collaborators in Australia (34), by selecting late-emerging flies, which Pimentel *et al.* had found 6 years earlier to be tolerant to DDT (72).

Although dehydrochlorinase provides the best-established mechanism of DDT resistance in houseflies, there is at least one case of a metabolic type of DDT resistance in houseflies not due to this enzyme. Oppenoorth (58) has described the Fe strain, which has only a little dehydrochlorinase (one-twentieth of that in a "normal" R strain) and therefore DMC* or FDMC,* both inhibitors of that enzyme, are not at all synergistic. Piperonyl butoxide, by contrast, is strongly synergistic, suggesting the possibility that the responsible breakdown enzyme is a microsomal hydroxylase (p. 219).

The above evidence is reason enough for it to be widely held that dehydrochlorinase action is the primary resistance mechanism in houseflies. The evidence is not, however, without flaws, as Perry has clearly indicated (63). There are at least four anomalies.

(1) The amounts of unchanged DDT in R flies are more than enough to kill the insect if the innate sensitivity of the R flies was the same as that of the S flies (7,67); thus 48 μg per fly were found in R insects treated at 60 μg per fly. This anomaly could be resolved if it were shown that the amount of DDT *at the active site* was not accurately mirrored by the amount in the whole fly; such a resolution has not yet appeared. A somewhat related problem, described in the same study, was that high levels of DDT actually blocked DDT conversion in R flies: 7.5 μg of DDT per fly gave rise to 1.2 μg of DDE (of the remainder, 3.7 μg was recovered as unchanged DDT); whereas 30 μg per fly gave only 0.24 μg of DDE (of the remainder 23 μg was recovered as DDT); and no DDE was produced at the heroic, but not lethal, dose of 60 μg per fly! These findings suggest that dehydrochlorination might only play a small role when large doses are applied.

(2) Some DDT-resistant flies have cross resistance to compounds which cannot be dehydrochlorinated, such as Prolan (65) and dianisyl neopentane (19).

(3) Some insect species, such as the milkweed bug, can metabolize DDT as fast as R flies, yet are susceptible to DDT poisoning (63). It may of course be that the milkweed bug has far more innate sensitivity to DDT than do houseflies, so that its ability to degrade it is inadequate compensation. A related

* DMC is an analog of DDT, with

$$CH_3\overset{|}{\underset{|}{C}}OH \text{ replacing } Cl_3\overset{|}{\underset{|}{C}}H$$

which inhibits DDT-dehydrochlorinase. FDMC is an analog of DDT with

$$F_3C\overset{|}{\underset{|}{C}}OH \text{ replacing } Cl_3\overset{|}{\underset{|}{C}}H.$$

"anomaly" is even more easily disposed of; this is the fact that some insects, such as the Khapra beetle, cannot metabolize DDT yet are insensitive to it (63). This merely indicates that the Khapra beetle has some nonmetabolic defense mechanism.

(4) In 1953, Pratt and Babers showed (77) that DDT applied to the thoracic ganglion of houseflies caused leg tremors; more DDT was required for R than for S flies. Yet the S–R difference with respect to the number tremoring 5 minutes after application was fairly small (e.g., at the lower dose, 88% of S and 64% of R); the difference was great 1 hour later (64% of S and 16% of R), a finding compatible with a contribution owing to DDT metabolism. Later, Yamasaki and Narahashi (91) confirmed and amplified the finding with electrophysiological techniques, as discussed more fully below (p. 250). It seems probable that differences in the innate sensitivity of the nerve are involved, and it is likely that this phenomenon contributes, at least in part, to the resistance. In at least one fly, the stable fly *Stomoxys calcitrans*, R and S strains absorb, metabolize, and excrete DDT identically (82); perhaps in this case, innate nerve sensitivity is the primary factor in resistance.

There is some evidence (2) that the DDT-resistance mechanism in *Aedes aegypti* larvae is the same as in the housefly, i.e., probably by dehydrochlorination, but with minor variations. Extensive experiments were performed with six R and five S strains. The most direct approach involved measurement of the DDT absorbed and DDE produced. Certainly the most resistant strain produced much more DDE than the most sensitive (either on a percent or an absolute basis), but the correlation over all the strains was not excellent. However, in support of the view that resistance was due to dehydrochlorination, DMC and also (70) WARF antiresistant (see p. 129) synergized DDT's toxicity and inhibited its dehydrochlorinase (16), and there was no resistance to Dilan. In these respects the case was parallel to that in R houseflies. In the R housefly, *o*-chloro-DDT is very toxic, presumably because it cannot be dehydrochlorinated; but in R *Aedes*, resistance to *o*-chloro-DDT was pronounced, and extensive dehydrochlorination was observed. It would seem that dehydrochlorinases differ a good deal in different organisms, and this conclusion is confirmed by the finding (71) that DDT containing deuterium instead of hydrogen on the 2-carbon atom (deutero-DDT) was very poorly dehydrochlorinated by R *Aedes aegypti*, and consequently was very toxic to them, whereas it is readily dehydrochlorinated by R houseflies and was nontoxic to them.

A subsequent study (35) cleared up in a very interesting way the question of the rather poor correlation in *Aedes* between dehydrochlorinase activity and resistance by examining many strains, 14 in all. As Fig. 15.2 shows, the correlation was good for 8 American strains (correlation coefficient 0.81), and nonexistent for 6 Asiatic strains. Furthermore, a comparison of S and four R substrains of one of the American strains (Trinidad strain) using *o*-chloro-DDT and methoxychlor as substrates for dehydrochlorination, showed an excellent correlation between dehydrochlorination and DDT resistance. It therefore appears that dehydrochlorination is the cause of resistance in American, but not in Asiatic, strains of *Aedes aegypti*. A curious additional mechanism of resistance was found in American strains of *Aedes aegypti*: R larvae excreted an extremely large quantity of peritrophic membrane (the gut lining which is common in insects, and is normally continuously extruded or "excreted"), to which was bound a great deal of unchanged DDT (1).

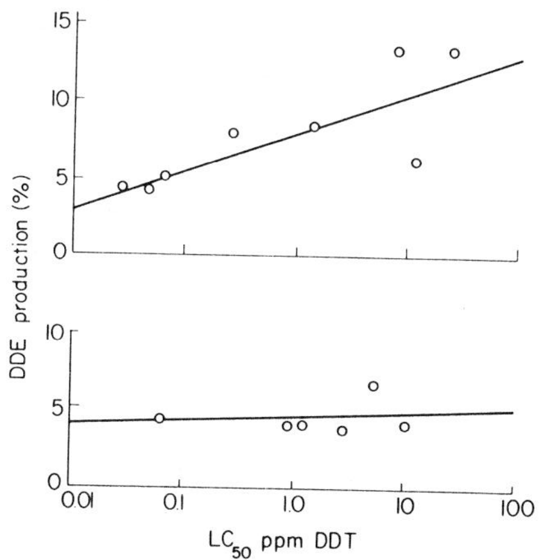

FIG. 15.2. Relationship of DDT-dehydrochlorinase activity to DDT resistance in *Aedes aegypti*; American strains (top) and Asiatic strains (bottom). Redrawn from Kimura and Brown (35).

Opinions vary about the role of dehydrochlorination in resistance to DDT of *Culex* mosquito larvae. Workers of Brown's group (36) consider the role an important one, on the grounds that in both *Culex tarsalis* and *Culex fatigans* the R strain dehydrochlorinates vigorously *in vivo*, and with homogenates the R strain contains 4 times (in *C. tarsalis*) and 10 times (in *C. fatigans*) the dehydrochlorinase activity of the S counterpart. But the study was not altogether conclusive. For instance, the difference between R and S strains in dehydrochlorination *in vivo* was small in *C. fatigans*, in which R and S strains dehydrochlorinated 96 and 83% of a dose, respectively, scarcely enough difference to account for the 250-fold resistance, and at odds with the above data on homogenates showing a 10-fold dehydrochlorinase difference. The findings with *C. tarsalis* seemed more satisfactory; *in vivo* the R and S strains dehydrochlorinated 40 and 0%, respectively, and in homogenates a 5-fold difference in dehydrochlorinase activity was found. The resistance was at least 25-fold.

Let us call "Type I" the dehydrochlorinase of *Aedes aegypti*: it is 3 times as active on DDT as on *o*-chloro-DDT, and inactive on deutero-DDT; and "Type II" that of houseflies, which does not dehydrochlorinate *o*-chloro-DDT, and is very effective on deutero-DDT. Both I and II dehydrochlorinate DDD better than DDT. The enzyme of the *Culex fatigans* mosquito is like Type I except that it is only one-tenth as active on DDD as on DDT; that of the *C. tarsalis* mosquito is of Type II (36).

An almost simultaneous study by Plapp *et al.* (74) on *Culex tarsalis* reached a conclusion opposite to the above. They noted that the DDT resistance extended to compounds which could not be dehydrochlorinated, such as Prolan and *o*-chloro-DDT (but the degree of resistance was much less, e.g., 1875 times for DDT, 200 times for Prolan, and >167 times for *o*-chloro-DDT). Resistance was little affected by agents, such as DMC and WARF antiresistant, which block dehydrochlorination. Studies on metabolism were performed with C^{14}-DDD, and showed, in addition to the dehydrochlorination product, fairly substantial amounts of other products, including bis(*p*-chlorophenyl)-methanol, DDA, *p*-chlorobenzoic acid, and unidentified, relatively polar compounds. Under some circumstances, these other oxidative metabolites were as plentiful as the dehydrochlorination product, and the authors felt that a nondehydrochlorination mechanism was responsible for resistance. But unfortunately, R and S strains were compared at different DDD concentrations; furthermore, the R strain had only 250-fold resistance to DDD compared with 1875-fold resistance to DDT. Consequently, it is not easy to accept the authors' conclusions about the relevance of their findings for DDT resistance.

Studies on DDT-resistance mechanisms in agriculturally important pests are surprisingly few. In the pink bollworm, *Pectinophora gossypiella*, a study in 1963 showed (20) that R strains were three times as effective as S strains in converting DDT to DDE; this difference undoubtedly accounts, at least in part, for the resistance. In 1965, work with the adult spotted root maggot, *Euxesta notata*, showed (31) that an R strain absorbed half as much C^{14}-DDT as an S strain. The finding was strengthened by the observation that DDT absorption in a dieldrin-resistant strain was only 20% less than in S strain. When C^{14}-dieldrin was studied, both DDT and dieldrin-resistant strains absorbed rather *more* than the S strain! As for the ability to convert DDT to DDE, there was no consistent difference between R and S strains; in spite of the DDT sensitivity of the S insects, their ability to convert DDT to DDE was remarkable; females (LD_{50}, 0.55 μg per fly) converted 59% of a 0.5-μg dose in the course of 6 hours. Since resistance in these insects is monofactorial (85), it is possible that absorption is the only R mechanism; but one would like to see the corollary, i.e., that injected DDT is as toxic to R as to S insects.

In the human body louse, the first studies from Perry's laboratory (64) showed that a Korean R strain degraded DDT to an unidentified acidic metabolic (probably DDA), whereas the Orlando S strain did not. But later work (68) showed that homogenates of S were a trifle more active than those of R lice in degrading DDT; the degradation in this case was to mixed products including DDA, DDE, and dichlorobenzophenone. In brief, the role of metabolism in louse resistance remains obscure.

There is a suggestion that resistance to DDT can be developed in mammals. Morrison's group showed in 1962 a 107-fold decrease in sensitivity after treating nine generations of mice with DDT and breeding from survivors (61); the difference is associated with a lesser stimulation of respiration by DDT in the resistant or tolerant mice (62).

Cyclodiene Resistance

The consensus is that in spite of determined attempts to discover it the mechanism of resistance to cyclodienes is unknown (63). Studies on houseflies by English (11,12) and American (24,69) workers show that dieldrin is not metabolized by insects, that aldrin is converted only to dieldrin, and that these processes occur to the same extent in S and R strains. Nor do R and S strains vary in the amount of aldrin or dieldrin they absorb from topical application, nor in the distribution of the absorbed material within the body. There is some evidence (55) that the housefly thoracic ganglion is innately less sensitive to dieldrin applied directly to it.

In German cockroaches, Ray has shown (78) that when dieldrin is applied to R and S strains the absorption through the cuticle and also the amounts of dieldrin that appear in the nerve cord are virtually identical. This finding implies that there were no differences in uptake, distribution, or penetration to what is most probably the target. In a recent study, Brooks and Harrison (13) argued that if resistance to cyclodienes was due to enhanced degradation, then compounds that block degradation should be much better synergists for R than for S insects (as was indeed found by others for carbamate synergism). The argument was tested on houseflies with dieldrin and five other novel analogs which were poor insecticides; but in all cases for which answers were obtained, R strains were synergized no more than S. This was evidence against a metabolic mechanism for resistance.

The residual hypothesis available is that the innate sensitivity of the nerve differs in R and S strains (see p. 249).

Lindane Resistance

Our knowledge of the mechanism of this resistance is also small. Most of the studies on uptake and metabolism in S and R houseflies have had to be done with isomers of lindane because of the high toxicity of lindane itself. In one experiment performed in 1959 (10) in which differences in metabolizing ability were studied, it was found that R and S strains of houseflies metabolized C^{14}-α-HCH (used as a hoped-for indicator of lindane metabolism) at similar rates. But the weight of evidence supports Oppenoorth's classic study of 1956 (56), in which he showed an excellent correlation between absorption of α-HCH and resistance to lindane (Fig. 15.3). One would expect that, as far

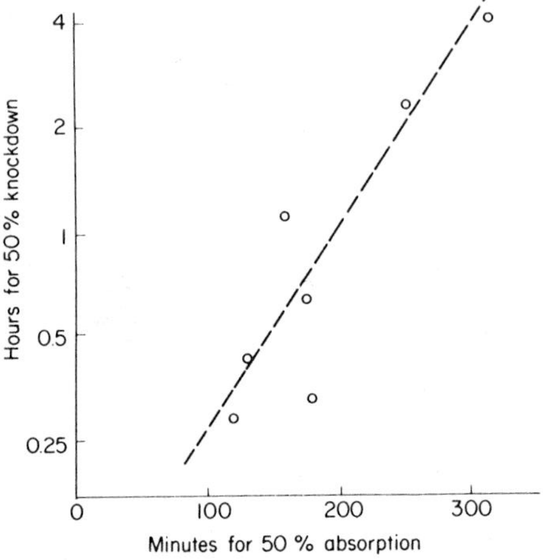

FIG. 15.3a. Relationship of α-HCH metabolism (measured as time to 50% absorption) to lindane resistance in houseflies. Redrawn from Oppenoorth (56).

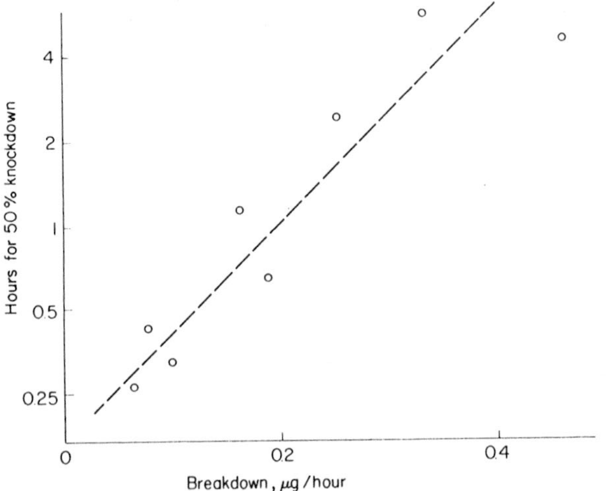

FIG. 15.3b. Relation of α-HCH metabolism (measured as amount metabolized per hour) to lindane resistance in houseflies. Redrawn from Oppenoorth (56).

as absorption is concerned, the stereoisomers would be essentially equivalent; and indeed δ-HCH behaved like α-HCH.

A less clear-cut experiment (56) showed that S flies degraded topically applied lindane much more than did R flies: in 17 hours, two R strains had degraded 90 and 95% of the dose, whereas the S had degraded only 27%; but unhappily the dose needed to conduct this experiment was 0.3 μg of lindane per fly, and since this is five times more than enough to kill 90% of the S flies, these must have been moribund throughout the experiment, casting doubt upon the meaning of the results. Yet in other experiments, Oppenoorth observed a very good correlation between metabolism of α-HCH and lindane resistance; and although the metabolism of α-HCH and lindane might be more stereospecific than their penetration, one is moved to concur with Oppenoorth that both metabolic and penetrative factors contribute to lindane resistance. But the metabolic involvement should be regarded as still unproved in view of the 1959 study with C^{14}-α-HCH quoted above, and in view of the fact that the breakdown values in Fig. 15.3 had to be computed rather indirectly, to attempt correction for the varying degrees of penetration of the various compounds.

Organophosphate Resistance

Malathion

In view of the complicated patterns of cross resistance among organophosphates, it is a fortunate simplification that for malathion, strains exist which are resistant almost exclusively to this compound. The reason is, as we shall see, that the mechanism involved is one that could not affect most organophosphates.

Matsumura and Brown (44) showed in 1961 that larvae of a malathion-resistant strain of *Culex tarsalis* mosquito had a carboxyesterase that was active against the $COOC_2H_5$ group of malathion; the enzyme was three times higher in the R than in the S strain, and its existance led to lower malaoxon levels in R than in S insects after malathion poisoning. An important procedural point was that the difference in carboxyesterase products could be shown in intact larvae only if the larvae were "cleaned" after exposure to the radioactive malathion by transferring them to fresh water so that their gut contents were voided. The difference could also be shown in homogenates, in which case it was shown that the K_m of carboxyesterase of R and S were identical, suggesting that the difference was in quantity rather than kind. Back-crossing studies showed that resistance and high carboxyesterase were inseparably linked; and the functional importance of the extra carboxyesterase for the R strain was demonstrated by showing that EPN (a carboxyesterase inhibitor; see p. 223) synergized malathion's toxicity for the R but not for the S strain.

The carboxyesterase of *Culex* was later partially purified (45); 13 times more could be obtained from R than from S mosquitoes. It was a small protein of M.W. 16,000 and of low turnover number (7 per minute for the R strain). Since the malathion-resistant strain showed no resistance at all to the compound carboxymethyl malathion (which has $COOCH_3$ in place of $COOC_2H_5$), it may be inferred that the carboxyesterase is highly specific and can only attack $COOC_2H_5$ (23).

The situation in *Culex* is essentially paralleled by that in the housefly, as Matsumura has shown. It too has a malathion-resistant strain (called the G strain) with little cross resistance to other organophosphates; the R and S strains differ *in vivo* 2-fold in carboxyesterase, not at all in phosphatase (47). Unfortunately, carboxyesterase *in vivo* is responsible for one-fifth as much degradation as phosphatase, so the 2-fold difference is correspondingly less exciting. Nevertheless, the outcome was that four times more malaoxon and twice more malathion was found in intact S than in intact R insects. These *in vivo* effects were magnified in other preparations; homogenates of the R degraded twice as much as those of the S strain, and this difference was attributable to a 3-fold difference in carboxyesterase. On partial purification with columns of DEAE-cellulose, one fraction from the R had over 7 times the activity of the S strain. This column-purified preparation was very unstable (the half-life at 32°C was 20 minutes). As in *Culex*, EPN (47) synergized the toxicity of malathion for R but not for S strains, and resistance to the $COOCH_3$ analog of malathion was much reduced, from 200-fold to 60-fold (46). [But this latter finding was not confirmed by Plapp *et al.* (75).]

The housefly story is therefore much like that for *Culex* in outline, but there are disturbing anomalies. It seems to me that magnified differences, in homogenates or fractions thereof, did not affect the most relevant experiments, i.e., those *in vivo*, where the R/S difference was small. It was encouraging that substituting $COOCH_3$ for $COOC_2H_5$ in the molecule reduced resistance for houseflies—but one would prefer to have seen it abolished. But this is not a serious criticism, for it may simply be that the housefly is less specific; that it does differ from the *Culex* enzyme is suggested by the finding (76) that although many inhibitors of carboxyesterase could synergize malathion for both *Culex* and houseflies, tricresyl phosphates were good synergists for *Culex* while poor for houseflies. A more serious problem is the observation that resistance to malathion analogs in houseflies was very dependent on the alkoxy end of the molecule (46); the ratios of the resistance for malathion itself, $(CH_3O)_2P$, to the $(C_2H_5O)_2P$ analog to the $(C_4H_9O)_2P$ analog was 200:5:1. Either the carboxyesterase is astonishingly "fussy" about the rather distant alkoxy configuration, or phosphatases do play a role. But if so, one would expect cross resistance to other organophosphates. In fact, one finds resistance to acethion, $(C_2H_5O)_2P(S)OCH_2C(O)OC_2H_5$, and not to dimethoate, $(CH_3O)_2P(S)SCH_2C(O)NHCH_3$; thus the overall conclusion must surely be that, in spite of the anomalies, cleavage of the carboxyester group is all-important in this particular kind of resistance.

Recently, it was shown (87) that malathion-resistant German cockroaches, like *Culex* and houseflies, have little cross resistance to other organophosphates. The insects were 167-fold resistant to malathion, but in no case more than 15-fold resistant to seven other organophosphates. This situation contrasted strongly with that in a diazinon-selected strain; its 5.5-fold resistance to diazinon was coupled with better than 2.3-fold resistance to all seven other organophosphates, including a 14-fold resistance to malathion! A plausible interpretation of the facts is that malathion selection induces a resistance having a carboxyesterase mechanism, and diazinon induces resistance having a phosphatase mechanism. However, the carboxyesterase is fairly specific, for malathion-resistant cockroaches were little resistant to GC 3707 in which there are $COOCH_3$ rather than $COOC_2H_5$ groups.

$$\begin{array}{l} (CH_3O)_2P(O)OC{=}CHCOOCH_3 \\ \qquad\qquad\qquad\quad | \\ \qquad\qquad\qquad CH_2COOCH_3 \end{array}$$

GC 3707

Other Organophosphates

It seems that only malathion enjoys the privilege of having "its own resistance mechanism." For most other organophosphates, selection with one compound typically induces resistance to most other organophosphates. For this reason, it is normal to find complex resistance patterns or "resistance spectra" such as that shown in Fig. 15.4, based on Busvine's data (21), or that described by Oppenoorth (57). There is no simple way to predict what spectrum will be induced by a particular compound. Frequently, the inducer is not the compound to which highest resistance is developed: selection of houseflies with parathion led to $6\times$ R (that is, a 6-fold resistance) for parathion and $74\times$ R for malathion; and selection with diazinon gave $9\times$ R for diazinon but $57\times$ R for malathion. [It will be noted that although selection with malathion usually gives uniquely malathion resistance, yet one often obtains malathion resistance (presumably of a different mechanism) by selecting with other organophosphates.]

The most coherent theory for generalized organophosphate resistance is the "mutant aliesterase" theory of van Asperen and Oppenoorth, who have reviewed it fairly recently (4,59). In essence, it states that such resistance involves the mutation of a gene which normally causes aliesterase synthesis, so that the mutant gene causes synthesis of a phosphatase which can degrade many organophosphates. For present purposes, "aliesterase" can be considered a nonspecific enzyme hydrolyzing many simple aliphatic and aromatic

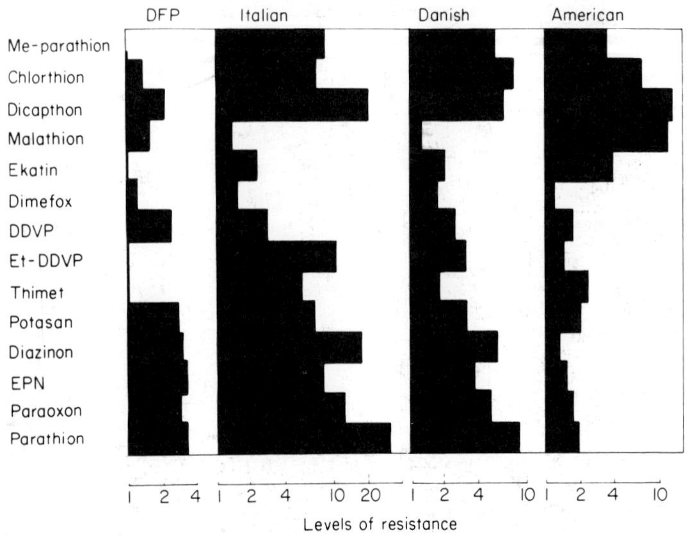

FIG. 15.4. Organophosphate resistance spectra of four housefly strains. Redrawn from Busvine (21).

esters, and best assayed by its hydrolysis of methyl acetate; it is inhibited by organophosphates. The difference between an aliesterase and a phosphatase is in some ways quite small; both can be phosphorylated by organophosphates, but only phosphatases are easily dephosphorylated again, so that they catalyze organophosphate hydrolysis. The basis of the theory is that usually aliesterase is markedly lowered (e.g., by 50%) in R compared with S strains of houseflies; and that the ability to degrade organophosphates is greater in homogenates of R than of S strains. Furthermore, low aliesterase and high phosphatase are genetically linked, judged by back-crossing studies.

In the following account, the case in favor of the theory will be stated first, and some of the counterarguments will then be considered.

It was found independently by van Asperen and Oppenoorth (6) in 1959 and Bigley and Plapp (8) in 1960 that aliesterase is about half as active in R as in S strains of housefly. Later (60) it was found that homogenates of R strains of houseflies broke down certain organophosphates faster than those of S flies. The method used to establish this was the addition of organophosphate [P(O) compounds only can be used in this method] to fly homogenates; then incubation, usually for 2 hours; then addition of housefly heads as a cholinesterase source, followed by incubation to permit residual organophosphate to inhibit the added cholinesterase; and finally, assay of the remaining cholinesterase. With this method, S flies degraded 5 ng of diazoxon per fly in 2 hours, whereas various R flies degraded from 7 to 76 ng depending on strain. Three R strains broke down relatively large amounts (76, 75, and 55 ng), which Oppenoorth and van Asperen attribute to their having two alleles of gene *a*, the gene which they believe to have mutated to produce phosphatase in place of aliesterase. Among about eight R strains, the overall correlation of resistance and breakdown was not good, and it was therefore suggested that unspecified secondary factors play a role.

Evidence was provided for the existence of several mutant phosphatases, all having very small turnover numbers (from 0.05 to 0.7 molecules of organophosphate destroyed per minute for each molecule of enzyme). One was said to act exclusively against diethyl phosphates; another acts primarily on diethyl but to some extent on dimethyl phosphates; a third acts only upon malaoxon; a fourth* was construed to be active on malaoxon on the basis of synergism experiments (see below), but enzyme activity could not be detected in the homogenate studies. And there was an embarrassing fifth enzyme which broke down chlorthion vigorously, yet imparted little resistance to chlorthion.

A final report (5) before van Asperen's tragic death in 1964 described electrophoretic migration of the phosphatase of one particular housefly strain (C strain), and it was also shown that the phosphatase concentration was highest in the abdomen, lower in the thorax, and lowest in the head; the relative activities were 3:2.2:1. Other electrophoretic studies (4) showed the multiple nature of aliesterases in flies and the great variation between strains; for instance, the C strain had 10 and the susceptible strain only 4. It would therefore seem that numerous changes in esterase patterns accompany development of resistance. The extent of these changes does not appear to relate to resistance, and indeed no change in response to organophosphate poisoning is anticipated from such changes. This observation reinforces (for the writer) the view that the minor increase in phosphatase activity, like the other numerous changes in hydrolases (i.e., aliesterases and phosphatases), accompanies resistance rather than causes it.

There are three objections to the "mutant aliesterase" theory. One is that homogenates reflect very poorly the degrading ability of whole houseflies. Whereas whole houseflies degrade readily all organophosphates which have been tested (e.g., see 39,52), homogenates of susceptible houseflies show very small breakdown (38,60). This breakdown can be improved almost 4-fold by adding cofactors (38), but even so the rate is far less than typical *in vivo* rates. A second objection is that the amounts of extra paraoxon, for instance, which the extra phosphatase of resistant flies can degrade are extremely small. For example, a homogenate of a diazinon-resistant strain whose topical LD_{50} for diazinon is 133 γ/g (52) can degrade 8 γ/g of diazoxon in 4 hours (60). Susceptible houseflies have an LD_{50} of 3.6 γ/g (52). Consequently, the proponents of the

* Probably this enzyme was not a mutant phosphatase, but the carboxyesterase described earlier in this chapter; the G strain was the basis of both studies.

theory suppose a special strategic location of the phosphatase, so that it acts only on the small fraction of the P(O) compound which would find the target. There is no experimental evidence for this supposition. Third, as Matsumura (private communication) has pointed out, the evidence that a phosphatase is involved is not very good, for the assay method simply follows loss of anti-cholinesterase activity. In fact there are three possible explanations of the extra loss in R flies: phosphatase activity, binding to a component, or phosphorylation of unknown substance. One would like to know more about the time course of the loss. All that is known is that the rate of loss falls; e.g., 220 $\mu\mu$moles per fly are destroyed per hour in the first hour for malaoxon, and 75 for the second hour (Table V in ref. 60).

One might hope that more vigorous degradation in intact houseflies of various strains would parallel that in homogenates; such is not the case. The above diazinon-resistant strain does not degrade *in vivo* substantially more diazinon than a susceptible strain (27,39,52), and two different groups agree that in fact the susceptible strain produces *in vivo* substantially less P(O) than does the resistant (39,52)! This finding casts further doubt on the validity of the mutant aliesterase theory, and suggests that in fact resistance is not connected with rapid degradation. With a different diazinon-resistant strain (the K_a strain, see below) Matsumura and Hogendijk (48) found *in vivo* no differences between S and R in rate of parathion degradation, but a significant (50%) increase in P(O) production in the R compared with the S strain.

Interesting supporting evidence for the mutant aliesterase theory is that *n*-propyl paraoxon can inhibit the phosphatase *in vitro*, which implies that the phosphatase can cleave a diethyl phosphate but not a dipropyl phosphate group, and can also reduce the resistance of intact houseflies to diazinon (60). Thus propyl paraoxon and isopropyl paraoxon profoundly blocked diazoxon synthesis in homogenates, and synergized diazinon toxicity *in vivo*. The results were not totally conclusive, however, for S flies were also synergized 4-fold by propyl paraoxon used at a concentration that gave, for four resistant strains, synergisms of 10-fold, 2-fold, 8-fold, and 1.6-fold, respectively. One might well argue, in fact, that the S and R strains showed no great difference in this synergistic test. The authors rest their case also upon a finding that malathion toxicity to other R strains (G and H) is synergized by *n*-propyl paraoxon. But it seems at least equally likely that in this case blockade of carboxyesterase is involved (79), and again the S strain is substantially synergized; furthermore the data for the H strain are unacceptable because *n*-propyl paraoxon has very high toxicity by itself to this strain. Consequently the above evidence is by no means conclusive support.

Matsumura and Hogendijk (48) continued explorations on the mutant aliesterase theory with homogenates, but using radioactive parathion, and consequently following primarily degradation of the P(S) rather than the P(O) compounds. Strong support for the view that extra phosphatase is indeed derived from aliesterase, was the finding that the K_a strain selected for low aliesterase but never exposed to organophosphates, yet nevertheless 20-fold resistant to parathion, had indeed a 2-fold increase in phosphatase. But the amount of parathion degradation by homogenates was only twice as high in R as in S strains. However, after purification and batch fractionation with DEAE-cellulose, the difference between R and S was magnified, e.g., in one fraction to the extent of 7-fold. This fraction could also hydrolyze paraoxon and diazinon; it was inhibited by $10^{-5}M$ *n*-propyl paraoxon; and it hydrolyzed parathion only to $(C_2H_5O)_2P(S)OH$, unlike the cruder preparations. When this DEAE fraction was further subfractionated (by ethanol and a DEAE-cellulose column), a profound difference between the K_a R-strain and the K_a S-strain appeared: the phosphatase activity of R was all in one peak, and that of S was all in another. It seems then that qualitative as well as quantitative differences occur.

In spite of the value of these new observations, the three objections given above apply to them. Furthermore, homogenate studies now show two quite separable differences between S and R, in "thionase" and in "oxonase," whereas the genetic work suggested a monogenetic control of resistance. And the recent finding by Smissaert that spider mites (*Tetranychus urticae*) have a lower aliesterase level than S, whereas all the resistance is attributable to the insensitive cholinesterase of the R (81), leads one to wonder if minor variations in quantities of hydrolases are not a common and unimportant concomitant of resistance.

Mengle and Casida (52) found that, when paraoxon or malaoxon were incubated with whole housefly homogenates and the rate of inhibition of the cholinesterase was followed, inhibition was more rapid in S than in R strains. This was not due to differences in cholinesterase, for when homogenates of heads were examined, S and R strains were similar; nor was it due to differential degradation of inhibitor, for chloroform extraction of the homogenates showed similar levels of P(O) to be present. They suggest instead that an unknown factor exists in the thorax and/or abdomen of resistant houseflies. The factor (which is destroyed by boiling) protects cholinesterase from inhibition, but without hydrolyzing the inhibitor. Nobody has followed up this interesting suggestion. In the same paper the extraordinary observation was made that the toxicity of eight anticholinesterases for S or R flies was not influenced by decapitation!

Let us consider the role of penetration in resistance. Forgash *et al.* (27) found that in a diazinon-resistant strain of houseflies (Rutgers A strain; the strain mentioned several times above) diazinon penetrated relatively slowly into R insects, so that they absorbed only 40% as much as the S strain in 30 minutes. This difference they considered an important factor, although not the sole one, because R insects also showed substantial resistance to injected diazinon. Earlier studies on the same R strain by Krueger *et al.* (39) showed that there was only a 7% difference in penetration rate between R and S houseflies, a difference they considered unimportant. In this case the S strain was the CSMA strain, rather than the Wilson strain used by Forgash *et al.* The CSMA strain was also compared with the above R strain by Mengle and Casida (52), who found a difference in diazinon penetration intermediate between the findings of the other two groups. They discounted the difference in penetration, in part because in their hands resistance was almost as pronounced with injected as with topically applied compounds; the factors were 30-fold and 37-fold, respectively, for diazinon. The corresponding factors reported by Forgash *et al.* (27) were 125-fold and 14-fold. Furthermore, with malathion, parathion, and methyl parathion, the penetration differences were smaller; with methyl parathion the penetration difference between R and S, which was negligible at 30 minutes, thereafter increased in the opposite of the expected direction, with more penetration into resistant insects! The consensus thus appears to be that penetration differences play only a minor role in organophosphate resistance in the above cases.

In the case of an English strain, the SKA, compared with a Rothamstead normal strain, there was a distinct indication of a penetration factor in diazinon resistance (26). Thus diazinon resistance in old flies was 100-fold by topical application, and 29-fold by injection. This 3.3-fold difference (i.e., topical factor/injection factor) was magnified to 6.5-fold when diazoxon was used. One would anticipate this magnification if penetration was important, for inundation (by injection) should be relatively more serious when the toxicant acts immediately, with no saving time lag owing to a need for activation, during which time degrading enzymes can get to work (e.g., "opportunity factor," p. 267). Furthermore, there was a drastic difference in penetration of diazinon (judged by surface disappearance); the half-time was 7 hours for R and 2 hours for S strains when old flies were used. This large penetration difference was also seen in young houseflies, for whom the half-lives were 1 hour for R and 20 minutes for S strains; the R/S ratio therefore was similar. In addition to this large penetration contribution, there were lesser indications of a difference in degradation between S and R strains.

It is generally agreed that in houseflies, the cholinesterases of S and R strains do not differ in quantity or intrinsic sensitivity to organophosphates (e.g., 9,27,52). A recent report by Smissaert (80) has shown that in a demeton-resistant strain (Leverkusen strain) of spider mites, the cholinesterase was 150 times less sensitive to diazoxon than that in susceptible strain. Smissaert's findings were confirmed in our laboratory (88), with an interesting addition: although the Leverkusen strain had indeed a less sensitive cholinesterase, the Blauvelt resistant strain had a normal cholinesterase. This is a delightful example of two strains of a species developing very different pathways to accomplish the same end. The properties of the normal and abnormal cholinesterases have how been described in some detail (89). The resistance of the Blauvelt strain was shown to owe to the development of additional phosphatase and carboxyesterase (49) and the latter enzyme has been purified and characterized (50).

In the rice stem borer, there is a strain whose larvae are 10-fold resistant to parathion. Kojima (37) has shown the strains are similar with respect to penetration and activation, but differ about 2-fold or more in their ability to degrade parathion or paraoxon. This difference was shown in intact larvae, and therefore it seems quite possible that it may be causal in resistance.

Carbamate Resistance

Relatively few studies have appeared on the mechanism of this kind of resistance; all have dealt with houseflies. In 1961, Georghiou and Metcalf (29) showed for one carbamate, MIP (3-isopropylphenyl methylcarbamate) that although R took up almost twice as much carbamate as S houseflies from topical applications, there was much faster metabolism in the R flies, so that at 2 hours, for instance, about 85% was metabolized in R and 23% in S flies. The "extra" metabolism in the R flies was very severely blocked by piperonyl butoxide. Later work (28) showed that in some strains, piperonyl butoxide virtually abolished resistance. But in two strains resistant to MIP, one obtained by selecting with MIP and another by selecting with the organophosphate ronnel, piperonyl butoxide only lowered the resistance somewhat, retaining MIP resistance of 3.2-fold (compared with 5-fold without piperonyl butoxide) and 6.6-fold (compared with 10.8-fold without piperonyl butoxide) for the two strains, respectively. It therefore seems that in carbamate resistance at least two mechanisms may be involved; one, very probably metabolic, which is sensitive to piperonyl butoxide; another, whose nature is unknown, which is insensitive to piperonyl butoxide.

These workers subsequently showed (30) the corollary of the piperonyl butoxide studies, i.e., that S flies destroyed MIP slowly, for example, 48% at 8 hours, and R flies more rapidly, 93% at 8 hours; and that piperonyl butoxide partially blocked the "extra" metabolism of R flies, reducing it to 77% at 8 hours (values interpolated from data given).

A subsequent study by Plapp *et al.* (73) on houseflies resistant to Isolan also attributed the phenomenon to more vigorous breakdown of Isolan in the R strain, although the difference was not very large, e.g., at a high dose, 92% breakdown in 1 hour by the R and 70% by the S flies. This study also revealed that aliesterase in the R was about 50% of that in the S; and genetic studies showed that low aliesterase and resistance were inseparably linked. In this regard, the resistance resembled that of organophosphates as described above (p. 244), with the exception that Plapp's degradation studies were far more satisfactory, for they involved injection into whole flies rather than additions to homogenates.

Conclusion

In spite of the evidence for a catabolic basis for resistance, especially well documented for DDT and houseflies, there is evidence that such an explanation may not be fully adequate. Thus DDT-resistant insects tolerate, without symptoms, amounts of insecticides which would kill susceptible ones (see p. 235). Such findings might, of course, be due to substantial storage in areas, such as fat body, remote from the target site, But Yamasaki and Narahashi (55,91), for instance, have shown differences in the sensitivity of exposed housefly nerve which, for DDT (discussed above) and also lindane and dieldrin, but not for diazinon and diazoxon, are related to resistance. The precise values are not linearly related, but lie in the right direction; thus for DDT the ratio of three strains for resistance to poisoning was 1:16:217 and the ratio for nerve sensitivity to poisoning was 1:6.2:7.7. For lindane, the resistance ratio for two strains was 1:6000 and the insensitivity ratio was 1:162. For dieldrin, the resistance ratio was 1:40 and the insensitivity ratio was 1:1.5. These differences in nerve sensitivity must surely play an important and perhaps a fully determining role in some cases of toxicity. A genetic analysis (86) has shown that insensitivity is controlled by an incompletely recessive gene pair on chromosome 2 of the housefly, whereas dehydrochlorination is controlled by a dominant gene on chromosome 5. It remains to be seen if the differences in nerve sensitivity reflect differences in the nature of the target membrane, or in the ability of the whole nerve to exclude or metabolize DDT and other compounds.

The question of irritability as a general resistance mechanism was recently raised for the case of the spotted root maggot fly (32). Strains selected by exposure to malathion, parathion, and methyl parathion, respectively, using treated papers, gave rise in about 10 generations to flies that survived longer in the exposure situation, surviving, for example, 6.1 hours before 50% mortality, in contrast to 1.8 hours for the parent strain. Yet in these three cases, the *physiological* sensitivity was actually reduced; the topical LD_{50} was about halved in each case. This example of behavioral resistance is therefore clearly distinguishable from physiological resistance. Its mechanism was relatively simple: flies of the resistant strain tended to rest on the untreated end of the exposure tube, rather than on the treated papers that lined the tube. Interestingly enough, the same experiment when performed with exposure to DDT or dieldrin led instead to physiological resistance in the flies.

REFERENCES

1. Abedi, Z. H., and Brown, A. W. A., *Ann. Entomol. Soc. Am.* **54**, 539 (1961).
2. Abedi, Z. H., Duffy, J. R., and Brown, A. W. A., *J. Econ. Entomol.* **56**, 511 (1963).
3. Anonymous, *World Health Organ. Expert Comm. Insecticides, 7th Rept. World Health Organ. Tech. Rept. Ser.* No. 125 (1957).
4. Asperen, K., van, *Entomol. Exptl. Appl.* **7**, 205 (1964).
5. Asperen, K. van, van Mazijk, M., and Oppenoorth, F. J., *Entomol. Exptl. Appl.* **8**, 163 (1965).
6. Asperen, K. van, and Oppenoorth, F. J., *Entomol. Exptl. Appl.* **2**, 48 (1959).
7. Babers, F. H., and Pratt, J. J., *J. Econ. Entomol.* **46**, 977 (1953).
8. Bigley, W. S., and Plapp, F. W., *Ann. Entomol. Soc. Am.* **53**, 360 (1960).
9. Bigley, W. S., and Plapp, F. W., *J. Econ. Entomol.* **54**, 904 (1961).
10. Bridges, R. G., and Cox, G. T., *Nature* **184**, 1740 (1959).
11. Brooks, G. T., *Nature* **186**, 96 (1960).
12. Brooks, G. T., and Harrison, A., *Nature* **198**, 1169 (1963).
13. Brooks, G. T., and Harrison, A., *J. Insect Physiol.* **10**, 633 (1964).
14. Brown, A. W. A., "Insecticide Resistance in Arthropods," World Health Organ., Geneva, 1958.
15. Brown, A. W. A., *Bull. Entomol. Soc. Am.* **7**, 6 (1961).
16. Brown, A. W. A., *Mosquito News* **24**, 402 (1964).
17. Brown, A. W. A., "Handbook of Physiology, Vol. 4," p. 773. Am. Physiol. Soc., Washington, D.C., 1964.
18. Brown, A. W. A., and Abedi, Z. H., *Mosquito News* **20**, 118 (1960).
19. Brown, H. D., and Rogers, E. F., *J. Am. Chem. Soc.* **72**, 1864 (1950).
20. Bull, D. L., and Adkisson, P. L., *J. Econ. Entomol.* **56**, 641 (1963).
21. Busvine, T. R., *Entomol. Exptl. Appl.* **2**, 58 (1959).
22. Crow, J. F., *Ann. Rev. Entomol.* **2**, 227 (1957).
23. Dauterman, W. C., and Matsumura, F., *Science* **138**, 694 (1962).
24. Earle, N. W., *J. Agr. Food Chem.* **11**, 281 (1963).
25. El Basheir, E. S., and Lord, K. A., *Chem. Ind.* (*London*) p. 1598 (1965).
26. Farnham, A. W., Lord, K. A., and Sawicki, R. M., *J. Insect. Physiol.* **11**, 1475 (1965).
27. Forgash, A. J., Cook, B. J., and Riley, R. C., *J. Econ. Entomol.* **55**, 544 (1962).
28. Georghiou, G. P., *J. Econ. Entomol.* **55**, 768 (1962).
29. Georghiou, G. P., and Metcalf, R. L., *J. Econ. Entomol.* **54**, 150 (1961).
30. Georghiou, G. P., and Metcalf, R. L., *J. Econ. Entomol.* **54**, 231 (1961).
31. Hooper, G. H. S., *J. Econ. Entomol.* **58**, 608 (1965).
32. Hooper, G. H. S., and Brown, A. W. A., *Bull. World Health Organ.* **32**, 131 (1965).
33. Hoskins, W. M., and Nagasawa, S., *Botyu-Kagaku* **26**, 115 (1961).
34. Kerr, R. W., Venables, D. G., Roulston, W. J., and Schnitzerling, H. J., *Nature* **180**, 1132 (1957).
35. Kimura, T., and Brown, A. W. A., *J. Econ. Entomol.* **57**, 710 (1964).
36. Kimura, T., Duffy, J. R., and Brown, A. W. A., *Bull. World Health Organ.* **32**, 557 (1965).
37. Kojima, K., *Botyu-Kagaku* **28**, 55 (1963).
38. Krueger, H. R., and Casida, J. E., *J. Econ. Entomol.* **54**, 239 (1961).
39. Krueger, H. R., O'Brien, R. D., and Dauterman, W. C., *J. Econ. Entomol.* **53**, 25 (1960).
40. Lipke, H., and Kearns, C. W., *Advan. Pest Control. Res.* **3**, 253 (1960).
41. Lovell, J. B., and Kearns, C. W., *J. Econ. Entomol.* **52**, 931 (1959).
42. March, R. B., *Entomol. Soc. Am. Misc. Publ.* **1**, 13 (1959).
43. Martin, H., "The Scientific Principles of Crop Protection," 4th Ed. Arnold, London, 1959.

44. Matsumura, F., and Brown, A. W. A., *J. Econ. Entomol.* **54**, 1176 (1961).
45. Matsumura, F., and Brown, A. W. A., *J. Econ. Entomol.* **56**, 381 (1963).
46. Matsumura, F., and Dauterman, W. C., *Nature* **202**, 1356 (1964).
47. Matsumura, F., and Hogendijk, C. J., *Entomol. Exptl. Appl.* **7**, 179 (1964).
48. Matsumura, F., and Hogendijk, C. J., *J. Agr. Food Chem.* **12**, 447 (1964).
49. Matsumura, F., and Voss, G., *J. Econ. Entomol.* **57**, 911 (1964).
50. Matsumura, F., and Voss, G., *J. Insect Physiol.* **11**, 147 (1965).
51. Meltzer, J., *Indian J. Malariol.* **12**, 579 (1958).
52. Mengle, D. C., and Casida, J. E., *J. Agr. Food Chem.* **8**, 431 (1960).
53. Metcalf, R. L., "Organic Insecticides." Wiley (Interscience), New York, 1955.
54. Miyake, S. S., Kearns, C. W., and Lipke, H., *J. Econ. Entomol.* **50**, 359 (1957).
55. Narahashi, T., *Japan. J. Med. Sci. Biol.* **17**, 46 (1964).
56. Oppenoorth, F. J., *Arch. Neerl. Zool.* **12**, 1 (1956).
57. Oppenoorth, F. J., *Entomol. Exptl. Appl.* **2**, 216 (1959).
58. Oppenoorth, F. J., *Mededel. Landbouwhogeschool Opzoekingssta. Staat Gent* **30**, 1390 (1965).
59. Oppenoorth, F. J., *Ann. Rev. Entomol.* **10**, 185 (1965).
60. Oppenoorth, F. J., and van Asperen, K., *Entomol. Exptl. Appl.* **4**, 311 (1961).
61. Ozburn, G. W., and Morrison, F. O., *Nature* **196**, 1009 (1962).
62. Ozburn, G. W., and Morrison, F. O., *Can. J. Zool.* **43**, 709 (1965).
63. Perry, A. S., *In* "The Physiology of Insecta" (M. Rockstein, ed.), Vol. 3, p. 285. Academic Press, New York, 1964.
64. Perry, A. S., and Buckner, A. J., *Am. J. Trop. Med. Hyg.* **7**, 620 (1958).
65. Perry, A. S., and Buckner, A. J., *J. Econ. Entomol.* **52**, 997 (1959).
66. Perry, A. S., and Hoskins, W. M., *Science* **111**, 600 (1950).
67. Perry, A. S., and Hoskins, W. M., *J. Econ. Entomol.* **44**, 850 (1951).
68. Perry, A. S., Miller, S., and Buckner, A. J., *J. Agr. Food Chem.* **11**, 457 (1963).
69. Perry, A. S., Pearce, G. W., and Buckner, A. J., *J. Econ. Entomol.* **57**, 867 (1964).
70. Pillai, M. K. K., Abedi, Z. H., and Brown, A. W. A., *Mosquito News* **23**, 112 (1963).
71. Pillai, M. K. K., Hennessy, D. J., and Brown, A. W. A., *Mosquito News* **23**, 118 (1963).
72. Pimentel, D., Dewey, J. E., and Schwardt, H. H., *J. Econ. Entomol.* **44**, 477 (1951).
73. Plapp, F. W., Chapman, G. A., and Bigley, W. S., *J. Econ. Entomol.* **57**, 692 (1964).
74. Plapp, F. W., Chapman, G. A., and Morgan, J. W., *J. Econ. Entomol.* **58**, 1064 (1965).
75. Plapp, F. W., Orchard, R. D., and Morgan, J. W., *J. Econ. Entomol.* **58**, 953 (1965).
76. Plapp, F. W., Bigley, W. S., Chapman, G. A., and Eddy, G. W., *J. Econ. Entomol.* **56**, 643 (1963).
77. Pratt, J. J., and Babers, F. H., *J. Econ. Entomol.* **46**, 700 (1953).
78. Ray, J. W., *Nature* **197**, 1226 (1963).
79. Seume, F. W., and O'Brien, R. D., *Toxicol. Appl. Pharmacol.* **2**, 495 (1960).
80. Smissaert, H. R., *Science* **143**, 129 (1964).
81. Smissaert, H. R., *Nature* **205**, 158 (1965).
82. Stenersen, J. H. V., *Nature* **207**, 660 (1965).
83. Sternburg, J., Kearns, C. W., and Bruce, W. N., *J. Econ. Entomol.* **43**, 214 (1950).
84. Tahori, A. S., *J. Econ. Entomol.* **56**, 67 (1963).
85. Telford, J. N., and Brown, A. W. A., *Can. Entomologist* **96**, 625 (1964).
86. Tsukamoto, M., Narahashi, T., and Yamasaki, T., *Botyu-Kagaku* **30**, 128 (1965).
87. Van den Heuvel, M. J., and Cochran, D. G., *J. Econ. Entomol.* **58**, 872 (1965).
88. Voss, G., and Matsumura, F., *Nature* **202**, 319 (1964).
89. Voss, G., and Matsumura, F., *Can. J. Biochem.* **43**, 63 (1965).
90. Winteringham, F. P. W., and Hewlett, P. S., *Chem. Ind.* (*London*) p. 1512 (1964).
91. Yamasaki, T., and Narahashi, H., *Nippon Oyo Dobutsu Konchu Gaku Zasshi* **6**, 293 (1962).

CHAPTER 16

Selectivity; Penetration

By selectivity is meant selective toxicity for one species (or genus or order or class or phylum) compared to another. The definition is a somewhat loose one, and not intended to be taken too seriously. For instance, resistance presents a clear case of selective toxicity between susceptible and resistant strains, and only on grounds of convenience, rather than logic, it is dealt with in a separate chapter. One ought also to be able to discuss selectivity between strains whose difference is not due to development of resistance, for instance, between two susceptible housefly strains, which invariably differ a little in susceptibility; and on a yet more refined level, one would like to know (especially in the case of humans) what factors determine variations in susceptibility of individuals. But the fact is that our knowledge of the causes of selective toxicity is very imperfect and, up to now, convincing proof of these causes can only be found when the selectivity, i.e., the ratio of the toxicities for the two groups of organisms, is very high. In this case, the ratio of the causative factors should be correspondingly high. Attempts to provide explanations for a toxicity difference between species which is only 4-fold, for instance, would be difficult because differences of this magnitude could be caused by very small differences in any one of a variety of factors. In this stage of the development of our knowledge, it is profitable to select for study toxicity differences of 100-fold or more where possible; if the difference is less than 10-fold, chances of successful explanation are small.

Before embarking on an account of general principles and then examining actual cases, I would like to beg future researchers in this area to avoid one of the main pitfalls: comparison under unequal conditions. It is fairly common (and has a spurious ring of logic about it) to compare metabolism or penetration of a compound in two species at some dose level related to the LD_{50}, for instance, using the $\frac{1}{2}LD_{50}$ for each species. Basic principles would suggest, and indeed experimental data confirm, that most biological processes are linearly related to dose only over limited ranges, and these ranges are not predictable. For instance (7), after 24 hours houseflies absorb 95% of a low dose (1 μg) of allethrin, but only 47% of a high dose (12 μg); and in rat liver, when dimethyl dichlorovinyl phosphate (DDVP) was $2 \times 10^{-2} M$, only 5% of its cleavage was at the O—CH_3 bond, but at $5 \times 10^{-4} M$, 32% of its cleavage was at this bond (22). Consequently, it is quite impossible to draw conclusions from a finding that, for instance, a malathion-tolerant animal degrades 90% of a high dose of malathion, whereas a malathion-sensitive animal degrades only 10% of a low dose. The comparison must be made at identical doses. Unfortunately, one must also assume that at the dose employed, no animal is manifestly affected by the toxicant. Commonly, this means that one must use a dose which is much less than the LD_{50} for the more sensitive animal; since this may be a low dose indeed, such as 1 mg/kg, the sensitivity of one's detection techniques is likely to be severely pushed.

General Principles

The logic of the discussion of selectivity is simple. It has been outlined in reviews by the author 5 and 6 years ago (70,72) and has not changed in its essentials since that time. There are only a limited number of steps that can occur when any toxicant acts upon any animal. Any difference in the susceptibility of two animals to a toxicant is therefore due to a difference in one or more of these steps. If one can develop experimental approaches to the measurement of all these steps, then one should be able to determine the factors responsible for selectivity. The seven steps are as follows:

(1) Contact of toxicant and organism
(2) Penetration into the organism
(3) Metabolism (almost invariably within the organism), which commonly renders the compound inactive (detoxification, or degradative metabolism), but not infrequently converts it from a latent to a directly active toxicant (toxification, or activative metabolism)
(4) Storage and excretion
(5) Penetration to the target, most frequently the nervous system
(6) Attack upon the target
(7) Consequences of successful attack upon the target

These steps will be considered one by one below. The fairly recent developments in knowledge of penetration, both into and within the organism, will be discussed here in detail, because so much of their interest lies in their relevance to selective toxicity.

Contact of Toxicant and Organism

Ripper in 1951 coined the term "ecological selectivity" to describe the case where differences in behavior or habitat brought the toxicant into contact with some organisms in preference to others, and contrasted it with "physiological selectivity," a term used to describe all other types of selectivity, which are apparent even when toxicant is applied directly to the organisms involved (90).

One aspect of this component of selectivity is merely commonsensical: one typically applies toxicants so that the intended victims are exposed and the applicator is not. More sophisticated attempts have been made in this area, such as the use on plants of DDT coated with a cellulose preparation, so that only phytophagous insects which actually consumed the plant, and therefore the DDT, would digest off the coat and become poisoned (91). The ingenious idea was prohibitively expensive.

The use of plant-systemic insecticides may lead to ecological selectivity, for (once the toxicant is safely within the plant) only phytophagous insects will suffer contact with the insecticide.

Penetration into the Organism*

One would have imagined that our knowledge of the factors which determine skin penetration into mammals and integument penetration into insects would be substantial, for it would seem probable that only a few physical factors would be involved; the experimental techniques are not excessively difficult; and complications caused by metabolism of the compounds are minimal. But in fact an astonishing deficiency exists in our knowledge of this area, offering rich dividends to future investigators.

When one contemplates the (often damp) flexible keratinized skin of a mammal and contrasts it with the (usually greasy) rigid chitinized integument of insects, it is natural to suspect that their permeability properties might be radically different. Such intuitive thinking, coupled with the evident lipophilic character of DDT, has lured many writers to make such incautious claims as "the apparently specific insecticidal properties of DDT are in reality due to very efficient absorption through the insect cuticle" (54) and "the specific toxicity of DDT to insects is therefore a result of the high permeativity of the insect cuticle to DDT to which the vertebrate skin is an effective barrier" (48). Both conclusions are based upon the well-known fact that for mammals, and not for insects, there is a large difference between the LD_{50} of DDT administered by the cutaneous and intravenous routes. Table 16.1 provides examples,

* I am indebted to Dr. A. A. Buerger's thesis (10) for much of the critical literature review of this section.

showing that the rat, rabbit, Japanese beetle, and American cockroach conform to this toxicity pattern, although the bee "behaves like a mammal" in this regard. In spite of this persuasive evidence, direct measurement of DDT penetration has shown that it penetrates at essentially equal rates into vertebrate and insect integuments*; the times for half-penetration are 26 hours for rats (76) and 26.4 hours for American cockroaches (85).

TABLE 16.1

DEPENDENCE OF DDT TOXICITY UPON ROUTE OF ADMINISTRATION

	LD_{50} (mg/kg)			
	Cutaneous	Oral	Intraperitoneal	Intravenous
Rat	3000	400	150	50
Rabbit	300–2820	300	2100	50
Milkweed bug	409	301	31	—
Bee	114	1.7	0.2	—
Japanese beetle	93	205	162	—
American cockroach	10	—	7	—

[a] Data approximated from Negherbon (60).

How can the toxicity data be reconciled with the direct measurements of penetration? The answer must for the present be speculative, but it suggests the way in which two factors can interact in affecting selectivity. Rats and cockroaches both have integuments very impermeable to DDT. Suppose that rats can metabolize DDT fairly rapidly, and cockroaches very slowly. Then an *injected* dose of DDT, which is delivered instantly into the body in both species and can initiate its effects at once in both, will have comparable potency for both if their innate sensitivity is the same. But a *cutaneous* dose of DDT, delivered absorptively very slowly in the body, can readily be destroyed by the metabolic competence of the rat, but not of the cockroach.

The mode of application of agents to an integument profoundly influences the results obtained, and only with this realization can the apparently contradictory reports in the literature be explained. Let us first consider the relatively simple case of diffusion through cockroach cuticle. We observed (85) that when an agent is applied in a small volume, such as 1 μliter, of a

* The term "integument" can conveniently be applied to skin, cuticle, and other body coverings.

volatile solvent which rapidly volatilizes, then polar agents diffuse most rapidly from the surface and the apolar ones most slowly; thus the half-times for the surface loss were 16 minutes for H_3PO_4 and 26.4 hours for DDT. There were no exceptions to this rule in the six compounds studied. This finding, the reverse of what one might at first have expected, probably owes to the fact that, with this mode of application, one introduces agent directly into the least polar phase, the epicuticular grease. Diffusion into the underlying layer is therefore necessarily into a more polar layer, and is promoted by hydrophilic character. A very different state of affairs is seen if one applies agent in a polar phase; thus when H_3PO_4 was applied to cockroach integument in a drop of water, which evaporated only slowly because a grease film formed on it, no

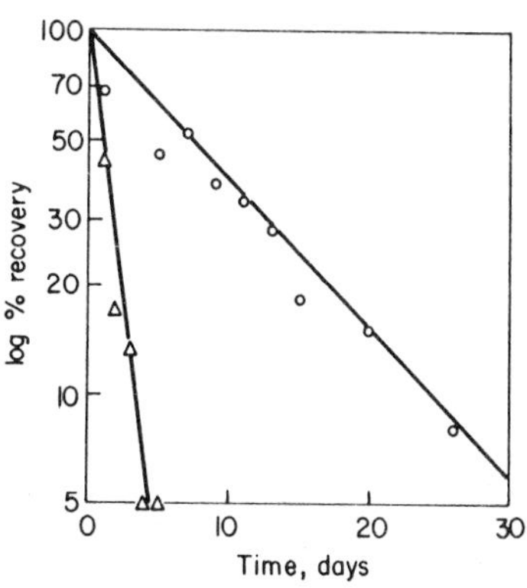

FIG. 16.1. Penetration of piperonyl butoxide (△) and DDT (○) in the Madeira cockroach, measured by the wash-off technique (see text). From Olson and O'Brien (85).

penetration occurred until the water evaporated, after which the usual 16-minute half-time for penetration was observed.

The commonest way to determine extent of penetration in insects is to apply solute (frequently, radioactive solute is used) to the cuticle, and then to rinse the treated insect with solvent (commonly acetone) to determine what remains in the acetone-soluble epicuticular grease or wax. One insect is needed for each time period. In most cases where this procedure is used, the kinetics of penetration follow the simple first-order form which is predicted either from Fick's law of diffusion, or more simply from the consideration that the amount penetrating at any given moment is proportional to the amount in the epicuticular grease at that moment [see Buerger (11) for a more complete theoretical discussion]. Then a plot of the logarithm of the amount remaining as a function of time should be linear. This is the desirable way of plotting such penetration data, but unfortunately is not extensively used. Figure 16.1 shows data so plotted. With results such at these, the half-time of penetration ($t_{0.5}$) is a meaningful parameter, and can be used to calculate the rate constant of penetration, k, from the relationship

$$k = 0.693/t_{0.5}$$

Such results have been reported for penetration of diazinon into houseflies (18), dimethoate, paraoxon, H_3PO_4, K_2HPO_4, and dieldrin into American cockroaches (85), piperonyl butoxide (96) and DDT (43) into Madeira cockroaches, and DDT into rats (76). However, other studies show biphasic penetration, with a first extremely rapid phase followed by a slower first-order phase; this has been reported for malathion penetration into houseflies, German and American cockroaches (39,49), and rats (76), diazinon penetration into houseflies (40), DDT, famphur, and dimethoate penetration into mealworms and crickets, and DDT penetration into horned toads, chameleons, and toads (12). The fact that different results are listed above for cases of one compound in one organism makes it clear that the differences reported are not always in the organisms but in the techniques employed.

The "wash-off" technique described above is usually thought to evaluate penetration *through* the integument. In fact it does not; it evaluates penetration *into and through* the integument, i.e., loss from the outermost soluble layer into underlying layers. In order to study penetration through the integument of intact organisms, one must use what could be called the "disk technique," which has been applied to rats (76), insects, and other animals (12). One applies the radioactive solute to the integument, then after a given time removes a disk or patch of integument large enough to contain any solute that has spread laterally from the point of application, digests it, and counts the residual radioactivity. That the disk and wash-off techniques may give different values in some cases is indicated by the observation (76) that, in contact with rat skin, dieldrin becomes progressively less extractable by acetone (e.g., 90% is extractable at 1 hour, 20% at 15 hours), presumably owing to some binding or other interaction with the skin; but famphur does not show this effect.

The techniques described above have all dealt with intact organisms. Better replication but (in the author's view) less relevance to physiological affairs can be obtained by using excised integuments, as has been done by Treherne for rabbit skin (103) and locust integument (104), as well as by earlier workers interested in electrolyte permeability. In such a technique, the integument is removed and placed in a cell which exposes both sides of the integument to water. Compounds may then be applied to one side and their rate of appearance on the far side observed. The data necessarily give information about waterlogged integuments, unlike the normal integument.

Finally, less direct techniques should be mentioned. The least desirable make use of time-to-death values obtained with a variety of solutes, applied usually to insects, as an index of permeability for the compounds (26,89). But clearly it is impossible to sort out the contributions of variations in penetration, in excretion, in degradation, in distribution, and (above all) in innate toxicities of the various solutes. Others have used urinary outputs as the measure of skin absorption, for instance, in absorption of various salicylates by human skin (9). Once again, the variations owe as much to differences in metabolism and excretion as in permeability. Somewhat more direct is the measurement of blood levels of agents applied to the skin, as has been done in rabbits (19), but again, variation in the factors described above introduces uncertainty.

The vehicle used for application of agents has an important effect upon penetration rate. Thus sulfanilamide penetration into rabbit skin, expressed in milligrams absorbed in 8 hours, was 14 with application in lard, 7 with an emulsifying ointment, and 6 with water (19). And in rats treated with 1 μg of carbaryl, the percent remaining in the skin after 3 hours was 63 with application in benzene, 88 in corn oil, and 42 in acetone (76). Unfortunately, no generalizations serve to unify such observations.

Now let us turn to the problem of primary interest: what factors determine penetration rates, and do different factors operate in different organisms, thus permitting selectivity based on penetration differences? It has been stated above that a study on the cockroach cuticle (85) using solutes applied in a small drop of organic solvent showed that penetration of various compounds increased with their polarity. Under similar conditions, the same is true of the mealworm adult, the toad, the Carolina chameleon, and the Mexican horned toad (12). A similar conclusion emerges from the data (1) on penetration of four hexachlorocyclohexane isomers into the grain weevil (using an unsatisfactory procedure consisting of exposure to impregnated papers). Unfortunately, in the rat no such correlation was observed (76); of five compounds, the two least polar were the slowest penetrating (DDT, half-penetration time 26 hours) and the fastest penetrating (dieldrin, half-penetration time 3.5 hours). But as Fig. 16.2 shows, the penetration kinetics were complex in the rat, and the half-penetration times are therefore less meaningful.

Three other studies on insects and mammals come to exactly the opposite conclusion, that is, that polarity decreases penetration rate! This is claimed for salicylate penetration into intact human skin (9); and for urea, alcohols, and related compounds penetrating excised locust integument (104) and rabbit skin (103). The explanation undoubtedly lies in the fact that, in these three studies, the solutes were applied in a polar phase (water) and that the limiting rate was that of partition into the most apolar integumental layer from the polar phase.

Let us try now to draw together these complex considerations into tentative

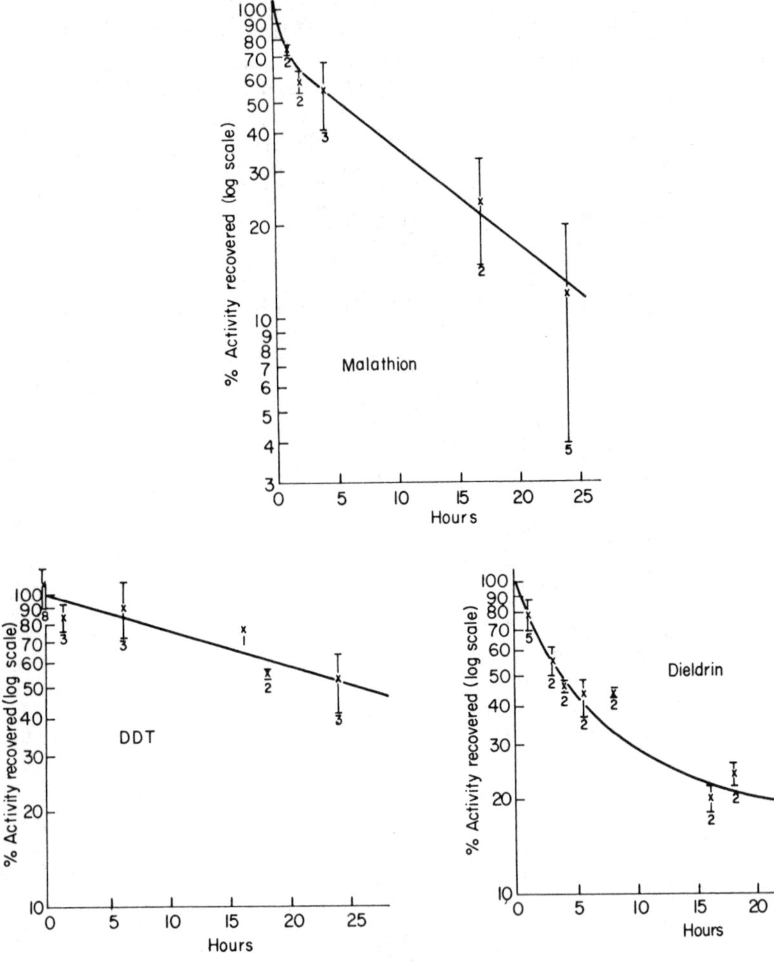

FIG. 16.2. Penetration of insecticides through skin of the female rat, measured by the disk technique (see text). From O'Brien and Dannelley (76).

principles that may aid in understanding penetration with relation to selectivity. (*a*) There is no evidence that insects, reptiles, amphibia, or mammals have integuments whose permeabilities differ in any consistent way one from another with respect to the role of polarity in permeability; nor that selective toxicity of a general sort, e.g., toward insects compared with mammals, is associated with differential skin permeability (*b*). In many organisms (the rat is an exception) polar compounds penetrate more rapidly than apolar compounds if they are introduced directly into the outermost integumental layer, e.g., by application in a small volume of organic solvent. The reverse is true

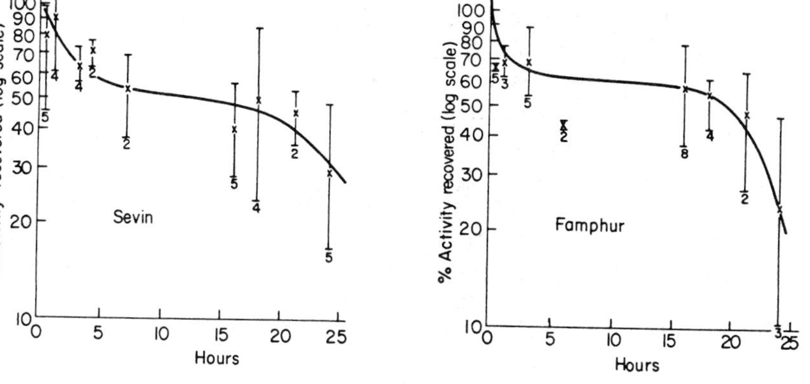

FIG. 16.2 (*continued*)

if they are applied in a polar phase, from which they must partition into the outermost integumental layer.

A somewhat different case arises when application is from the vapor phase, a case that has been studied in some detail with respect to insect eggs. In these experiments (5,116) the eggs were exposed to a variety of agents in vapor phase at room temperature, and attempts were made to explain the rather capricious pattern of toxicity, using in many cases radioactive compounds, including chlorinated hydrocarbons, organophosphates, and carbamates. It was found that, as one might expect, vapor pressure was a major factor in determining uptake and toxicity; in effect, if one compound has twice the vapor pressure of the other, then under saturation conditions the eggs are exposed to twice as much toxicant in the first as in the second case. Thus with compounds of comparable partition coefficient, uptake was observed to be proportional to the logarithm of the saturated vapor pressure. Another important factor was liposolubility; using compounds with similar vapor pressures, the uptake was directly proportional to the oil/water partition coefficient, so that carbaryl (partition coefficient 61) gave only 0.06 mg/kg, whereas dieldrin (partition coefficient 12,000) gave 1.3 mg/kg. However, as in the case of adult insects discussed above, the apolar compounds tended to remain in the epicuticular wax, and thus paradoxically presented excellent *total* uptakes, but very poor *internal* levels of toxicant. Thus with DFP (partition coefficient 8) 53% of the total taken up appeared internally; but with dieldrin only 6% appeared internally.

The optimal situation appeared to be extremely high vapor pressure (to get good uptake) with rather low liposolubility (to get a high internal proportion), so that DFP and dichlorvos were the only excellent ovicides.

In conclusion, I would offer an experimental note and two speculative comments. The most direct experiments have been made with radioactive solutes; frequently (especially in the disk technique), it is not possible to characterize the radioactivity which is measured, and therefore one may be seeing, for instance, in Fig. 16.2, the diffusion of derivatives rather than of the compound applied. Speculatively, unless one is applying compounds in a polar solvent, amines should be particularly rapid in their skin penetration. They could be applied as the free base, which could be very apolar, but because each molecule that diffuses into the lower polar phases would become hydrated, there would be negligible back-diffusion. Along a different line, the role of promoters of penetration deserves study: dimethyl sulfoxide (DMSO) is popularly reported to be such a compound. Perhaps it complexes with solutes and bestows upon them some solventlike properties.

Metabolism

Differences in rates of breakdown of compounds in different organisms are probably the commonest causes of differential toxicity. Later we shall see that differences in activation rates, i.e., conversion of a latent to a direct toxicant, have not proved to be important in most cases studied.

Perhaps the best-known cases of "metabolic selectivity" are the fast dehydrochlorination of DDT in resistant houseflies and the fast hydrolysis of malathion by resistant insects and tolerant insects and mammals. The former is dealt with in the Chapter 15; the latter will now be described in detail.

Malathion shows a remarkably useful pattern of selective toxicity; it is toxic to most insects and is of low toxicity to all mammals, and to a lesser extent, birds. This pattern, demonstrated in Table 16.2, is ideal for a commercially effective compound as well as of much academic interest, and hence worthy of detailed study.

TABLE 16.2

TOXICITY OF MALATHION FOR INSECTS AND VERTEBRATES[a]

Vertebrates, oral LD_{50} (mg/kg)		Insects, topical LD_{50} (mg/kg)	
Rats	1509	American cockroach	8.4
Mice	1609	Housefly	30
Guinea pigs	570	Pea aphid	0.75
Chickens	275	Black carpet beetle	10
Ducks	1107	Southern armyworm	18
		German cockroach	120

[a] Data averaged from Spiller (99) and Krueger and Casida (38).

March *et al.* (46) first noted in 1956 that mice and cockroaches metabolized malathion to very different (unidentified) metabolites. In 1957, O'Brien observed that mouse liver degraded malaoxon very rapidly, but cockroach tissues did not (66). This suggested that the nontoxicity of malathion for mice

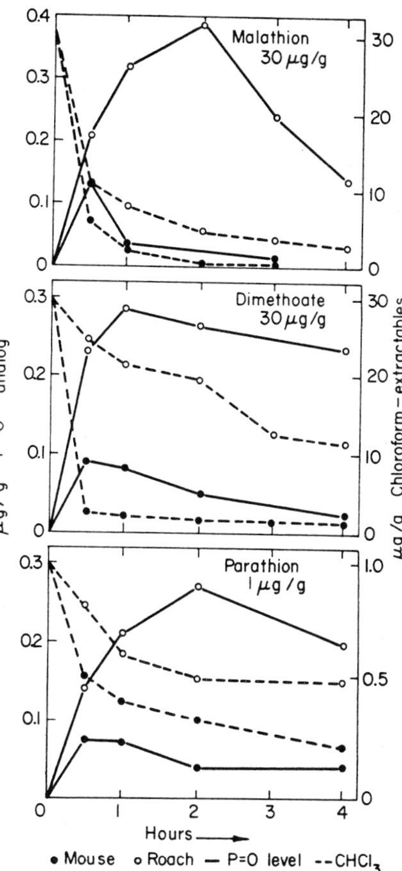

FIG. 16.3. Production of P(O) analogs when mice and cockroaches are treated with phosphorothionates. $CHCl_3$ refers to chloroform extractables, i.e., parent compound plus P(O) analog. From Krueger *et al.* (40).

was due to vigorous degradation at one carboxylic ester bond. The speculation was confirmed by the more meaningful studies on intact animals by Krueger and O'Brien (39), which showed that the net operation of activative and degradative processes led to little accumulation of the activation product, malaoxon, in cockroaches compared with mice (Fig. 16.3), and also that the extra degradation in mice was due almost entirely to cleavage at the carboxyester group. Typically, the mouse degraded 68% by carboxyesterase, whereas insects (houseflies, German and American cockroaches) degraded about 30% by this route (Fig. 16.4).

It should be stressed that multiple products were found. As Fig. 16.4 would imply, eleven products were formed, and every product was found in every organism. The metabolic differences were in overall degradation (high in mice, low in insects) and in pathway (primarily carboxyesterase in mice, primarily phosphatase in insects).

The generality of carboxyesterase as a sort of "saving enzyme" in malathion poisoning has been established by the findings: (*a*) that its blockade in mammals, using EPN for instance, reduces them to an insectlike sensitivity to malathion (see p. 223); (*b*) that houseflies and mosquitoes which have "developed" resistance to malathion do so by "developing" a high titer of carboxyesterase—and simultaneously develop a sensitivity to EPN synergism;

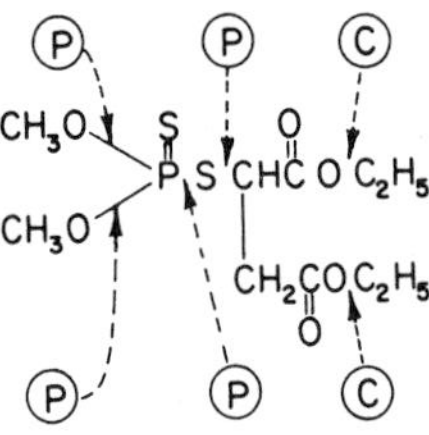

FIG. 16.4. Points of degradation of malathion: circled P, phosphatases; circled C, carboxyesterases.

and (*c*) certain naturally tolerant species appear to degrade malathion faster than susceptible species of the same genus, and only in the tolerant species can the degradation be synergized by carboxyesterase blockade. This was shown by Dyte *et al.* (36) with larvae of two hide beetles: the susceptible *Dermestes lardarius* (LD_{50}, 1.9 mg/kg) and the tolerant *D. maculatus* (LD_{50}, 19.1 mg/kg). Triphenyl phosphate synergizes malathion toxicity for the latter, reducing its LD_{50} to 1.6, whereas it somewhat antagonizes malathion toxicity to the susceptible species.

The relationship between malathion carboxyesterase and the enzyme(s) called "aliesterase" is uncertain in most cases. For the cases of rat and human liver and rat serum, the carboxyesterase is the aliesterase called B-aliesterase. Human serum has no B-aliesterase, and does not hydrolyze malathion (47).

As the cause of malathion selectivity became clarified, it was apparent that one might be able to develop a useful generalization. It seemed unlikely that the malathion carboxyesterase was very specific, since malathion is an exotic compound, and so in 1957 it was proposed that "the introduction of a carboxyester group into an organophosphorus anticholinesterase should confer the property of selective toxicity towards the insect as compared with the mammal; that this effect would be strongest if the carboxyester group were near the phosphorus* and that it would be particularly marked in thionophosphates [now called phosphorothionates], where the lag in poisoning, which is caused by the need for oxidation of the thiono group, would give time for the detoxifying hydrolysis to occur" (64). This third consideration, to be reviewed in detail later, was later called the "opportunity factor" (69).

The hypothesis, or group of hypotheses, was tested in 1958 by preparing seven new organophosphates, of which the best known is acethion $(C_2H_5O)_2P(S)SCH_2COOC_2H_5$, whose selectivity, for houseflies compared with mice, was 136-fold, about twice as good as that of malathion (83). It has never become a commercially successful compound, primarily because it did not have a wide spectrum of insect toxicity. Nevertheless, it suggests the validity of the notion that the carboxyester group is a "selectophore" [a term introduced in 1961 (72)], i.e., a group whose introduction into a molecule confers selective toxicity of some kind.

Our studies on dimethoate, $(CH_3O)_2P(S)SCH_2C(O)NHCH_3$, began with the hope that the *N*-methylcarboxamide group $C(O)NHCH_3$ might be a selectophore, and that mammals might be high in amidase just as they are in carboxyesterase. The first studies compared the mouse and cockroach and showed (Fig. 16.3) the 70-fold difference in LD_{50} (the cockroach was the sensitive organism) was associated with about 10-fold more breakdown in the mouse, and hence a 3-fold greater level in dimethoxon, the P(O) analog assumed to be the actual toxicant (40). However, it became apparent subsequently (109,111) that dimethoate's pattern of toxicity was utterly unlike malathion's, for there is a spectrum of sensitivity to dimethoate found in both insects and vertebrates. Thus there are sensitive vertebrates (e.g., hen, LD_{50} about 30 mg/kg) and insects (e.g., housefly LD_{50}, 0.53 mg/kg), and there are insensitive vertebrates (e.g., rats, 240 mg/kg) and insects (e.g., Colorado potato beetle, 770 mg/kg).

Here the story takes two paths. In vertebrates, a great simplification was evident when it was shown (109) that dimethoate is broken down almost exclusively in the liver (unlike malathion, for instance, which is degraded in numerous tissues). Furthermore, the rate of dimethoate breakdown in liver homogenates was excellently correlated (inversely) with toxicity, as Fig. 16.5 shows, in spite of the fact that the breakdown was by phosphatase action (cleaving the S—C bond) in some species, by amidase only in others (such as sheep), and by both systems in most animals. The correlation makes it possible to predict, in a tentative way, the toxicity of dimethoate for vertebrates whose livers only are available for study. This prediction has recently been made for man, and a tentative LD_{50} of 30 mg/kg was assigned (110).

* "Near" either in the primary structure, or else brought near as a consequence of folding in the molecule.

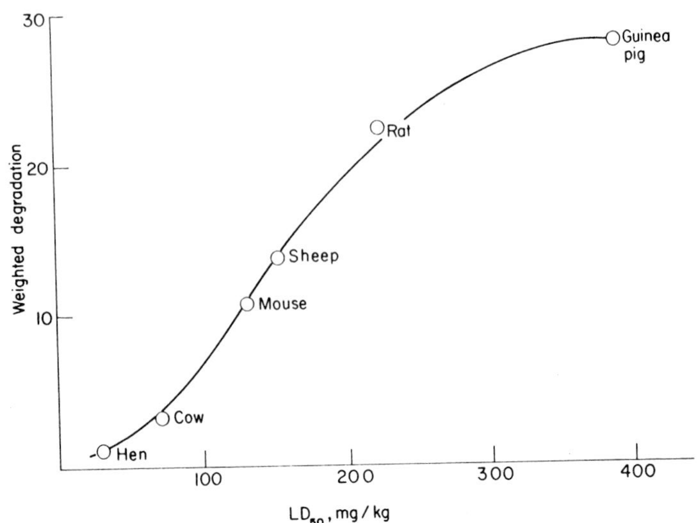

FIG. 16.5. Relationship between dimethoate degradation by liver *in vitro* and toxicity of dimethoate. Toxicities are oral except for guinea pig, for which they are intraperitoneal. Weighted degradation = AB, where A = liver weight as percent of body weight; B = dimethoate hydrolysis in micrograms per gram wet liver in 30 minutes. From data of Uchida and O'Brien (110).

TABLE 16.3

DIMETHOATE: ACTION IN ADULT INSECTS[a]

	LD_{50} (μg/g)	Degradation (%)	P(O) Production (%)	Penetration (%)	I_{50} for ChE (M)
Housefly	0.53	15	31	80	5×10^{-7}
Cricket	3.1	35	8	—	—
American cockroach	7.0	44	5	25	2×10^{-5}
Milkweed bug	205	9	4	75	5×10^{-5}
Colorado potato beetle	770	34	17	40	—

[a] The LD_{50}'s were topical at 24 hours; the degradation and P(O) production at 1 hour after an injected dose of 0.5 mg/kg and the penetration at 1 hour after a topical dose of 3 mg/kg. The I_{50} values are molar concentrations for 50% inhibition *in vitro*. Data from Uchida *et al.* (111).

In insects, the position is much more complex, and virtually every factor *except* degradation plays a role in accounting for the remarkable species specificity (Table 16.3). The most sensitive species was the housefly, whose cholinesterase was 100 times more sensitive than that of the others; which activated dimethoate to an unheard-of extent (31% in 1 hour); and was most readily penetrated by a topical dose. With all these factors, the great sensitivity of the housefly is readily understood. However, the reason why, for instance, dimethoate is 100 times less toxic to the Colorado potato beetle than to the American cockroach is not apparent.

Let us now review the notion of the opportunity factor mentioned above. When a toxicant arrives in the body, numerous simultaneous events occur; some of the molecules react with the target and others are degraded, excreted, or stored. It has been pointed out above (p. 256) that the limited ability* of degrading systems to "handle" toxicant can be manifested in a susceptibility to an injected dose, which arrives promptly in the body, whereas the same topical dose, which diffuses in relatively slowly, may be degraded fast enough to forbid accumulation of toxic levels.

A precise analog of delivery of toxicant by slow inward diffusion is the process of activation of latent inhibitors, which also leads to a slow progressive appearance of actual toxicant. One would therefore expect that differences in the abilities of two organisms to degrade a compound would, under favorable circumstances, result in a larger differential toxicity when there was a requirement for activation. Put in another way, the requirement for activation imposes a delay in intoxication which may permit an opportunity for degrading enzymes to act.

The most favorable case for observing the opportunity factor is that of phosphorothionates, which in virtually every case require an activation that is usually rather slow. In 1965 it was possible to say (74) that "it is almost invariably true that P(S) compounds are ... more selectively toxic to insects as compared with mammals" and support the statement with data for selective toxicity (expressed as LD_{50} for rat or mouse compared with housefly) for several phosphorothionates contrasted with their phosphate analogs as follows: dimethoate 1390 [550 for its P(O)]; acethion 136 [63 for its P(O)]; malathion 1590 [5 for its P(O)]; and parathion 6.9 [5.5 for its P(O)]. However,

* It is worthy of note that many degrading systems are of very low efficiency, judged by their remarkably small turnover numbers; one molecule of DDT-dehydrochlorinase degrades 2.3 molecules of DDT per minute (44) and one molecule of phosphatase in various resistant houseflies degrades 0.05, 0.25, 0.4, or 0.7 of organophosphate per minute, depending upon strain (86). The values can be contrasted with turnover numbers for their substrates: catalase, 1,250,000; β-amylase, 250,000; fumarase, 100,000; and serum cholinesterase, 19,600 (33). Clearly, the reason is that these insecticides are exotic compounds, not "designed" for the enzymes.

the author was incautious enough to test a corollary of these observations by preparing P(S) analogs of some peculiarly toxic P(O) compounds. It was hoped that the innately high toxicity of these compounds would be retained in good insecticidal action, whereas selectivity would be "built in" by making P(S) analogs. Unfortunately (79), this prediction was not confirmed; the P(S) analogs of dimefox and DFP proved to be less selective than the parent compounds, and that of mipafox was only a trifle better than its parent. Detailed arguments about this finding will be found in the reference; for present purposes, suffice it to say that thiono compounds are frequently, but not necessarily, more selective than their P(O) analogs.

Many claims that differences in degradation have caused differential toxicity are based on very inadequate evidence, such as differences noted in one tissue only (other tissues were often not examined). Thus the remarkable insensitivity of frogs and toads, compared with mice, to organophosphates was claimed to stem from a 3-fold difference in DFP degradation in toad and mouse blood (37). A later study showed that after injection of paraoxon, the levels of paraoxon in body and brain of frogs and mice was almost identical; virtually all the selectivity was due to differences in cholinesterase activity, i.e., selectivity was "target" and not "metabolic" (87). Another pitfall in studies of this type is that differential metabolism may be compensated for by other differences. For instance, famphur is degraded enormously faster by mice than by milkweed bugs: in 1 hour, mice degrade 90% of an injected dose, milkweed bugs 10%. Yet the LD_{50} is about the same: 11.6 for mice and 8.0 for milkweed bugs. The paradox is resolved by the finding that milkweed bug cholinesterase is 32 times less sensitive than that of the mouse (80).

One of the most provocative recent reports of selectivity has concerned a new compound, Sumithion (dimethyl 3-methyl-4-nitrophenyl phosphorothionate), named after the Sumitomo Company (Japan) where it was synthesized and reported by Nishizawa in 1960 (61,63).

$(CH_3O)_2P(S)O$–C_6H_3(CH_3)–NO_2

Sumithion

The remarkable fact is that simply by inserting a *m*-methyl group into methyl parathion, the mammalian toxicity is substantially reduced. As Table 16.4 shows, this reduction does not hold for compounds very closely related to Sumithion, including the diethyl analog and sumioxon, the P(O) analog. Thus what one might call "the magic *m*-methyl" is only magical in a very restricted context.

TABLE 16.4

TOXICITY OF SUMITHION AND ANALOGS[a]

Formula (X=3-methyl-4-nitrophenyl)	Mouse oral LD_{50} (mg/kg)		
	Nishizawa *et al.* (62,63)	Miyamoto *et al.* (59)	Metcalf and March (57)
$(CH_3O)_2P(S)X$ (Sumithion)	870	870	—
$(CH_3O)_2P(O)X$ (sumioxon)	20	90	—
$(C_2H_5O)_2P(S)X$	17.5	—	—
$(C_2H_5O)(C_6H_5)P(S)X$	30	—	—
Methyl parathion	26	17	100–200
Methyl paraoxon	—	11	—
Ethyl parathion	9.5	—	24–32

[a] The value of 100–200 for methyl parathion seems high in view of reports of values for rat oral LD_{50}'s of 15 or 13 or 14–42 or 9–25 (60).

In seeking an explanation for Sumithion's low toxicity, rapid degradation by liver has been claimed (113). The claim was based upon the report that (*a*) mouse liver slices degraded sumioxon [the P(O) analog of Sumithion, assumed to be the actual toxicant] about 4 times more rapidly than an equal weight of American cockroach fat body; (*b*) the slices degraded Sumithion 1.4 times faster than methyl parathion (but this small difference is surely negligible). However, no attempt was made to show whether difference (*a*) *in vitro* was associated with a difference in the intact animal, and gave rise to significantly different levels of methyl paraoxon and sumioxon. In another study, methyl parathion-P^{32} and sumithion were fed to rats and guinea pigs; after several days, more of the Sumithion radioactivity appeared in the urine of both animals; but in the first half day, the reverse was true for the guinea pig, and there was no difference in the rat (58). One would imagine that the early hours of poisoning would be of greatest importance with acute toxicants. A more serious criticism is that methyl parathion was used at 10 times the dose of Sumithion, and it is known that routes and extents of degradation of toxicants are dose-dependent (22,109). For this reason one cannot evaluate the importance of the otherwise valuable additional data on levels of sumithion and methyl parathion in brain. The toxicity of sumithion and of methyl parathion was related to cholinesterase inhibition *in vivo*; that is, a much higher dose of Sumithion than of methyl parathion was needed to inhibit, say, 75% of brain cholinesterase in rat or guinea pig. However, such observations are compatible with several possible mechanisms of selectivity. Finally, the selectivity of Sumithion is not a case of "target selectivity," for sumioxon is not a selective inhibitor of cholinesterase *in vitro* (62). The interesting mystery therefore remains unsolved.

So far we have discussed primarily one kind of metabolic selectivity: the kind we might call *degradative selectivity*, i.e., that owing to differences in ability to degrade toxicants. The term degrade in this context very specifically means "reduce the direct or the latent toxicity"; it does *not* mean "catabolize." Thus there are cases where metabolic removal of groups increases the toxicity; deacetylation of acetyl trichlorfon doubles the anticholinesterase potency (2):

$$\underset{\text{Acetyl trichlorfon}}{(CH_3O)_2P(O)CH(OCOCH_3)CCl_3} \rightarrow \underset{\text{Trichlorfon}}{(CH_3O)_2P(O)CH(OH)CCl_3}$$

Similarly, hydrolysis of fluoroacetamide to fluoroacetate is a first step in its conversion to fluorocitrate (the actual toxicant), and is therefore not a degradation from the toxicological viewpoint (50):

$$\underset{\text{Fluoroacetamide}}{FCH_2C(O)NH_2} \rightarrow \underset{\text{Fluoroacetate}}{FCH_2C(O)OH}$$

These two reactions are therefore activations; the best known activation is that of conversion of phosphorothionates to phosphates, as discussed in Chapter 3.

Clearly, differences in activating reactions of this type between species could lead to a differential toxicity, which could be called *activative selectivity*. Indeed, it has been suggested that the fact that cockroaches hydrolyze fluoroacetamide 4 times faster than do mice is the cause of the 25-fold greater toxicity of fluoroacetamide for cockroaches (50). It was mentioned above that the remarkable ability of houseflies to activate dimethoate [by conversion of P(S) to P(O)] was a factor in the sensitivity of that insect to dimethoate.

The great similarity between the properties of the liver microsomal systems that activate phosphorothionates and degrade numerous drugs has been commented on elsewhere (p. 210). Following a report (8) that the drug-degrading system was extremely deficient in aquatic vertebrates (including fish, turtles, frogs, and salamanders), a study was undertaken (88) to see if a similar deficiency existed with respect to parathion activation. It was found that the variation in ability of liver slices in this respect was surprisingly small in the six aquatic and seven terrestrial vertebrates studied, and that there was no consistent difference between aquatic and terrestrial forms, a finding which is in harmony with the sensitivity of fish to phosphorothionate poisoning.

The present status of our knowledge therefore suggests that metabolic selectivity is common, and most frequently is of the degradative type. The above discussion has dealt primarily with organophosphates, simply because they are the most-studied group, but other cases exist. A good example is the finding of Tombes and Forgash (100) that adults of the Mexican bean beetle steadily develop DDD-dehydrochlorinase, and this development correlates excellently with the LD_{50} for DDD (Fig. 16.6), leaving little doubt that the

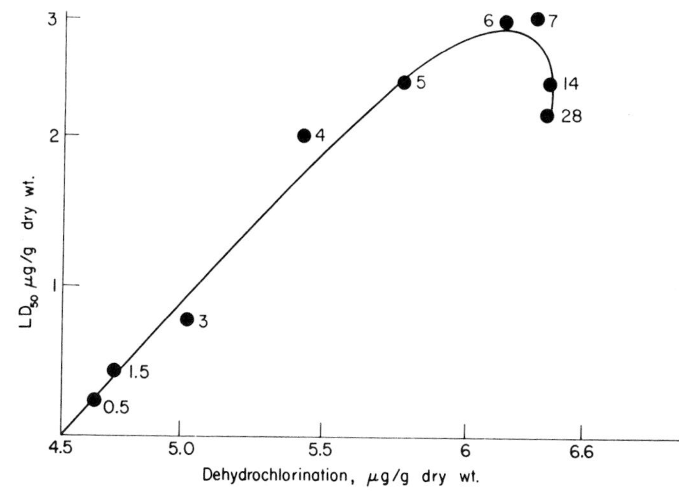

FIG. 16.6. Relation between dehydrochlorinating ability and sensitivity to DDT for Mexican bean beetles of various ages. The numbers show the age in days. From data of Tombes and Forgash (100).

enzyme controls the toxicity. After 7 days other factors appear to take over, for the LD_{50} proceeds to drop while the enzyme level remains stable.

I would hazard a guess that the remarkable variations in the susceptibility of various insects to carbamates owes to metabolic selectivity, for metabolism is most complex with these compounds (42). It also seems probable that the selective toxicity of rotenoids to cold-blooded animals is metabolic in origin, for the target is sensitive in mammals as well as in insects (p. 161).

Penetration to the Target

The commonest target for toxicants is the nervous system. One of the most tangled cases in insect toxicology will now be reviewed. It is well known that vertebrates have a blood-brain barrier, which slows the access of many compounds, especially ions, from blood to brain (32,52). Do insects have a similar barrier between their central nervous system, i.e., their ganglia, and their hemolymph? The question is of extreme toxicological importance, for the fact (p. 20) that insect cholinesterase is entirely ganglionic, and that there is none in the neuromuscular junction, means that for insects (unlike vertebrates) anticholinesterases must penetrate the ganglia if they are to have a toxic action.

In the last half of the 1950's, a variety of pieces of evidence from different workers using different techniques all suggested that insect ganglia have a barrier to cations including both metallic, such as K^+, and organic cations, such as acetylcholine and ionic drugs and toxicants. Rather than give the account in a strictly historical way, let it first be stated that some new evidence throws doubt on the existence of this barrier. Consequently, after presenting each piece of evidence in favor of a barrier, a short critique is given in suitable cases, enclosed in square parentheses.

Potassium Penetration

In 1953, Hoyle (25) observed that locust nerve was astonishingly insensitive to K^+, applied in concentrations which would promptly block conduction in mammalian nerve. Thus 140mM K^+ blocked only after 4 hours. The American cockroach ganglion was also insensitive, but to a lesser extent, blocking in 30 minutes at this concentration (107). Hoyle noted that if he injected 140mM K^+ into locust nerve, blocking was immediate. He therefore argued that a potassium-impermeable sheath invested the nerve; the term "Hoyle's sheath" has sometimes been applied to it by subsequent workers. The existence of such a sheath accounted very satisfactorily for the ability of phytophagous insects to tolerate with equanimity profound fluctuations in their hemolymph K^+ resulting from ingestion of plant juices.

[But in 1961 Treherne published four papers (105) describing the use of radioactive K^+ and Na^+ to show that their influx and efflux from cockroach ganglia was quite rapid; thus after injection into the whole cockroach, the half-time for exchange was 24 minutes for K^+ and 14 minutes for Na^+. He was able to explain the insensitivity of intact nerve to high K^+ as a case of a Donnan equilibrium, in which nondiffusible anions in the nerve, coupled with a semi-permeable (and therefore K^+-permeable) membrane would suffice to buffer *net* changes in internal K^+. The relatively rapid flux of K^+ and Na^+ has been independently confirmed, and extended to Ca^{++} (51).]

Acetylcholine Penetration

In 1948 Roeder (92) observed that acetylcholine, at $10^{-2}M$, had no action when applied to the American cockroach ganglion. Ten years later, Harlow showed the same insensitivity for a locust ganglion (20). At the time, Roeder felt this was evidence against a transmitter role for acetylcholine in the ganglion. However, in 1956 and 1957 Twarog and Roeder (107,108) reported that if one desheathed the ganglion, that is, peeled off the outer connective tissue sheath or neural lamella along with its adherent inner cellular layer or perilemma, then a partial sensitivity to blockade by acetylcholine was found; but the rather high concentration of $3 \times 10^{-3}M$ was required. Other ionic drugs also were effective on the desheathed preparation, but ineffective on the intact ganglion. These findings were interpreted to mean that the ganglion was invested with a sheath, presumably the neural lamella or the perilemma, which was a barrier to ions.

[But Treherne and Smith in 1965 (106) used radioactive acetylcholine to show that rapid penetration does indeed occur in the cockroach ganglion, but that there is enough acetylcholinesterase in the rind of the ganglion to destroy even $10^{-2}M$ acetylcholine and prevent its penetration to the neuropile, in which the vital synapses are buried. (It is important to note that, in insect ganglia, the peripheral portion or cortex contains the cell bodies of the neurons, but their synapses are axodendritic and situated in the central neuropile.)]

Another indication of acetylcholine exclusion from American cockroach ganglia was the finding by Winton *et al.* (114) that when acetylthiocholine was used as the staining reagent of cholinesterase of whole ganglia staining was only obtained where the surface was cut or damaged, at which sites the reagent presumably leaked in. [But the procedure involved drying the ganglion at 38°C for 15 minutes prior to staining, so there is no guarantee that the ganglion behaves in a similar way *in situ*.]

O'Brien in 1957 also showed (65) that a cockroach with its intact nerve cord in place, and only the gut and dorsum removed, could not hydrolyze the acetylcholine solution with which it was irrigated, even though homogenates readily hydrolyzed it. By contrast, nonionized esters such as phenyl acetate were readily hydrolyzed. [But it was not shown that phenyl acetate was hydrolyzed by enzymes in the nerve cord. Perhaps cholinesterase was located only in nerve cord, whereas phenyl acetate-hydrolyzing enzymes were in many tissues and hydrolysis of phenyl acetate was simply more plentiful.]

Effects on Ganglionic Transmission

In addition to the insensitivity to acetylcholine already described, several other drugs which should interfere with cholinergic transmission have little or no effect on insect ganglia, and their inactivity is in many cases interpretable as owing to an ion barrier, because weak bases are of low activity and cationic compounds are almost inactive.

In 1948 Roeder (92) showed that $10^{-2}M$ scopolamine and atropine (medium strength bases) and curare (a cation) were virtually inactive on the American cockroach ganglion; these three compounds are potent antagonists of acetylcholine in mammals. The ganglion was highly sensitive to un-ionized anticholinesterases such as tepp (e.g., at $10^{-6}M$), but of fairly low sensitivity to the base eserine, or the cation prostigmine, requiring about $10^{-4}M$ for ganglionic blockade. In the desheathed preparation, by contrast (108), a moderate sensitivity to several ionic cholinergic agents was revealed, including $10^{-4}M$

muscarine and $10^{-3}M$ tetramethylammonium, decamethonium, or urocanylcholine. Unfortunately, direct comparisons with sheathed and desheathed preparations are only available for eserine, which blocked at $10^{-5}M$ in the desheathed and $10^{-4}M$ in the intact preparations. With the intact locust ganglion, Harlow (20) showed that eserine was of low activity, requiring $2 \times 10^{-4}M$ for blockade compared with $10^{-5}M$ for the unionizable compounds tepp or paraoxon; that prostigmine was even less active, requiring $10^{-2}M$; and that acetylcholine antagonists, such as curare and decamethonium (cationic) or atropine (basic), were entirely inactive at the highest concentration tested, $10^{-3}M$.

[But the data of Twarog and Roeder for desheathed ganglia lack precise comparisons with the intact preparation. They also found (92) that DFP had a low activity against intact ganglia, requiring $10^{-3}M$ for blockade, but was more effective on desheathed ganglia, blocking at a 17-fold lower concentration. I suggest the following interpretation: DFP is a relatively poor inhibitor of true cholinesterase; it is 100–1000 times poorer than against serum cholinesterase (23,73). This is one factor in its poor performance. For all agents, desheathing improves penetration substantially, in part by loosening of the ganglionic texture; this improvement has been shown with radioactive cations and alcohols (16). Desheathing, therefore, does not remove some special barrier with unique properties, but it does improve accessibility of the interior to all agents.]

Ionization and Toxicity

In 1956, O'Brien (67) noted that many ionic compounds which were toxicants for mammals were virtually nontoxic to insects; putting this information together with the finding of Hoyle's sheath and the well-known fact that acetylcholine is nontoxic to insects (24), he suggested a general "ion-impermeable barrier" in the cockroach. In 1958 with Fisher (77) he elaborated the case and studied the toxicity of 35 neurotoxicants to five insects and to mice, showing that the data were interpretable in terms of an ion barrier protecting the synapses of insects but not of mice. For instance, nicotine has a pK_a of 8.1, so that at pH 7 over 90% is in the ionized form; if the un-ionized fraction alone were effective in insects, but all of the compound was effective in mammals, and if the innate sensitivity of insects and mammals were identical, one can predict a toxicity ratio of 14. Experiments showed the actual ratio, when the mouse was the mammal, to be 25 for the housefly, 28 for the cockroach, 7.3 for the milkweed bug, and 25 for the squash bug. The many problems in calculating and interpreting such ratios have been discussed at length (70, p. 331; 77).

If insect ganglia were totally protected from cations, then cationic anticholinesterases should be entirely ineffective, and basic anticholinesterases should have their toxicity inversely related to their basicities.* In addition to the O'Brien-Fisher study just described, many other observations tend in the same way: thus prostigmine, a permanent cation, kills only 10% of migratory locusts at 1200 μg/g, whereas eserine has an LD_{50} for these insects of 23 μg/g. Kolbezen *et al.* (27) found in 1954 that whereas *m*-dimethylaminophenyl methylcarbamate was a good anticholinesterase and toxic to houseflies, its quaternary analog was a better anticholinesterase but devoid of toxicity to houseflies; this finding they attributed to the ganglionic ion barrier. But since the toxicities were measured by topical application, there is a small possibility that differences in integumental penetration were in fact responsible.

It has been known for a long time that the organophosphate Amiton, a base of pK_a 8.5, is of very low toxicity to most insects, but highly toxic to mammals (a case of inverse selectivity, from the utilitarian viewpoint).

$$(C_2H_5O)_2P(O)SCH_2CH_2N(C_2H_5)_2$$

Amiton

Experiments described below suggested that Amiton penetrated cockroach ganglia slowly because of its ionization at pH 7. A corollary should be that less basic analogs should penetrate insect ganglia better, and show less inverse selectivity. Fluorination of the *N*-ethyl group did indeed reduce basicity and selectivity (78): the pK_a's of Amiton, the monofluoro, and the difluoro analogs were, respectively, 8.5, 6.5, and 4.7, and the selectivities (housefly LD_{50}/mouse LD_{50}) were 330, 50, and 13. Unfortunately, the LD_{50}'s for the housefly had to be measured topically because of solubility considerations, so again it is possible that integumental penetration was a factor in the variation. And recently we have had indications (6) that an analog of Amiton, in which C replaces N, shows inverse selectivity in spite of its nonionizable character.

Measurements of Penetration of Drugs and Insecticides

The last section described toxicity data which are not easy to interpret except in terms of a ganglionic ion barrier. However, much preferable to such indirect studies are direct measurements of penetration. Such studies have been infrequent; those on K^+ and acetylcholine have been described above. Let us first consider what one might call semidirect measurements, which involve measuring not the penetrating compound itself, but its effect upon some endogenous system.

* As in the case of the toxicity predictions described above, the inverse correlation of basicity and toxicity caused by an ion barrier would be entirely accurate only if toxicity were determined by the amount that penetrates such a barrier very soon after injection, for an ionizable basic compound, unlike a permanent cation, will eventually achieve equilibrium on both sides of a cation barrier because of the diffusion of its free-base form (70, pp. 164, 331).

Schradan is an amidic organophosphate with a curious pattern of toxicity. It is toxic to all mammals, to mites, and to aphids and other hemiptera, but not to most other insects (Table 16.5). The insensitivity of cockroaches to it has

TABLE 16.5

SELECTIVE TOXICITY OF SCHRADAN[a] $[(CH_3)_2N]_2P(O)OP(O)[N(CH_3)_2]_2$

Species	Route	LD_{50} (mg/kg)
Susceptible		
Willow aphid	Topical	22
Squash bug	Topical	16
Rat	Intraperitoneal	8
Guinea pig	Intraperitoneal	10
Nonsusceptible		
Housefly	Topical	1932
American cockroach	Topical	2170
Blowfly	Injection	175
Green rice leafhopper	Topical	160
Rice bug	Topical	< 23

[a] Data of Saito (95) and O'Brien and Spencer (81).

been attributed to a failure of the activated form (schradan is a latent anti-cholinesterase) to penetrate the intact ganglion, for it was shown that a solution of activated schradan that caused 9% cholinesterase inhibition in intact nerve cords caused 73% in excised cords or 69% in cords which were slashed (82). This rather crude experiment was partially confirmed when Saito (95) showed by electron microscopy that schradan-insensitive insects had a thick protective sheath, presumably the neural lamella—in the housefly about 0.5 μ, in cockroach 4 μ thick—whereas schradan-sensitive insects such as the rice bug had very thin lamellae—in the black rice bug about 0.25 μ, and in the rice bug about 0.05 μ. [However, the variation in thickness among susceptible species or among nonsusceptible species is so large that it dwarfs the differences between the susceptible and nonsusceptible species. Inspection of Table 22 of Saito's study strongly suggests that the toxicity of schradan is a reflection of a high level in the nerve cord, which in turn is a reflection of great differences in schradan breakdown, since the residual percent of a given schradan dose after a fixed time is 33% in the susceptible rice bug and 2% in the nonsusceptible housefly (A. Toppozada, personal communication). This suggests that selectivity is metabolic in origin.]

Saito also was able to show a difference of penetration of P^{32}-schradan into intact and desheathed cockroach ganglia, but the difference was rather small, never exceeding 1.5-fold.

Although it is not at all clear why an un-ionized compound like activated schradan should encounter a ganglionic barrier, it is relevant to note that mammals poisoned by schradan, or those of its analogs which contain di-methylamide groups, show no sign of disturbances of the central nervous system, nor is their brain cholinesterase inhibited (4,34,35,84). Consequently, activated schradan behaves in mammals, too, like those ionized compounds which cannot penetrate the blood-brain barrier. In general, amidic compounds penetrate the mammalian barrier poorly (98).

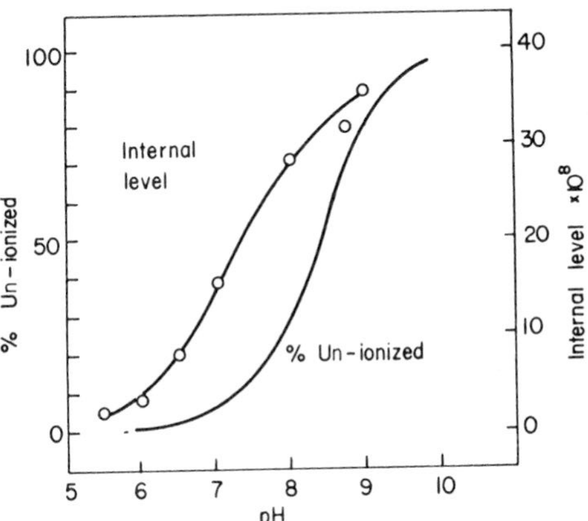

FIG. 16.7. Penetration of Amiton in intact American cockroach nerve cord. Ordinates: (left) scale for the titration curve of Amiton, shown right of center; (right) molar concentration ($\times 10^8$) of Amiton inside the cord. From O'Brien (68).

A more refined use of cholinesterase as an index of penetration involved the organophosphate Amiton mentioned above (p. 275), which is ionizable; tepp, which is un-ionized; and quaternized Amiton, which is ionic (68). Inhibition of endogenous cholinesterase was used as an index of penetration into excised and intact American cockroach nerve cords. The findings strongly suggested that intact, but not excised, cords had their cholinesterase protected by an ion barrier: tepp penetration was about equal in intact and excised cords and was pH-independent; quaternized Amiton penetrated about 30-fold less in intact than in excised cord, independently of pH; and Amiton penetrated in a pH-dependent way (Fig. 16.7). From the figure one may calculate that in the course of 1 hour, when 50% of Amiton was ionized (pH 8.5), about 8-fold more penetrated than when all was ionized (pH 6), suggesting a difference in penetration rates of ionized and un-ionized forms of 15-fold.* At first it was expected (68) that the pH dependence should overlap the titration curve of Amiton (also shown in Fig. 16.7) which shows the amount un-ionized at any given pH. The nonoverlap probably has two causes. The major one has been pointed out before (70) and is illustrated in Fig. 16.8. The titration curve predicts *initial* penetration rates; if one considers instead an infinite time of penetration, then total equilibrium is achieved on both sides of an ion-impermeable membrane. In practice, one selects an exposure time as small as is convenient, and obtains a penetration intermediate between that for zero time and that for infinite time. In the experiments on which Fig. 16.7 is based,

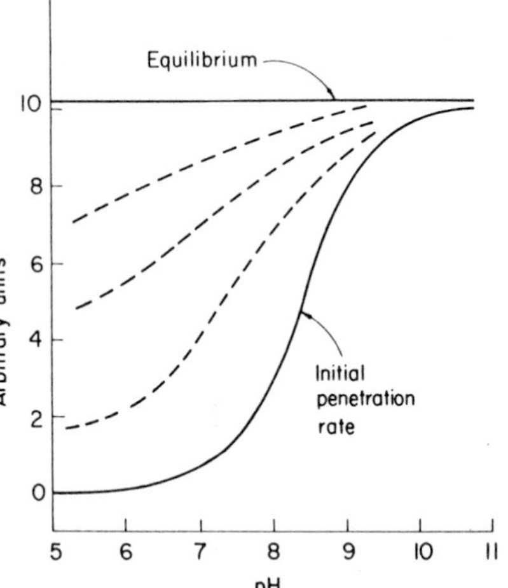

Fig. 16.8. Theoretical penetration rate of a base of pK_a 8.4 through an ion-impermeable membrane as a function of pH. From O'Brien (70).

the exposure time was 1 hour, and there was the added complexity that the cholinesterase inhibition observed owed to an amount of Amiton that progressively increased between $t=0$ and $t=60$ minutes; the resultant represents a rather complex integral, for extra weight was given to the Amiton that arrived first, thus enjoying a 60-minute period of inhibition.

A minor cause for nonoverlap in Fig. 16.7 is that prediction based on the titration curve is only correct when the contribution of the ionized form is zero, and in fact the ionized form contributes one-fifteenth as much as the un-

* Calculated as follows: If penetration per hour of ionized form $=i$ and of un-ionized form $=u$, and if at pH 8.5 one-half is ionized and the hourly penetration $p_1=0.5i+0.5u$, at pH 6 virtually all is ionized and $p_2=i$. From Fig. 16.6, $p_1/p_2=8$, hence $u=15i$. The newer value for the pK_a of 8.5 (ref. 78) is more precisely measured than the original value of 8.4 (ref. 68).

ionized form. Correction for this consideration would shift the predicted curve in the direction of that observed, but only to a small extent.

By far the most convincing evidence for the existence of an ion barrier was the demonstration (Fig. 16.9) that the permeability of cockroach abdominal ganglia to butyric acid, which is ionizable, decreases profoundly with increasing

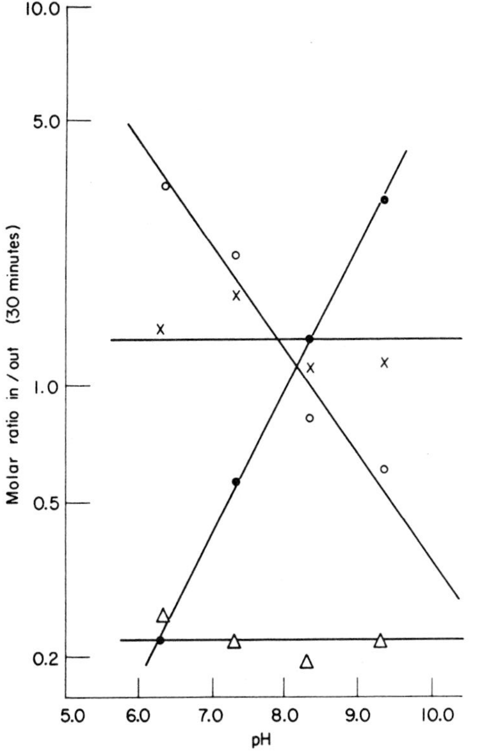

FIG. 16.9. Penetration of compounds into the abdominal nerve cord of the American cockroach, as a function of pH: ● $C_4H_9NH_2$; ○ C_3H_7COOH; × C_4H_9OH; △ $C_4H_9N^+(CH_3)_3$. From Eldefrawi and O'Brien (17).

pH; that the opposite is true for butylamine, also ionizable; and that the penetration of un-ionizable butanol or ionic butyltrimethylammonium is pH-independent (17). In essence, the examples of the amine and the acid compare compounds directly with their protonated analogs, a comparison that cannot be bettered, for the steric differences are thus virtually eliminated. Furthermore, the combined findings absolutely rule out the possibility of an artifact owing to pH effects upon the cord itself.

Another approach to studying the permeability of insect ganglia involves comparison of radioactive molecules of different size and charge. Several series of compounds have been examined by Eldefrawi and O'Brien (13,14,15) working with the abdominal nerve cord of the American cockroach. It was found that anions (specifically, seven fatty acids from acetate to octanoate), cations (ten alkylammonium compounds), and alcohols all pass fairly freely into and out of the nerve cord. Penetration (judged by influx) is promoted: (*a*) by metabolism, which under appropriate circumstances* removes the diffusing species internally, thus eliminating back-diffusion; metabolism can be evaluated in part by suitable blocking agents such as 2,4-dinitrophenol; (*b*) by liposolubility—if one ascends a homologous series, the penetration rate increases as does the liposolubility, judged by octanol–water partition coefficients. (*c*) By small size—if one increases the size of a molecule in such a way that the smallest diameter is increased, e.g., by proceeding from $(CH_3)_3N^+(C_2H_5)$ to $(C_2H_5)_3N^+(C_2H_5)$, the influx rate decreases. But as one continues this series, and passes from the $(C_4H_9)_3$ to the $(C_5H_{11})_3$ compound, the influx rate increases; presumably the additional methylene groups are progressively less effective in enhancing diameter whereas the compensating gain in liposolubility continues steadily. Thus the progressive increases of maximum diameter as one proceeds $C_1:C_2:C_3:C_4:C_5$ are, respectively, 1.3, 1.3, 1.2, and 1.2, whereas the corresponding values for increases in octanol–water partition coefficient are 1.5, 4.3, 7.7, and 12.0.

Because of the several factors which determine penetration, it is not extremely easy to compare compounds from different classes in order to examine the role of charge. One might compare, however, a multiply hydroxylated molecule, such as glucose, with an ionic compound of similar polarity and molecular volume, such as $(CH_3)_3N^+C_2H_5$. The influx of glucose is 3.6-fold faster, but undoubtedly metabolism aids glucose penetration; by contrast, the quaternary ammoniums are not metabolized at all.

Let us now try to drawn together the numerous tangled skeins of data on ionization and penetration. Many of the early studies seemed to suggest a potent ion barrier; indeed it was sometimes spoken of as if it were absolute, i.e., that ions (or, more usually, cations) could not penetrate it at all. Yet the analogous blood-brain barrier of vertebrates is far from an absolute. Thus several amino acids suffer a 3–15-fold barrier effect in 1 hour (41); in 2 hours, the Na^+ effect is 2-fold, the I^- and sucrose effect is 100-fold (32). These values are based on inside/outside concentration ratios at the indicated times. A better measure is of the actual rate constant of penetration (52). Using the constants of several compounds with identical and high permeability constants (thiopental, aniline, aminopyrine) as a basis representing a no-barrier effect,

* If one considers only the flux of radioactivity in such studies, then back-diffusion is lessened only if the metabolic product is incorporated into a nondiffusible or slowly diffusing compound.

the barrier effect in rabbit brain for antipyrine was 3-fold, for acetanilide 20-fold, and for salicylic acid 276-fold. These variations were related to the pK_a of the compounds and to the liposolubility (judged by organic solvent–water partition coefficients) of their un-ionized forms. In a similar way, the "barrier" in insects is relative rather than absolute; it slows the penetration of polar molecules. One can show (15) that it is the polarity of ions, rather than their charge *per se*, that causes their penetration to be slowed.

Direct measurements indicate barrier effects in insect ganglia associated with ionization which are of the order of 5–15-fold. A most important factor to consider is that the "direct measurement" experiments might be examining influxes and effluxes in the periphery (cortex) of the ganglion, whereas the neuropile, containing the functionally vital synapses, might enjoy much greater immunity from cations. Histological studies with methylene blue support this view (16,102). Such a case was reported (93) for acetylcholine penetration into squid axon: the "envelope" of the axon achieved 47% of the concentration of the bathing solution, the axoplarm achieved only 0.5%. However, the fact that, in insect ganglia, measurements with radioactive cations and anions at various pH's tell the same story as comparable measurements based on cholinesterase inhibition by Amiton, strongly suggests that ionized compounds penetrate to the cholinesterase zone 10–15 times less effectively than their un-ionized analogs; whether this is due to a true ion barrier, i.e., either a discrete or diffuse zone which specifically limits penetration of ions [a consideration that led Lajtha (41) to speak of a "brain barrier system" in place of a "blood-brain barrier"] cannot be decided from presently available experiments. There is strong evidence that the ganglionic sheath is not "the barrier," because desheathed ganglia show pH-dependant penetration similar to intact ganglia (16).

In contemplating the extent to which a barrier of this magnitude might lead to toxicological consequences of the extent described above, one must consider that a magnification phenomenon can occur, as discussed above for the case of the opportunity factor. For instance, one can readily suggest two systems, both having a fairly brisk rate of metabolism, such that a 10-fold difference in nerve-cord penetration could give rise to a 100- or 1000-fold difference in toxicity.

Many authors have noted that compounds such as Amiton and schradan, often suspected to owe their generally low toxicity to insects to a nerve-penetration problem, are toxic to aphids (70). This thought led Toppozada and O'Brien (101) to explore the permeability of the ganglion of an aphid (the willow aphid) to anions and cations. They found that the aphid ganglion behaved remarkably like that of the American cockroach, and concluded that the unusual toxicity of the above compounds for aphids was not connected with any special feature of the aphid ganglion. One alternative possibility is that the neuromuscular junction of aphids, which is probably more exposed to ions and perhaps amides, is cholinergic.

In conclusion of this section on penetration to the target, the statement made in 1959 (68) still remains appropriate: "The introduction of an ionized or readily ionizable group into an anticholinesterase will make the compound a selective mammalicide. However, some arthropods (mites, aphids) may be susceptible. If other pests than these are to be poisoned, it is desirable to avoid ionizable compounds, unless the pK_a is low in the case of bases (e.g., below 7) or high in the case of acids (e.g., above 7)." One can say that for all insects studied, compounds penetrate *as if* there were a barrier which slows ion penetration 10–15-fold; but that this barrierlike property probably resides in the ganglion as a whole rather than in a specific layer of cells. The insect and vertebrate central nervous systems therefore enjoy qualitatively similar protection from polar substances. The above selectivity is caused by the existence of peripheral, ion-sensitive cholinesterase in the vertebrate but not in the insect.

Disposal (Storage and Excretion)

A former discussion in 1961 (72) has pointed out that one might well expect there to be cases of selectivity to be attributable to differences in disposal, especially in view of the relative efficiency of the mammalian, compared with the insect, excretory apparatus. Probably the reason for the absence of documented cases of such selectivity is that most toxicants are relatively apolar, and such compounds are rarely excreted as such. Since prior metabolism of a kind which renders the compound more polar (e.g., hydrolysis; and glycoside formation, often following hydroxylation) is a normal prerequisite for effective excretion in such cases, and since these prior reactions are usually detoxifying in themselves, it is clear why the primary focus of interest centers upon metabolism as a determinant in selectivity.

In one case at least, a suspicion of the importance of different storage capabilities has been raised. Saito (95) argues quite convincingly that the reason that schradan is twice as toxic to the male as to the female American cockroach (relative LD_{50}'s, 2710 and 4416 mg/kg) is, at least in part, the immobilization of the compound in the female fat body. Not only does the female have three times as much fat body as the male, but it stores in it five times (or more) as much schradan, representing a large fraction of the dose. At 250 μg/g, the female stores 66 μg in her fat body, the male only 13 μg.

Attack upon the Target

This aspect, dealing with the existence of "target selectivity," has expanded greatly since its last review in 1961 (72), and it is clearly of major importance in many cases. Clearly, a detailed discussion is possible only when the nature of the target is understood in detail; in effect, this limits discussion to the anticholinesterases.

Let us first consider the problem in general, insofar as it relates to organophosphates, in order to make clear the problems in interpretation that arise. If one is to attribute observed differences in toxicity, for instance, in insects compared with mammals, to differences in anticholinesterase activity, one wants to know first that nonselective toxicants are about equally potent against insect and mammalian cholinesterase. Our own laboratory findings go partway to providing this assurance: using compounds which are not much more toxic (i.e., not more than 10-fold) for houseflies than for mice or rats, plus those compounds (asterisked below) whose selective toxicity either to insects or mammals has been firmly attributed to factors other than target selectivity, we find differences between anticholinesterase activity for human red cells compared with housefly heads, expressed as I_{50} red cells/I_{50} fly head, as follows: Amiton* 5, quaternary Amiton* 1.6, DFP 0.8, paraoxon 0.5, propyl paraoxon 1, malaoxon* 13, P(O) of phorate 4, sulfone of P(O) of phorate 4. Without claiming that this is a sufficiently exhaustive list, it is clear that it is a commonplace to find anticholinesterase potency ratios in the range 0.1–10.

Next we come to compounds which are selectively toxic, are selective anticholinesterases and, in the absence of precise comparative data on metabolism or penetration, are therefore, one strongly suspects, possessed of differential toxicity by virtue of target selectivity. These include DDVP, suggested by van Asperen in 1958 (3), which is 10 times more toxic to houseflies (topically) than to mice (subcutaneously) and has a cholinesterase ratio* of 501; and ruelene, whose P(S) analog is 70 times more toxic to houseflies than to mice (71,97) and whose cholinesterase ratio is 794.

Two detailed studies (31,55) were performed in different laboratories on an early and intriguing report of 1949 that diisopropyl parathion was 250 times more toxic to flies than to bees, and 1000 times better *in vitro* against fly than against bee cholinesterase (56). The situation needed clarification because soon after 1949 it was realized that phosphorothionates [P(S) compounds] of the parathion class, when purified, have negligible *in vitro* anticholinesterase activity, and owe their *in vivo* potency to metabolic conversion of P(S) to P(O). Any apparent *in vitro* potency is therefore due to impurities. Studies on diisopropyl paraoxon [the P(O) analog which is probably the potent metabolite of diisopropyl parathion *in vivo*] showed it also to be selectively toxic to flies (22 times more than to bees) and to be 40 times better against fly than against

* Defined as potency for cholinesterase *in vitro*, for housefly: human red cell. In all cases quoted, the data are unpublished findings from our laboratory, even though the investigator under discussion may have used other enzymes or assays. It is hoped in this way to permit better comparisons. In no case has the investigator's data been much different from ours.

bee cholinesterase *in vitro*. Pure diisopropyl parathion was found to be 100 times more toxic to flies than to bees, and it is plausible that the selective toxicity of both the P(S) and P(O) compounds is attributable to the selective anticholinesterase activity of the P(O). But faith in this attribution was somewhat shaken by findings with closely related compounds. Di-*n*-propyl paraoxon showed much greater selective toxicity than the isopropyl compound (150 times more toxic to flies than to bees) yet was a less selective anticholinesterase (20 times better against fly than against bee enzyme). Diethyl paraoxon and dibutyl paraoxon were also selective anticholinesterases for fly compared with bee (1.6 and 2.0 times, respectively), yet actually showed the *reverse* pattern of toxicity in that they were more toxic to bees than to flies (10 and 1.7 times, respectively). Consequently, it is clear that in such compounds, target selectivity is not the only factor, and although it may be the predominant factor when of sufficiently great magnitude, yet it can be profoundly modified by other factors, probably metabolic. For instance, *n*-propyl paraoxon is probably less selective than its target selectivity would suggest because it is degraded at a disproportionately great rate by houseflies.

Such considerations lead to a concept of polyfactorial selectivity, which is probably much more common than monofactorial selectivity. That is to say, selective toxicity is normally caused by several factors; occasionally one factor is so large that experimentally it seems like the only one. In some cases, two factors may cancel each other out. This has been shown for the organophosphate, famphur, which is degraded eight times faster by mice than by milkweed bugs, yet is 20 times better against mouse than against milkweed bug cholinesterase *in vitro*. The combination of these two opposing factors led to a very small selective toxicity; famphur is only 1.5 times more toxic to milkweed bugs than to mice (80). A similar phenomenon might explain why azinphosmethyl is as toxic to mice as to flies (23,71) even though its cholinesterase ratio is 125. An even more complicated case was reviewed above: that of dimethoate, whose selectivity among mammalian species was monofactorial, since it was dictated exclusively by the rate of degradation in liver. In insects, by contrast, variations in penetration, activation, and target sensitivity were all profound, and target selectivity played only a partial role in causing the relatively great sensitivity of the housefly, for whose cholinesterase it was 100 times more inhibitory than for that of the other insects (Table 16.3).

A case of relatively "pure" target selectivity was uncovered in an examination of the reasons why organophosphates are almost nontoxic to frogs and toads (37). It was shown in this case that variation in metabolism and distribution of paraoxon in frogs, mice, and American cockroaches was negligible, and the only significant feature was that the cholinesterase of the frog was 79 times more sensitive to inhibition than that of the mouse (87). And indeed it has been known since 1946 that frog brain cholinesterase is very unusual, for it is 100 times less sensitive to the carbamate eserine than is human plasma, erythrocyte, or dog brain cholinesterase (21).

From what has been said, it is clear that target selectivity is a fairly common phenomenon. One might hope to be able to approach the problem in another way, by exploring differences in cholinesterase (not necessarily using inhibitors) and then designing selective inhibitors, hopefully producing selective toxicants thereby. Most such work has been done with housefly head cholinesterase as an example from an insect, and human or bovine red-cell cholinesterase as a mammalian enzyme. (Whether or not there is any consistent difference between insect and mammalian cholinesterases is, of course, undetermined as yet; such a difference could exist in spite of the several differences *between* insect cholinesterases described above, e.g., between bee and housefly enzyme.)

Let it first be said that the similarities of housefly and red cell cholinesterase are very striking (115) with respect to inhibition, optimal substrates, and kinetics (for instance, in the existence and extent of inhibition by excess substrate). One attempt to explore differences in the active sites of housefly head and human red-cell cholinesterases examined the ability of simple alkylammonium salts, which presumably bind to the anionic site, to interfere with phosphorylation of the esteratic site by eight organophosphates (73). In the red cell enzyme, tetraethylammonium (TEA) and tetrapropylammonium (TPA) interfered equally well with phosphorylation, suggesting that both could mask the esteratic site when their N^+ was bound to the anionic site. By contrast, in the fly enzyme, TPA interfered up to 32 times better than TEA, suggesting that it masked the ester site better than TEA, so that the distance between the sites must be less than the diameter of TPA and more than that of TEA, i.e., between 4.5 and 5.9 Å; whereas the distance for the red cell enzyme must be less than 4.5 Å, since TEA and TPA overlapped the ester site.

Valuable studies by Dauterman and Mehrotra have compared 17 acetylcholine analogs (varying primarily in the R of the R_3N^+ group) as substrates for cholinesterase of rat (30), spider mite, and housefly (53,53a), and revealed substantial differences. For the rat and fly enzymes, analogs containing $(CH_3)_2N^+$ and $(C_2H_5)_2N^+$ were about equally good substrates, whereas the corresponding $(C_3H_7)_2N^+$ and $(C_4H_9)_2N^+$ compounds were very poor substrates; but the mite enzyme was almost equiactive against all these compounds. Inhibition by excess substrate was profound for all good substrates for the rat enzyme, minor or absent with all substrate for the mite, and very variable for the fly, where, for instance, it was great with the $(C_2H_5)_3N^+$ compound yet absent with the $(C_2H_5)_2(C_4H_9)N^+$ compound.

It is not easy to use such data to deduce unambiguously the different topographies of the enzyme surface, but it is very clear that important differences do exist, and in principle they present an opportunity for design of selective inhibitors.

This discussion has centered, so far, exclusively upon cholinesterase as a target. Yet the brightest prospects for a rational approach to selective toxicants surely lie in other targets. It is perhaps extraordinary that target selectivity has so far been shown only in that most unpromising case, where the very same enzyme (and with remarkably similar properties overall) is in mammalian friend and insect enemy alike. Obviously the best target would be one that was present only in the enemy; the neuromuscular junction of insects, since it is not cholinergic (p. 20), presents a particularly attractive case, one whose nature still awaits elucidation. We studied (75), abortively, another such case: the so-called α-glycerophosphate shuttle, which would seem to be the primary mechanism for oxidizing extramitochondrial $NADH_2$ by mitochondria; Sacktor and Dick (94) had shown for the blowfly that the alternative mechanisms of this oxidation available to mammals, involving lactic dehydrogenase or the malate–oxalacetate shuttle, are absent. We therefore hoped that inhibition of the α-glycerophosphate shuttle would be more embarassing for insects than mammals. We examined six analogs of α-glycerophosphate (most of which we had to synthesize) and eleven cinnamates, and found some quite good inhibitors of the shuttle *in vitro*; the best was *m*-hydroxycinnamic acid. Alas, this and the other compounds were completely nontoxic to houseflies. We may never know whether the reason was that the shuttle is not vital, or that it was inadequately inhibited because the compounds were not potent enough, or that the compounds were rapidly metabolized.

In spite of this failure, other such targets which might be peculiarly important for insects *must* be studied. The possibility of interference with metamorphic processes is being widely studied in several laboratories. There are many other special features of insect metabolism that might be exploited: the existence of special compounds (chitin, trehalose) and the enzymes for their metabolism; the absence of steroid-synthesizing enzymes, the low lactic dehydrogenase of muscle; the existence of peripheral (and therefore relatively unprotected) inhibitory neurons, of which γ-aminobutyric acid is very probably the transmitter (28,112).

However, there is still room for imagination in developing "biochemical bullets" for targets not unique to insects, just as has been done for the anticholinesterases. Dauterman and Mehrotra have explored differences in choline acetylase of rat (29), spider mite, and housefly (53,53a), using as substrates the choline moieties of the 17 acetylcholine analogs described above, and they found striking species differences. The rat enzyme could only utilize choline analogs having $(CH_3)_2N^+$ present; mite and fly enzyme could, in addition, utilize analogs with $(C_2H_5)_2N^+$ present. Presumably, therefore, one should be able to find inhibitors of this enzyme which are effective only on the insect (or mite) enzyme. It is well known that in the mammal inhibitors of choline acetylase, such as hemicholinium, are extraordinarily toxic (LD_{50} for mice is 0.05 mg/kg, by an unstated route) (45).

Consequences of a Successful Attack upon the Target

This is the most difficult aspect of selectivity to examine experimentally, and the easiest to speculate about. The basic principle is: If one organism can survive when a particular target is obliterated, and another organism cannot, then compounds attacking such a target will show selective toxicity with respect to these organisms. Or, at a more quantitative level, a similar consequence will follow if one organism can tolerate a substantially greater degree of target damage than another.

At present, only for the anticholinesterases do we know the target with some certainty. Although it seems plausible, *a priori*, that insects might tolerate more intensive or more prolonged inhibition of their cholinesterase, experimental evidence is lacking.

It has been mentioned elsewhere that amphibia can tolerate immense citrate levels in their hearts (p. 177), and this, or a parallel tolerance in other tissues, might be the cause of their insensitivity to fluoroacetate. The amazing insensitivity of insects to decapitation has also been described (p. 58), and it permits one to say that "decapitation is selectively toxic to mammals compared with insects." The statement happens to be true, as well as bizarre and rather useless. Insects are also very insensitive to prolonged oxygen deprivation, so that certain atmospheres lethal to mammals have little effect upon insects.

In general, one has the impression that all these differential sensitivities are such as to favor organisms lower on the evolutionary scale. Consequently, there is not much hope that one can utilize them in designing useful selective toxicants. But as we attempt to account more and more precisely for differential toxicity, I believe we shall find that this factor, which in a way is the ultimate expression of differences in "innate sensitivity" is one that must be considered.

REFERENCES

1. Armstrong, G., Bradbury, F. R., and Standen, H., *Nature* **167**, 319 (1951).
2. Arthur, B. W., and Casida, J. E., *J. Agr. Food Chem.* **5**, 186 (1957).
3. Asperen, K. van *Entomol. Exptl. Appl.* **1**, 130 (1958).
4. Barnes, J. M., *Chem. Ind.* (*London*) p. 478 (1954).
5. Bracha, P., and O'Brien, R. D., *J. Econ. Entomol.* **59**, 1255 (1966).
6. Bracha, P., and O'Brien, R. D., *Biochemistry* (in press, 1967).
7. Bridges, P. M., *Biochem. J.* **66**, 316 (1957).
8. Brodie, B. B., and Maickel, R. P., *Proc. 1st Intern. Pharmacol. Meeting, Stockholm,* 1961 **6**, 299 (1962).
9. Brown, E. W., and Scott, W. O., *J. Pharmacol. Exptl. Therap.* **50**, 373 (1934).

10. Buerger, A. A., Penetration of non-electrolytes through animal integuments, M.S. Thesis, Cornell Univ., Ithaca, New York, 1964.
11. Buerger, A. A., *J. Theoret. Biol.* **11**, 131 (1966).
12. Buerger, A. A., and O'Brien, R. D., *J. Cellular Comp. Physiol.* **66**, 227 (1965).
13. Eldefrawi, M. E., and O'Brien, R. D., *J. Insect. Physiol.* **12**, 1133 (1966).
14. Eldefrawi, M. E., and O'Brien, R. D., *J. Exptl. Biol.* (in press, 1967).
15. Eldefrawi, M. E., and O'Brien, R. D., *J. Insect Physiol.* (in press, 1967).
16. Eldefrawi, M. E., Toppozada, A., Salpeter, M. M., and O'Brien, R. D., *J. Exptl. Biol.* (in press, 1967).
17. Eldefrawi, M. E., and O'Brien, R. D., Unpublished findings (1966).
18. Forgash, A. J., Cook, B. J., and Riley, R. C., *J. Econ. Entomol.* **55**, 545 (1962).
19. Gemmell, D. H. O., and Morrison, J. C., *J. Pharm. Pharmacol.* **10**, 553 (1958).
20. Harlow, P. A., *Ann. Appl. Biol.* **46**, 55 (1958).
21. Hawkins, R. D., and Mendel, B., *J. Cellular Comp. Physiol.* **27**, 69 (1946).
22. Hodgson, E., and Casida, J. E., *J. Agr. Food Chem.* **10**, 208 (1962).
23. Holmstedt, B., *Pharmacol. Rev.* **11**, 567 (1959).
24. Hopf, H. S., *Ann. Appl. Biol.* **39**, 193 (1952).
25. Hoyle, G., *J. Exptl. Biol.* **30**, 121 (1953).
26. Hurst, H., *Nature* **147**, 388 (1941).
27. Kolbezen, M. J., Metcalf, R. L., and Fukuto, T. R., *J. Agr. Food Chem.* **8**, 198 (1960).
28. Kravitz, E. A., Kuffler, S. W., and Potter, D. D., *Federation Proc.* **22**, 220 (1963).
29. Dauterman, W. C., and Mehrotra, K. N., *J. Neurochem.* **10**, 113 (1963).
30. Dauterman, W. C., and Mehrotra, K. N., *J. Insect Physiol.* **9**, 257 (1963).
31. Dauterman, W. C., and O'Brien, R. D., *J. Agr. Food Chem.* **12**, 318 (1964).
32. Davson, H., and Spaziani, E., *J. Physiol.* (*London*) **149**, 135 (1959).
33. Dixon, M., and Webb, E. C., "Enzymes." Academic Press, New York, 1958.
34. DuBois, K. P., Doull, J., and Coon, J. M., *J. Pharmacol. Exptl. Therap.* **99**, 376 (1950).
35. DuBois, K. P., Doull, J., Okinaka, A. J., and Coon, J. M., *J. Pharmacol. Exptl. Therap.* **107**, 464 (1953).
36. Dyte, C. E., Ellis, V. J., and Lloyd, C. J., *J. Stored Prod. Res.* **1**, 223 (1966).
37. Edery, H., and Schatzberg-Porath, G., *Arch. Intern. Pharmacodyn.* **124**, 212 (1960).
38. Krueger, H. G., and Casida, J. E., *J. Econ. Entomol.* **50**, 356 (1957).
39. Krueger, H. R., and O'Brien, R. D., *J. Econ. Entomol.* **52**, 1063 (1959).
40. Krueger, H. R., O'Brien, R. D., and Dauterman, W. C., *J. Econ. Entomol.* **53**, 25 (1960).
41. Lajtha, A., *In* "Neurochemistry" (K. A. C. Elliott, I. H. Page, and J. H. Quastel, eds.), p. 399. Thomas, Springfield, Illinois, 1962.
42. Leeling, N. C., and Casida, J. E., *J. Agr. Food Chem.* **14**, 281 (1966).
43. Lindquist, D. A., and Dahm, P. A., *J. Econ. Entomol.* **49**, 579 (1956).
44. Lipke, H., and Kearns, C. W., *J. Biol. Chem.* **234**, 2123 (1959).
45. Long, J. P., *J. Med. Pharm. Chem.* **4**, 505 (1961).
46. March, R. B., Fukuto, T. R., Metcalf, R. L., and Maxon, M. G., *J. Econ. Entomol.* **49**, 185 (1956).
47. Main, A. R., and Braid, P. E., *Biochem. J.* **84**, 255 (1962).
48. Martin, H., "The Scientific Principles of Crop Protection," 4th ed. Arnold, London, 1959.
49. Matsumura, F., *J. Insect Physiol.* **9**, 207 (1963).
50. Matsumura, F., and O'Brien, R. D., *Biochem. Pharmacol.* **12**, 1201 (1963).
51. Matsumura, F., and O'Brien, R. D., *J. Agr. Food Chem.* **14**, 39 (1966).
52. Mayer, S., Maickel, R. P., and Brodie, B. B., *J. Pharmacol. Exptl. Therap.* **127**, 205 (1959).

53. Mehrotra, K. N., and Dauterman, W. C., *J. Neurochem.* **10**, 119 (1963).
53a. Mehrotra, K. N., and Dauterman, W. C., *J. Insect. Physiol.* **9**, 293 (1963).
54. Metcalf, R. L., "Organic Insecticides," Wiley (Interscience), New York, 1955.
55. Metcalf, R. L., and Frederickson, M., *J. Econ. Entomol.* **58**, 143 (1965).
56. Metcalf, R. L., and March, R. B., *J. Econ. Entomol.* **42**, 721 (1949).
57. Metcalf, R. L., and March, R. B., *J. Econ. Entomol.* **46**, 288 (1953).
58. Miyamoto, J., Sato, Y., Kadota, T., Fujinami, A., and Endo, M., *Agr. Biol. Chem. (Tokyo)* **27**, 381 (1963).
59. Miyamoto, J., Sato, Y., Kadota, T., and Fujinami, A., *Agr. Biol. Chem. (Tokyo)* **27**, 669 (1963).
60. Negherbon, W. O., "Handbook of Toxicology, Insecticides," Vol. 3, Saunders, Philadelphia, Pennsylvania, 1959.
61. Nishizawa, Y., *Bull. Agr. Chem. Soc. Japan* **24**, 744 (1960).
62. Nishizawa, Y., Fujii, K., Kadota, T., Miyamoto, J., and Sakamoto, H., *Agr. Biol. Chem. (Tokyo)* **25**, 605 (1961).
63. Nishizawa, Y., Nakagawa, M., Suzuki, Y., Sakamoto, H., and Mizutani, T., *Agr. Biol. Chem. (Tokyo)* **25**, 597 (1961).
64. O'Brien, R. D., *Proc. 4th Congr. Crop Protect., Hamburg*, 1957 **2**, 1183 (1960).
65. O'Brien, R. D., *Ann. Entomol. Soc. Am.* **50**, 223 (1957).
66. O'Brien, R. D., *J. Econ. Entomol.* **50**, 159 (1957).
67. O'Brien, R. D., *Proc. 10th Intern. Congr. Entomol., Montreal*, 1956 **2**, 377 (1958).
68. O'Brien, R. D., *J. Econ. Entomol.* **52**, 812 (1959).
69. O'Brien, R. D., *Can. J. Biochem. Physiol.* **37**, 1114 (1959).
70. O'Brien, R. D., "Toxic Phosphorus Esters," Academic Press, New York, 1960.
71. O'Brien, R. D., *Biochem. J.* **79**, 229 (1961).
72. O'Brien, R. D., *Advan. Pest Control Res.* **4**, 75 (1961).
73. O'Brien, R. D., *J. Agr. Food Chem.* **11**, 163 (1963).
74. O'Brien, R. D., *Ann. N.Y. Acad. Sci.* **123**, 156 (1965).
75. O'Brien, R. D., Cheung, L., and Kimmel, E. C., *J. Insect Physiol.* **11**, 1241 (1965).
76. O'Brien, R. D., and Dannelley, C. E., *J. Agr. Food Chem.* **13**, 245 (1965).
77. O'Brien, R. D., and Fisher, R. W., *J. Econ. Entomol.* **51**, 169 (1958).
78. O'Brien, R. D., and Hilton, B. D., *J. Agr. Food Chem.* **12**, 53 (1964).
79. O'Brien, R. D., and Hilton, B. D., *J. Agr. Food Chem.* **13**, 381 (1965).
80. O'Brien, R. D., Kimmel, E. C., and Sferra, P. R., *J. Agr. Food Chem.* **13**, 366 (1965).
81. O'Brien, R. D., and Spencer, E. Y., *J. Agr. Food Chem.* **1**, 946 (1953).
82. O'Brien, R. D., and Spencer, E. Y., *Nature* **179**, 52 (1957).
83. O'Brien, R. D., Thorn, G. D., and Fisher, R. W., *J. Econ. Entomol.* **51**, 714 (1958).
84. Okinaka, A. J., Doull, J., Coon, J. M., and DuBois, K. P., *J. Pharmacol. Exptl. Therap.* **112**, 231 (1958).
85. Olson, W. P., and O'Brien, R. D., *J. Insect Physiol.* **9**, 777 (1963).
86. Oppenoorth, F. J., and van Asperen, *Entomol. K., Exptl. Appl.* **4**, 311 (1961).
87. Potter, J. L., and O'Brien, R. D., *Entomol. Exptl. Appl.* **6**, 319 (1963).
88. Potter, J. L., and O'Brien, R. D., *Science* **144**, 55 (1964).
89. Richards, A. G., and Cutkomp, L. K., *Biol. Bull.* **90**, 97 (1946).
90. Ripper, W. E., Greenslade, R. M., and Hartley, G. S., *J. Econ. Entomol.* **44**, 448 (1951).
91. Ripper, W. E., Greenslade, R. M., Heath, J., and Barker, K., *Nature* **161**, 484 (1948).
92. Roeder, K. D., *Bull. Johns Hopkins Hosp.* **83**, 587 (1948).
93. Rosenberg, P., and Hoskin, F. C. G., *Biochem. Pharmacol.* **14**, 1765 (1965).
94. Sacktor, B., and Dick, A. R., *J. Biol. Chem.* **237**, 3259 (1962).

95. Saito, T., "Studies on the Selective Toxicity of Schradan," Bull. No. 1, Lab. Appl. Entomol., Nagoya Univ., Japan, 1961.
96. Schmidt, C. H., and Dahm, P. A., *J. Econ. Entomol.* **49**, 729 (1956).
97. Seume, F. W., and O'Brien, R. D., *Toxicol. Appl. Pharmacol.* **2**, 495 (1960).
98. Soloway, A. H., *Science* **128**, 1572 (1958).
99. Spiller, D., *Advan. Pest Control. Res.* **4**, 249 (1961).
100. Tombes, A. S., and Forgash, A. J., *J. Insect Physiol.* **7**, 216 (1961).
101. Toppozada, A., and O'Brien, R. D., *J. Insect Physiol.* (in press, 1967).
102. Toppozada, A., Salpeter, M. M. and O'Brien, R. D., Unpublished observations (1966).
103. Treherne, J. E., *J. Physiol.* (*London*) **133**, 171 (1956).
104. Treherne, J. E., *J. Insect Physiol.* **1**, 178 (1957).
105. Treherne, J. E., *J. Exptl. Biol.* **38**, 315, 629, 729, 737 (1961).
106. Treherne, J. E., and Smith, D. S., *J. Exptl. Biol.* **43**, 13 (1965).
107. Twarog, B. M., and Roeder, K. D., *Biol. Bull.* **111**, 278 (1956).
108. Twarog, B. M., and Roeder, K. D., *Ann. Entomol. Soc. Am.* **50**, 231 (1957).
109. Uchida, T., Dauterman, W. C., and O'Brien, R. D., *J. Agr. Food Chem.* **12**, 48 (1964).
110. Uchida, T., and O'Brien, R. D., *Toxicol. Appl. Pharmacol.* **10**, 89 (1967).
111. Uchida, T., Rahmati, H. S., and O'Brien, R. D., *J. Econ. Entomol.* **58**, 831 (1965).
112. Usherwood, P. N. R., and Grundfest, H., *Science* **143**, 817 (1964).
113. Vardanis, A., and Crawford, L. G., *J. Econ. Entomol.* **57**, 136 (1964).
114. Winton, M. Y., Metcalf, R. L., and Fukuto, T. R., *Ann. Entomol. Soc. Am.* **51**, 436 (1958).
115. Wolfe, L. S., and Smallman, B. N., *J. Cellular Comp. Physiol.* **48**, 215 (1958).
116. Zschintzsch, J., O'Brien, R. D., and Smith, E. H., *J. Econ. Entomol.* **58**, 614 (1965).

CHAPTER 17

Insecticides and Environmental Health

All the chlorinated hydrocarbon insecticides in common use share an amazing persistence in soils, vegetable matter, and the bodies of man and domestic and wild animals. The explanation for this persistence lies in part in a low susceptibility to enzymic attack in comparison with, say, organophosphates and carbamates, and in part in their marked apolarity, which allows storage in animal fats and plant waxes, where enzymic breakdown is absent. Because pesticides have become a virtually irreplaceable weapon of the agriculturist, they are used on a gigantic and growing scale. In the United States in 1962, an estimated 350 million pounds of pesticide were spread over 90 million acres, representing 5% of the continental area (39). Major components of this usage were the cyclodienes (78 million pounds) and DDT (63 million pounds). The amounts of cyclodienes and DDT in use have been dwindling slowly, so that only 51 million pounds of DDT were used in 1964 (42). It is perhaps not surprising that the extent and potential hazard from such widespread environmental contamination was publicized more by the dramatic and half-accurate writing of Rachel Carson (10) than by all the scientifically documented data in learned journals. A better background is provided by the very readable report (39) of the President's Science Advisory Committee published in 1963.

Nobody can be in doubt that the environment is widely contaminated in the United States and probably in all other advanced countries. Documentation will be provided below. The questions to be considered in this chapter are: Is there a real hazard to human health, and what are the effects upon wild life?

Problems of Human Health

There is extensive evidence that most humans regularly ingest small amounts of chlorinated pesticides, and thereby come to contain them in their body fat.

The data is most complete for the United States. We will first discuss the amounts in food, then the resultant amounts found in humans, then the evidence for any hazard.

An extensive study in 1954 (47) showed that DDT was present in all restaurant and institutional meals analyzed. Only 19 meals were analyzed, and from areas which were unstated, but presumably in the state of Washington, where the work was done. On the average, each meal had 55 μg of DDT and 28 μg of DDE. Meat almost invariably had DDT (24 out of 27 samples), but fruit juices and many vegetables were virtually free of it. In this work, the analyses were done by the colorimetric method of Schechter and Haller, and amounts below 1 μg could not be detected.

In 1966, researchers of the Food and Drug Administration (17) conducted an extensive survey on food contaminations, using gas chromatographic analysis. Analyses for 50 pesticides were performed on 216 composite samples collected during a year (1964–1965) in Boston, Kansas City, and St. Louis. The composites represented typical dietaries, and those foods which are normally cooked were cooked before analysis. Clearly, this was a painstaking study seeking to explore average exposure. The results (Table 17.1) reveal that contamination is common but always at low levels. The data do not tell the whole story; it is not stated how many samples had relatively high contamination, so the "maximum" figure could represent only a single unusual sample.

Even dwellers in remote areas do not escape. Alaskan Eskimos averaged 0.8 ppm of DDT and 2 ppm of DDE in their body fat (18). Their native foods (caribou, moose, beaver, seal, and other romantic items) contained no such residues, and occasional consumption of imported foods was the sole source. For instance, a dish of spaghetti and meat balls, consumed in a hospital, contributed 111 μg of DDT.

A 1961 review (26) of milk residues showed that contamination was almost universal. Using a method sensitive to 0.3 ppm of the major chlorinated compounds, and taking 4000 samples from all over the country, 91% were found to contain DDT, 43% had DDE, 29% had methoxychlor, and 12% had DDD. These findings are the more striking in that the United States Food and Drug Administration is officially supposed to seize milk samples containing any insecticide residues. Clearly, if regulations were followed, milk would be in short supply. The review emphasizes that, in an attempt to reduce residues, DDT is no longer used in or around dairy barns; the residues are caused by DDT intake in the food. The problem is exacerbated by the long persistence of DDT in the cow's body, typically of 10 months duration.

An additional factor contributing to the widespread contamination of agricultural commodities is the considerable persistence of the chlorinated hydrocarbons in soil, and their translocation into crops subsequently grown in these soils. These factors vary a good deal with compounds, soil, and crop.

TABLE 17.1

RESIDUES IN 216 COMPOSITE FOOD SAMPLES COLLECTED IN 1964–1965[a]

Insecticide	Detectable level (ppm)	Samples containing insecticide (%)	Maximum found (ppm)
DDT	0.001	39	0.802
DDE	0.001	38	0.915
DDD	0.001	22	0.291
Dieldrin	0.001	21	0.142
Lindane	0.001	17	0.21
Heptachlor epoxide	0.001	15	0.082
Carbaryl	0.2	7	0.5
Benzene hexachloride[b]	0.001	7	0.14
Aldrin	0.001	6	0.014
Endrin	0.001	5	0.017
Arsenic	0.1	3	4.7
Kelthane	0.001	2	0.166
Heptachlor	0.001	1	0.008
Tedion	0.001	1	0.006
Perthane	0.001	0.5	0.016
Chlordane	0.001	0.5	0.033

[a] Data of Duggan *et al.* (17). The "detectable level" was not always specified; when it was not, the "sensitivity" is given above in its place, although apparently in most cases compounds were detectable at levels somewhat below sensitivity.

[b] It is not clear whether or not this means "benzene hexachloride" isomers other than lindane.

Thus lindane is rapidly broken down in several soils to nontoxic derivatives within 2 weeks (31). Aldrin is steadily converted to dieldrin at moderate temperatures (26° or 46°C), but not at 7°C. In field use, 4 years after applying 2 lb/acre of aldrin, a muck soil had 0.07 ppm of aldrin and 0.21 ppm of dieldrin (31). Heptachlor is also epoxidized in soils: 17 months after applying 25 lb/acre of heptachlor to a loam soil, there were 3.7 ppm of heptachlor and 0.94 ppm of its epoxide; probably this epoxidation was microbial, for it was much reduced in dry or autoclaved soils (32) or by blocking agents such as typical pyrethrin synergists (33). These soil residues find their way into crops. Annual treatment of a silt loam soil with 3 lb/acre of aldrin or heptachlor gave rise annually to residues (measured as parent plus epoxide) which were typically 0.3 and 0.7 ppm, respectively, in carrots; 0.1 and 0.3 ppm in potatoes; 0.2 and 0.2 ppm in radishes; and 0.1 and 0.3 ppm in beets (34).

The data given above show that soils, crops, meat, and dairy products are fairly commonly contaminated with chlorinated hydrocarbon insecticides, certainly in the United States and presumably wherever else similar compounds are widely used. Let us now consider the residues which arise in humans as a consequence of ingesting contaminated foodstuffs.

Several early reports were summarized by Hayes *et al.* in 1958 (24) and amply reviewed in 1959 (25). Body fat samples from 342 humans were analyzed, and an average level of DDT plus DDE of 4.9 ppm was found. Many factors modified the level; thus vegetarians only had 2.7 ppm, and vegetarian meals had only one-quarter as much DDT as normal meals. Agricultural workers who applied DDT averaged 17 ppm, and formulators of DDT had up to 664 ppm of DDT plus DDE in their body fat! Of the DDT-like materials in the fat, a very large proportion (averaging 58%) was present as DDE, and the rest as DDT (but see p. 127 concerning DDD, which might have been reported as DDT in this study). There was no progression in the amount of storage of DDT between 1950 and 1958, a finding which is in accordance with data for several animals (rats, cows, dogs, monkeys, man, and others) showing that for any given regular level of DDT intake, the DDT in adipose tissue climbs initially, then reaches a plateau characteristic of that intake level. In different species, the plateau heights differ; thus 10 mg/kg each day gives about 440 ppm of DDT in the fat of the dog, and about 1500 ppm in rat or turkey (25). A similar plateau effect has been seen for dieldrin (21) and again the species vary: 0.1 ppm in the diet leads to 4.1 ppm deposition in the fat of hens, 0.4 in steers or hogs, 0.2 in cows, and 0.1 in lambs.

A natural question to ask is: Does this burden of DDT and other compounds, which we now carry, have any deleterious effect? Questions of this type are always difficult to answer because a mountain of negative evidence can, in principle, be overturned by a single positive finding; but unfortunately it is rather easy to perform bad experiments or draw wrong conclusions, so that isolated positive findings must be scrutinized with care. The problem is all the worse in the case of compounds such as the chlorinated hydrocarbons, whose precise mechanism of action is not known. Finally, there is always a real possibility that there may be no effect in the normal individual, but a harmful effect in some special pathological or physiological condition. The ghost of thalidomide, which has damaging effects only during early pregnancy, hangs over this discussion. It has been shown (20) that rats fed extremely high levels of DDT, such as 600 ppm, show no effects normally, but show marked tremors if starved for 24 hours, presumably because depletion of body fat releases extra DDT into the circulation. Effects were minor at lesser doses, such as 200 ppm.

One approach to the evaluation of hazard is to find what quantities are needed to produce poisoning in man. A detailed review of the reports of dozens of cases of accidental or experimental ingestion of DDT by man was presented by Hayes in 1959 (25). In acute cases, it took about 750 mg or more by mouth to produce symptoms, which included unsteadiness, dizziness, and a prickly sensation in the lower part of the face (paraesthesia). Much larger doses have been ingested accidentally; several episodes of mistaken use of DDT in place of flour for cooking have led to ingestion of 5–6 g, and in one case up to 20 g. Such high doses have caused severe symptoms (headaches, tremor, vomiting, paraesthesia), but almost invariably there is recovery. A few deaths have occurred, but the doses involved are unknown. Very many cases of severe poisoning have been reported following the ingestion of DDT along with other agents, usually solvents; and other anecdotal reports describe various symptoms hours or days after normal use of DDT. Such cases may cause alarm when dramatized, but tell us nothing of the effects unequivocally caused by DDT. In summary, acute exposure to DDT appears to produce marked effects only in extraordinary cases, and normal use appears to be free of any acute hazard.

Direct evidence that chronic DDT intakes which are greatly in excess of normal have no deleterious effects was provided by feeding it to volunteers. Doses of 1, 20, and 200 times the normal daily intake were given over a period of 2 years to healthy men. No effects were found by the examining physician, nor reported by the experimental subjects, nor detected by exhaustive clinical or laboratory tests (19,23). Furthermore, a study was made (37) of 40 men with intensive and prolonged occupational exposure to DDT, such that they ingested 200 times as much DDT as the average. No effects were noted apart from minor skin and eye irritations which were caused by the physical effects of DDT dust, and which cleared up when exposure was terminated. Finally, a Roumanian study (48) showed no ill effects from massive inhalation of DDT plus lindane in a forest spraying operation; some workers inhaled 21 mg/kg of DDT as well as 6 mg/kg of lindane daily for 30 days.

Studies on humans with cyclodienes are few. It has been stated (49) that blood levels of 0.7 ppm of dieldrin can be reached by those conducting spray operations with dieldrin, with no signs of poisoning.

Clearly, the studies on high-level intakes by man have revealed no alarming effects. Any biologically active compound will produce some kind of effect if given in heroic doses, and knowledge of just how high these doses must be is helpful in evaluating the significance of normal intakes. Such knowledge cannot be obtained (except in accident cases) for men, but has been for rats. Work in 1947 showed (20) the effects of feeding from 100 ppm and up to 800 ppm of DDT in the diet of rats over a 2-year period, which is longer than the average lifetime for a rat. Effects on growth and mortality were encountered only at huge intakes, such as 800 ppm (almost 0.1% of the diet), when mortality in males was increased 8% over the control mortality of 75%. Other effects were noted at lower intakes: liver weights increased in proportion with dose, with a 25% increase at 100 ppm, and there were characteristic microscopic changes in liver, along with necrosis in some cases, which the investigator felt was a terminal phenomenon in dying animals. In a few cases (4 out of the 192) hepatic tumors of uncertain type were seen. The microscopic effects on liver disappeared about 5 weeks after removal of DDT from the diet. Long-term studies on rats with aldrin and dieldrin (46) have shown that 25 ppm in the diet over 2 years causes mortalities no greater than those found in control animals.

As for subtler effects of chlorinated hydrocarbons on mammals, it has been reported for rats (46) that the numbers of pregnancies were reduced (to an unstated extent) by dieldrin at 2.5 ppm, or by aldrin at 12.5 ppm, but not by DDT at the highest dose employed (25 ppm). When dieldrin was fed at 2.5 ppm over several generations "the earlier evidence of reduction in the number of pregnancies tended to disappear." The numbers of offspring per litter were unaffected by 25 ppm of aldrin, dieldrin, or DDT, but if the offspring suckled mothers who were fed 12.5 ppm of dieldrin, mortalities among the offspring were "severe"; if mothers were fed 2.5 ppm of aldrin or dieldrin or 25 ppm of DDT the mortalities were "slight to moderate." It is very unfortunate that only these rather vague statements were made by the authors of this most interesting study. One wonders if the findings are connected with the report (3) that aldrin at 25 ppm in the diet of female rats caused a depression in the occurrence of estrus, but that within several weeks some kind of adaptation had occurred and estrus was normal again.

A line of evidence used to incriminate DDT has been to claim that upsurges of some "modern" disease have accompanied the large-scale introduction of DDT. However, detailed analysis of the statistics has shown that such diseases were increasing before the introduction of DDT, and did not increase any faster thereafter. Such analyses have been made for agranulocytosis, aplastic anemia, purpura, Hodgkin's disease, leukemia, and aleukemia (19).

Work of the effects of DDT upon oxidative phosphorylation in rat tissue (38) suggested "no evidence that the amounts of DDT likely to accumulate in human fat presents any toxicological hazard," largely because fatty tissues stored the DDT, and were themselves shown to be entirely unaffected by it metabolically.

To summarize the findings reported above, there is no evidence that persistent body burdens, even at levels greatly in excess of that found in the general population, have any adverse effect normally. A possibility does exist that if fat depots are rapidly utilized, as in severe fasting, enough DDT may be released to cause distinct symptoms. Nevertheless, one must consider the possibility of subtle effects, particularly on reproductive potential, which the above experiments would not have detected. The data in the next section have relevance for this consideration.

DDD has repeatedly been shown to cause degeneration of the adrenal cortex in the dog, e.g., when fed at 50 mg/kg daily. Amazingly enough, 2500 ppm in a rat's diet produces no such effect. In an even more drastic study (43), rats had their adrenal medulla removed, and the regeneration of the adrenal cortex was followed with and without DDD injected at 200 mg/kg three times a week. The cortex regenerated equally well in both cases. There is thus a large species variation in this phenomenon. In view of the fact that (quite apart from a moderate usage of DDD as such) DDT residues on foods cause DDD to accumulate in fatty tissues, it is rather surprising that DDT has not been shown to produce (by this indirect route) effects on the adrenal cortex and hence on the whole complex of functions controlled by adernocortical hormones, at least in some species, such as the dog.

Effects upon Wildlife

The effects to be considered are both gross responses, that is to say direct lethal effects, and what might be called "subtle effects," including effects upon fecundity and fertility. There is a rather extensive literature, and the studies prior to 1951, which were primarily on gross responses and especially concerned with DDT, have been excellently reviewed by Brown (7). In summary, they showed that mammals were unaffected even by high rates of application, such as 5 lb/acre. Such high rates depleted bird populations severely in a number of cases, but moderate treatments (1 lb/acre) had little effect. These observations are compatible with the data of Table 17.2, which show that wild animals, like laboratory animals, are rather insensitive to DDT poisoning. Amphibians and reptiles are more sensitive, and fish are most

TABLE 17.2

TOXICITY OF DDT TO WILDLIFE[a]

	Chronic lethal dose (ppm)	Acute lethal dose (mg/kg)
Bobwhite quail	250	300
Mallard and pintail ducks	500	> 2000
Starling	—	>600
Cottontail rabbit	> 2000	2000
Meadow mouse	3000	—
White-footed mouse	> 1000	1500

[a] The data [from Coburn and Treichler (12)] are all approximate and are based on small numbers of animals. The data are for crystalline DDT given orally.

susceptible, with a typical lethal concentration of about 0.005 ppm for adults and of as low as 0.001 ppm for fry. Such lethal concentrations are readily achieved by spraying at modest concentrations, such as 0.5 or 1 lb/acre. Of the invertebrates, molluscs are only moderately sensitive, earthworms are very insensitive, but crustaceans and (of course) insects and their larvae are extremely sensitive, and their depletion can affect wildlife populations indirectly.

A more recent survey in 1965 (11) has added to but not fundamentally changed the above body of knowledge, although now the interest is in many compounds in addition to DDT. It has been observed frequently (4,29) that the use of DDT for tree spraying, which gives rise to very high local contamination of the ground by DDT, is accompanied by large temporary reductions in populations of robins and (to a lesser extent) other insectivorous birds, presumably because of DDT accumulation in their prey. The most careful study on this subject (51) was done in 1965, when a reduction of 70% in robin population was observed, following a typical application averaging 2 lb/acre upon 670 acres, but of course in a very localized way. There was an indication that death resulted when brain levels of DDT plus DDD plus DDE rose above 50 ppm. In this study, a nearby unsprayed town served as a control. The robin population in the sprayed town recovered to almost normal levels within a few months, presumably by influx from other areas. It is notable that by use of methoxychlor in the following year, the bird mortality was almost abolished. Not all DDT treatments for Dutch elm disease cause such large effects, nor is the robin necessarily the most sensitive species. The selection of species for study greatly affects the apparent findings. For instance, in a carefully controlled study in Princeton, New Jersey (5), in which 30 species were tabulated, both treated and control areas showed a decline of 19.6% in bird numbers. If one selected from the data only the species common to both areas, one found a 22% decline in the treated, and a 6% increase in the control areas. But robin numbers remained unchanged in both areas.

There is evidence (4) that earthworms are a principal DDT source for robins. Various earthworm species in DDT-sprayed areas contained 33–164 μg/g of DDT without lethal effect on the worms; normal intake of these worms could readily yield the amounts of DDT found in poisoned robins.

These Dutch elm disease treatments involve unusually large amounts of DDT. At lower levels, effects are proportionately reduced. One extensive controlled study, conducted in 1951 in the Patuxent wildlife refuge in Maryland (40), examined the effects of spraying 2 lb/acre of DDT annually for 5 years (with the exception that in year two, only 1.1 lb/acre was used). Twenty-seven species of birds were studied; only three showed decreased populations over the 5 years, specifically 44% decrease in American redstarts, 40% in parula warblers, and 28% in red-eyed vireos. These are reassuring findings.

An extensive study on New Brunswick forests was reported in 1965 (50). In 6 years of regular spraying with DDT, using treatments between 0.25 and 1 lb/acre (but sometimes several treatments a year), the breeding success of woodcocks has slowly declined. (Breeding success is defined as the ratio of immature to adult females found in the fall.) More convincingly, there was a quite good correlation (correlation coefficient 0.82) between pounds of DDT applied in any year and breeding success in that year, even though the amount used varied rather randomly through the years. That the process is readily reversible is shown by the finding that in 1963, the last year of the study, when the amount sprayed was almost the smallest, the breeding success was maximal, i.e., reduced usage led promptly to increased success. The total levels of DDT in the birds were quite low, with a typical value of 1.7 ppm; in eggs the average was 1.3 ppm.

Buckley claimed in 1963 that, in the United States Department of the Interior laboratories, 68% of the 1928 specimens (representing 91 species of birds and 20 of mammals) analyzed during 1961–1962 contained chlorinated hydrocarbon residues, including heptachlor, dieldrin, toxaphene, or DDT. Eighty per cent of woodcocks studied had DDT or heptachlor residues, averaging 1.6 ppm of heptachlor epoxide and 1.7 ppm of DDT.

Although most data indicating widespread residues in wildlife have been reported from United States sources, a somewhat similar picture undoubtedly exists for all economically advanced countries, which necessarily employ pesticides on a large scale. In Britain, for instance, dieldrin was found at various levels up to 46 ppm in the tissues of wild pigeons, pheasants, and partridges in 1962, and heptachlor epoxide was found at up to 91 ppm in these same tissues (45).

In spite of the documented depletions of songbirds following insecticidal treatments, there is no evidence for a countrywide diminution in bird population in parallel with insecticide use. Indeed, Audubon Society figures show very large increases in robin and redwing blackbird populations between 1940 and 1960 (30). By contrast, populations of the scarce bald eagle (only 3,807 in the United States in 1962) have been declining steadily, and the presence of DDT residues in specimens which have been found dead [e.g., 32 ppm in heart muscle, less elsewhere (50)] has prompted queries about the causal role of DDT in the decline; but as of 1963 there was not concrete evidence either way (8).

Short-term exposure to high concentrations of DDT has no deleterious effects, gross or subtle. Spraying nests containing eggs of 12 common species of birds, including robins, various sparrows, and phoebes, at a rate equivalent to 5 lb/acre of DDT, had no effects on hatching or subsequent development (36).

More precise studies have been possible on birds that can be reared on a large scale in captivity. DeWitt (15) fed various chlorinated hydrocarbons to quail and pheasants (Table 17.3). Whereas aldrin, but not dieldrin or endrin, was very toxic at 1 ppm in the diet of chicks, DDT produced substantial numbers of deaths only at high levels, such as 50 ppm. The subtle effects which were explored proved to be relatively minor and were found only with DDT in quail, which at the high level of 200 ppm in the diet of the parents produced drastic mortality (85%) in the chicks which hatched from their eggs. Endrin in adult quail at 1 ppm in the diet had a similar but smaller effect, causing 25% mortality in chicks. The only other subtle effect (not shown in the table) was that the rather high level of 10 ppm of endrin in the diet of adult pheasants gave a 23% mortality in the chicks from their eggs. In similar studies on Japanese quail (41), it has been shown that dieldrin at up to 10 ppm, or heptachlor at up to 50 ppm, had no effects upon growth or reproduction.

Next, let us consider aquatic contamination and its consequences. A chain of 128 water-sampling stations was set up by the Public Health Service in 1957 to monitor water pollution in United States rivers and lakes. In 1962, DDT or dieldrin was detected in 14% of the locations sampled, with typical levels of 2 ppb. Contamination of lakes and streams is therefore fairly widespread. The level of contamination depends upon the recent history of treatment. For example, spraying a 4000-acre watershed with DDT at about 0.9 lb/acre gave rise to 0.3 ppb in stream water during the treatment, and 0.005 ppb 2 months later (22). Treatment of Clear Lake, California, with 14 ppb of DDD to control gnats gave rise to levels in flesh of fish (of numerous species) of 5–130 ppm, and in fat of 40–2690 ppm; frogs had only 5 ppm in fat, but grebes had 723 ppm in fat (28). In lakes and rivers of New York State, 0.02–0.3 ppb of DDT was found, and in whole fish of various species, typically 0.2–4 ppm were found; in fat, the levels were between 13 and 29 ppm (35). Probably as a result of such widespread contamination, fish kills have been widely reported; young salmon were said to be nearly eliminated in the Miramichi River (New Brunswick, Canada) in 1954 and 1956 after spraying 0.5 lb/acre of DDT, and coho salmon were said to suffer almost complete mortality in rivers of British Columbia (Canada) after 1 lb/acre of DDT (39). There have been other celebrated cases, including the hotly disputed charge that massive fish kills in the lower Mississippi in 1963 were caused by endrin poisoning, originally thought to owe to river contamination caused by normal agricultural use of endrin, but later attributed to industrial pollution (2), although it took Senator Dirksen to point out (16) the strangeness of the claim that the contamination, said to have occurred at Memphis, only had effects 700 miles downstream.

The normal use of chlorinated hydrocarbons as water treatments or as widespread aerial sprays leads to residues in mud of ponds and lakes, and this in turn leads to consistent reductions in bottom-dwelling invertebrates; but return to normal is usually relatively rapid, i.e., within a few months (14). In

TABLE 17.3

EFFECTS OF CHLORINATED HYDROCARBON INSECTICIDES FED TO PHEASANTS AND QUAIL[a]

	Level in diet (ppm)	Lethal effects[b]	
		Mortality in chicks (%)	Mortality in adults (%)
Pheasants			
DDT	50	13	39
Aldrin	5	100	—
Dieldrin	5	100	—
Endrin	5	100	—
Quail			
DDT	100	8	13
Aldrin	1	100	100
Dieldrin	1	100	4
Endrin	1	54	0

	Level in diet (ppm)	Reproductive effects[c]			
		Reduction in eggs (%)	Reduction in fertility (%)	Reduction in hatch (%)	Mortality of chicks at 6 weeks (%)
Pheasants					
DDT	100	60	0	9	8
Aldrin	1	17	0	3	9
Dieldrin	1	0	0	0	0
Endrin	1	6	0	1	0
Quail					
DDT	200	0	0	5	85
Aldrin	1	23	0	0	6
Dieldrin	1	0	9	3	10
Endrin	1	0	0	6	25

[a] Data calculated from Dewitt (15). Values are expressed as percent of corresponding controls. Thus if 10% of the controls died, and 50% of the treated birds,

$$\% \text{ mortality} = (50-10)/(100-10) = 44\%.$$

The data are selected from much more extensive data, with the primary objective of showing comparable treatments for the species compared. The treatments for lethal and reproductive data are different because in the latter case it was desired to use sublethal treatments.

[b] Chicks were fed during the summer only; adults during the winter only.

[c] All birds were fed during the reproductive period only.

the Yellowstone River area in 1957, 1 lb/acre of DDT was applied, resulting in about 90% kill of bottom invertebrates, vegetation residues up to 2.3 ppm, water residues up to 0.03 ppm, and fish residues up to 10 ppm of whole fish; but there were no fish mortalities (13).

A careful study on cutthroat trout, published in 1963 (1) showed that mortalities occurred if the DDT in the water or in food rose above a fairly clear-cut threshold of about 0.1 ppm in water or 1 mg/kg of body weight in food. The data suggested that these lethal levels were such as gave rise to DDD plus DDT levels in whole fish over 5 ppm, and in brain over 7 ppm. Happily, these exposure levels are larger than those anticipated in normal use. Apart from their lethal effects, no subtle damage was seen on fecundity or fertility, even in survivors from massive doses. In fact survivors, for instance, from 1 ppm in the water or 3 mg/kg in the food, were larger and healthier than control animals, presumably because poorer specimens had been killed off. With the survivors of the group of 636 fish given the highest level of DDT in the food (3 mg/kg) fecundity was almost abolished, the few eggs produced were 99% sterile, and the five fry that hatched soon died. However, under all less-stringent conditions, the DDT-treated animals grew and produced as well as did controls. These findings fit well with a 1964 study on lake trout (9) which was carried out after a hatchery in New York State suffered 100% mortality in trout fry for 4 successive years. Analyses in the subsequent 2-year experiment revealed again a threshold effect, this time expressed in terms of tissue residues: if the DDT plus DDD concentration in the whole fry was above 2.9 ppm, mortalities were substantial. If the concentration was below 2.9 ppm, mortalities were never found. Although DDE was always found in the fish (in this and the preceding study), its level of occurrence bore no relevance to mortality.

Most of the data described so far have been for DDT, simply because it is so widely used. As Table 17.4 shows, other chlorinated hydrocarbons, especially endrin and toxaphene, are more toxic to fish, by 70-fold and 5-fold, respectively, for rainbow trout, for instance. Toxaphene at 0.1 and at 0.05 lb/acre can kill most fish (44). Inspection of Tables 17.4 and 17.5 shows that the compounds safest for mammals are not necessarily very safe for fish; methoxychlor, for instance, is almost as toxic as DDT for minnows, yet is 53-fold less toxic than DDT for rats. In general, although many chlorinated hydrocarbons are rather safe for mammals, all of them are very toxic to fish. On the whole, fish are fairly uniform in their response; for instance for the seven very different fish species in Table 17.4, the species variation for any of the nine compounds was never more than 20-fold (for toxaphene) and was typically only 5-fold. One of the fortunate simplifications, therefore, is that predictions of fish kill can be based on laboratory studies to a far greater extent than can insect or mammalian kills. Finally, the compounds shown do vary greatly in their toxicity for fish;

TABLE 17.4

SPECIES VARIATION IN TOXICITY TO FISH[a]

Pesticide	Concentration that will kill 50% in 96 hours (ppb)						
	Bluegills	Minnows	Goldfish	Guppies	Chinook salmon	Coho salmon	Rainbow trout
Endrin	0.6	10	1.9	1.5	1.2	0.5	0.6
Toxaphene	3.5	5.1	56	20	2.5	9.4	8.4
Dieldrin	7.9	16	37	23	6.1	10.8	10
Aldrin	13	28	28	33	7.5	45.9	17.7
DDT	16	32	27	43	11.5	44	42
Heptachlor	19	94	230	107	17	59	19
Chlordane	22	52	82	190	57	56	44
Methoxychlor	62	35	56	120	28	66	62
Lindane	77	56	152	138	40	50	38

[a] Data of Tarzwell (44)

TABLE 17.5

COMPARATIVE TOXICITY TO FISH AND OTHER ANIMALS[a]

Insecticide	24-Hour LD_{50} to minnows (mg/liter = ppm)	Topical LD_{50} to houseflies (mg/kg)	Oral LD_{50} to rats (mg/kg)
Endrin	0.0013	—	17.8
Toxaphene	0.0051	31	90
Dieldrin	0.016	11	46
Aldrin	0.028	1.6	67
DDT	0.034	8–21	113
Methoxychlor	0.035	—	6000
Heptachlor	0.056	1.6	100
Lindane	0.056	1.0	125
Chlordane	0.069	4.0	335

[a] From Henderson and Pickering (27,27a).

whereas endrin obviously is extremely hazardous, lindane and methoxychlor are often 100-fold safer.

A brief note claims (6) that 5–15% of surviving pregnant mosquito fish abort when exposed for an unstated time to concentrations of DDT, DDD, methoxychlor, aldrin, dieldrin, endrin, toxaphene, heptachlor, or lindane which are sufficient to kill 10–40% of the adults. However, since no abortions were found with sublethal dosages, one may assume this is a rather unsubtle effect, seen when females are *almost* killed by these compounds.

In summarizing the data on wildlife implications, there can be little doubt that wildlife have become exposed to persistent pesticides, but the amount is not greatly in excess of that to which humans are routinely exposed. There is virtually no evidence that mammalian species are any the worse for this exposure. Birds, perhaps because of their feeding habits, which in certain cases lead them to pick up carriers of persistent compounds such as earthworms, may in special cases suffer substantial short-term losses. Usually these effects have not led to great population declines; this "resistance" may be due to repopulation from untreated areas, for it is still true that only a small fraction of the total land area is treated; or it may be that most animals reproduce themselves in abundance to counter the usual hazards of predation, sickness, and starvation, and this abundance serves equally well to counter the man-made hazard of pesticides. Only in a few cases is there any evidence for "subtle effects" in birds, e.g., upon reproductive potential.

Fish are highly sensitive to many insecticides. For reasons completely unknown, minute traces of chlorinated hydrocarbon pesticides are lethal to them. (It is noteworthy that we have almost no information whether fish have high intrinsic susceptibility, judged by injected doses, or whether they succeed in greatly concentrating these compounds from their watery milieu.) Consequently, even very modest treatments by the more hazardous compounds, especially endrin and toxaphene, are highly likely to cause massive kills.

A great fraction of the wildlife problem is economic rather than technical. The use of methoxychlor in place of other chlorinated hydrocarbons would perhaps double the cost of chemicals, which presumably represents an ever-dwindling proportion of the total treatment costs, and enormously reduce hazards for wildlife. It is not unreasonable that to enjoy the advantages of cheap agricultural commodities and undamaged flowers and trees, along with full streams and a noisy Spring, one should pay a little more.

REFERENCES

1. Allison, D., Kallman, B. J., Cope, O. B., and Van Valin, C. C., *Science* **142**, 958 (1963).
2. Anonymous, *Chem. Eng. News* **42**, 23 (1964).
3. Ball, W. L., Kay, K., and Sinclair, J. W., *Am. Med. Assoc. Arch. Ind. Health* **7**, 292 (1953).
4. Barker, R. J., *J. Wildlife Management* **22**, 269 (1958).
5. Benton, A. H., *J. Wildlife Management* **15**, 20 (1951).
6. Boyd, C. E., *Progressive Fish Culturist* **26**, 138 (1964).
7. Brown, A. W. A., "Insect Control by Chemicals." Wiley, New York, 1951.

8. Buckley, J. L., *In* "Pesticides—Their Use and Effect" (G. A. Swanson, ed.), p. 23. N.Y. State Legislative Symp. Albany, New York, 1963.
9. Burdick, G. E., Harris, E. J., Dean, H. J., Walker, T. M., Skea, J., and Colby, D., *Trans. Am. Fisheries Soc.* **93**, 127 (1964).
10. Carson, R. L., "Silent Spring." Houghton, Boston, Massachusetts, 1962.
11. Chichester, C. O., ed., "Research in Pesticides." Academic Press, New York, 1965.
12. Coburn, D. R., and Treichler, R., *J. Wildlife Management* **10**, 208 (1946).
13. Cope, O. B., *Trans. Am. Fisheries Soc.* **90**, 239 (1961).
14. Cope, O. B., *In* "Research in Pesticides" (C. O. Chichester, ed.), p. 115. Academic Press, New York (1965).
15. DeWitt, J. B., *J. Agr. Food Chem.* **4**, 863 (1956).
16. Dirksen, E. M., *Congressional Record* **110** (118), June 12, 1964.
17. Duggan, R. E., Barry, H. C., and Johnson, L. Y., *Science* **151**, 101 (1966).
18. Durham, W. F., Armstrong, J. F., Upholt, W. M., and Heller, C., *Science* **134**, 1880 (1961).
19. Durham, W. F., *In* "Research in Pesticides" (C. O. Chichester, ed.), p. 93. Academic Press, New York (1965).
20. Fitzhugh, O. G., and Nelson, A. A., *J. Pharmacol. Exptl. Therap.* **89**, 18 (1947).
21. Gannon, N., Link, R. P., and Decker, G. C., *J. Agr. Food Chem.* **7**, 826 (1959).
22. Grzenda, A. R., Nicholson, H. P., Teasley, J. I., and Patric, J. H., *J. Econ. Entomol.* **57**, 615 (1964).
23. Hayes, W. J., Durham, W. F., and Cueto, C., *J. Am. Med. Assoc.* **162**, 890 (1956).
24. Hayes, W. J., Quinby, G. E., Walker, K. C., Elliott, J. W., and Upholt, W. M., *Am. Med. Assoc. Arch. Ind. Health* **18**, 398 (1958).
25. Hayes, W. J., *In* "DDT: human and veterinary medicine," S. W. (Simmons, ed.), Birkhäuser, Basel, 1959.
26. Heineman, H. E. O., and Miller, C. B., *J. Dairy Sci.* **44**, 1775 (1961).
27. Henderson, C., and Pickering, A. H., *Trans. Am. Fisheries Soc.* **87**, 39 (1958).
27a. Henderson, C., and Pickering, A. H., *Trans. Am. Fisheries Soc.* **88**, 23 (1959).
28. Hunt, E. G., and Bischoff, A. I., *Calif. Fish Game* **46**, 91 (1960).
29. Hunt, L. B., *J. Wildlife Management* **24**, 139 (1960).
30. Jukes, T. H., *Am. Scientist* **51**, 355 (1963).
31. Lichtenstein, E. P., and Schulz, K. R., *J. Econ. Entomol.* **52**, 118 (1959).
32. Lichtenstein, E. P., and Schulz, K. R., *J. Econ. Entomol.* **53**, 192 (1960).
33. Lichtenstein, E. P., Schulz, K. R., and Cowley, G. T., *J. Econ. Entomol.* **56**, 485 (1963).
34. Lichtenstein, E. P., and Schulz, K. R., *J. Agr. Food Chem.* **13**, 57 (1965).
35. Mack, G. L., Corcoran, S. M., Gibbs, S. D., Gutermann, W. H., Reckahn, J. A., and Lisk, D. J., *N.Y. Fish Game J.* **11**, 148 (1964).
36. Mitchell, R. T., *J. Wildlife Management* **10**, 192 (1946).
37. Ortelee, M. F., *Am. Med. Assoc. Arch. Ind. Health* **18**, 433 (1958).
38. Parker, V. H., *Biochem. J.* **77**, 74 (1960).
39. President's Sci. Advisory Comm., "Use of Pesticides." U.S. Govt. Printing Office, Washington, D.C., 1963.
40. Robbins, C. S., Springer, P. F., and Webster, C. G., *J. Wildlife Management* **15**, 213 (1951).
41. Shellenberger, T. E., and Newell, G. W., *Lab. Animal Care* **15**, 119 (1965).
42. Shepard, H. H., and Mahan, J. N., *Chem. Eng. News* **43**, 108 Sept. 6 (1965).
43. Stoner, H. B., *Nature* **172**, 1044 (1953).
44. Tarzwell, C. M., *In* "Pesticides—Their Use and Effect" (G. A. Swanson, ed.), p. 30. N.Y. State Legislative Symp., Albany, New York, 1963.

45. Taylor, A., *Analyst* **87**, 824 (1962).
46. Treon, J. F., and Cleveland, F. P., *J. Agr. Food Chem.* **3**, 402 (1955).
47. Walker, K. C., Goette, M. B., and Batchelor, G. S., *J. Agr. Food Chem.* **2**, 1034 (1954).
48. Wasserman, M., Gliescu, S., Mandric, G., and Horvath, P., *Am. Med. Assoc. Arch. Ind. Health* **21**, 503 (1960).
49. Winthrop, G. J., and Felice, J. R., *Am. Med. Assoc. Arch. Ind. Health* **19**, 68 (1959).
50. Wright, B. S., *J. Wildlife Management* **29**, 172 (1965).
51. Wurster, D. H., Wurster, C. F., and Strickland, W. N., *Ecology* **46**, 488 (1965).

Author Index

Numbers in parentheses are reference numbers and are included to assist in locating references in which authors' names are not mentioned in the text. Numbers in italics refer to pages on which the references are listed.

C

D

E

F

G

N

Q

R

S

T

Z

Subject Index

A

D

E

I

K

L

M

N

O

Q

R

S